WITHDRAWN
UST
Libraries

DRUGS AND CEREBRAL FUNCTION

Panel participants of 1969 Symposium: *(From left to right)* Drs. Hakerem, Weinstein, Werry, Van Harreveld, Cherkin (front), Haward (rear), Bogen, Conners, Campbell, Leaf, Smith, Klein, Pollack, Essman, Davies. Missing: Drs. Adler, Goldberg, Moorman, and Pirkey.

DRUGS AND CEREBRAL FUNCTION

Compiled and Edited by

W. LYNN SMITH, Ph.D.

*Clinical Psychologist
Franklin Medical Center
Denver, Colorado
Director
Cortical Function Laboratory
Porter Memorial Hospital
Denver, Colorado*

With a Foreword by

George A. Ulett, M.D., Ph.D.

*Professor and Chairman
Department of Psychiatry
University of Missouri School of Medicine
Missouri Institute of Psychiatry
Director, Missouri Division of Mental Diseases
Columbia, Missouri*

CHARLES C THOMAS • PUBLISHER
Springfield • Illinois • U.S.A.

Published and Distributed Throughout the World by
CHARLES C THOMAS • PUBLISHER
BANNERSTONE HOUSE
301-327 East Lawrence Avenue, Springfield, Illinois, U.S.A.
NATCHEZ PLANTATION HOUSE
735 North Atlantic Boulevard, Fort Lauderdale, Florida, U.S.A.

This book is protected by copyright. No part of it may be reproduced in any manner without written permission from the publisher.

© *1970, by* CHARLES C THOMAS • PUBLISHER

Library of Congress Catalog Card Number: 70-119987

With THOMAS BOOKS *careful attention is given to all details of manufacturing and design. It is the Publisher's desire to present books that are satisfactory as to their physical qualities and artistic possibilities and appropriate for their particular use.* THOMAS BOOKS *will be true to those laws of quality that assure a good name and good will.*

Chapters 3, 7, 12, 14, and 16 may be reproduced royalty free for United States Governmental purposes.

Printed in the United States of America
GG-11

To
SYLVA
and to
MELANIE, KEVIN, BRIAN, LYNNETTE
SHAWN and BENJAMIN

Contributors

Adler, Martin W., Ph.D.

Associate Professor of Pharmacology
Department of Pharmacology
Temple University College of Medicine
Philadelphia, Pennsylvania

Bogen, Joseph E., M.D.

Senior Neurosurgeon
Ross-Loos Medical Group
Los Angeles, California
Consultant in Neurosurgery
California Institute of Technology
Pasadena, California

Campbell, Berry, Ph.D.

Professor and Acting Chairman
Physiology Department, College of Medicine
University of California, Irvine
Irvine, California

Cherkin, Arthur, Ph.D.

Chief
Psychobiology Research Laboratory
Veterans Administration Hospital
Sepulveda, California
Lecturer in Anesthesiology
Division of Anesthesia
University of California School of Medicine
Los Angeles, California

Conners, C. Keith, Ph.D.

Director
Child Development Laboratory
The Massachusetts General Hospital
Boston, Massachusetts
Harvard Medical School
Boston, Massachusetts

Davies, D. Hywel, D.M., M.R.C.P.

Associate Professor of Medicine
University of Colorado Medical School
Denver, Colorado
Chief
Cardiology Service
Veterans Administration Hospital
Denver, Colorado

Essman, Walter B., Ph.D.

Professor of Psychology and Biochemistry
Psychology Department
Queens College of the City University of New York
Flushing, New York

Goldberg, Solomon C., Ph.D.

Assistant Chief
Psychopharmacology Research Branch
National Institute of Mental Health
Chevy Chase, Maryland

Hakerem, Gad, Ph.D.

Associate Professor and Chairman
Department of Psychology
Queens College of the City University of New York
Flushing, New York
Associate Research Scientist
Biometrics Research
Department of Mental Hygiene
New York, New York

Haward, Lionel R.C., Dr. Psy.

Biometric Clinic
Chichester, Sussex
England

Klein, Donald, F., M.D.

Director of Research
Hillside Hospital
Glen Oaks, New York

Leaf, Russell C., Ph.D.

Associate Professor of Psychology
Rutgers University
New Brunswick, New Jersey

Moorman, Lemuel T., M.D.

Retina Surgeon
Franklin Medical Center
Denver, Colorado
Assistant Clinical Professor of Ophthalmology
Director, Retina Clinic
University of Colorado Medical School
Denver, Colorado

Pirkey, Will P., M.D.

Microsurgeon and Otologist
Denver Otologic Group
Republic Building
Denver, Colorado

Pollack, Max, Ph.D.

Professor
Department of Psychology
Queens College of the City University of New York
Flushing, New York
Senior Research Associate
Hillside Hospital
Glen Oaks, New York

Smith, W. Lynn, Ph.D.

Clinical Psychologist
Franklin Medical Center
Denver, Colorado
Director
Cortical Function Laboratory
Porter Memorial Hospital
Denver, Colorado

Turner, William J., M.D.

Consultant
Dreyfus Medical Foundation
New York, New York

Van Harreveld, Antonie, M.D., Ph.D.

Professor of Physiology
Division of Biology
California Institute of Technology
Pasadena, California

Weinstein, Stephen A., Sc.D.

*Associate Professor of Environmental Medicine
Director
Laboratory of Behavioral Physiology
Johns Hopkins University
Baltimore, Maryland*

Werry, John S., M.B., Ch.B.

*Director
Institute for Juvenile Research
Chicago, Illinois*

Foreword

History will record that following the accidental discovery of the psychotropic effects of largactil (chlorpromazine) in France, the specialty of psychiatry entered upon the most significant period of change in its existence. The important diagnostic observations of Kraepelin, the far-reaching psychodynamic theories of Freud, and the somatic therapies associated with such names as Sakel, Meduna, Cerletti, and Moniz, all affected and benefited the lives of untold thousands of mentally ill people. Despite this the number of patients behind asylum walls steadily increased until 1955, the year when psychotropic drugs became generally available. Since then the population of public mental hospitals has dropped—in some instances halved—despite a rise in admission rates and an ever-increasing number of persons seeking treatment for psychiatric illness. With the significant control of symptoms made possible through neuroleptic medications thousands can again live meaningful and productive lives in the community with family and friends.

Revolutionary and effective though they have been, the treatment methods in this age of psychopharmacotherapy have remained for the most part empirical, but unlike the elusive formulations of models for psychopathogenesis of the first half of this century, theories relating symptom relief to drug action are readily amenable to scientific test and investigation in the laboratory and in the clinic. Chemically induced therapeutic behavioral change can be observed as a direct result of alteration in cerebral function. All over the world, scientists of both basic and clinical persuasion are meeting, interrelating, and working cooperatively in an effort to bring some correlative understanding to brain behavior and to the biochemistry and physiology of central nervous system acting drugs. This first, *Cerebral Function Symposium,* represents yet another important thrust in the attack upon this prime problem area. It is symbolic both of the quality of the contributions and the lofty aspirations for this Symposium that it was held high in the mountains of Colorado. The assembly opened properly with a look at the anatomical underpinnings including the ancient yet exciting area of the hippocampus and the last large structure of the cerebrum to be developed in the human embyro one peculiar to mammals—the corpus callosum. With neuroanatomy closely tied to those basic central nervous system functions of conduction and inhibition the "go" and "stop" mechanisms of behavior, the Symposium then turned to a look at metabolism, the effect of psychoactive drugs on the brain, an assessment of the effect of drugs on the formation of engrams—learning facilitators—

and an important excursion through biochemistry of brain with emphasis on oxygenation and cerebral blood flow.

Although in three days it was not possible to review in depth all significant and related work in the area of focus, yet conceived as but the first of an ongoing series of related symposia, this first meeting well introduced the important areas and set the stage for later expansion and addition as facts and observations from the clinic and laboratory become available. Surely the interdisciplinary stimulation for those who attended and participated served only to more clearly define a common goal for many scientists of different persuasions. Surely too, from the dizzy heights of the Rocky Mountains at Aspen, Colorado, it was readily possible to see more clearly all the way to the distant horizon that lies ahead in psychopharmacological research.

GEORGE A. ULETT, M.D., PH.D.

Introduction

Drugs and Cerebral Function is the publication of the proceedings of the first Cerebral Function Symposium held at the Aspen Institute for Humanistic Studies at Aspen, Colorado, June 7, 8, and 9, 1969. Next June will be the second meeting of the ongoing series, the Annual Cerebral Function Symposium. Each year the Symposium is to have a specific focus; the 1970 Symposium's emphasis will be on developmental factors.

This series of annual meetings evolved out of a growing awareness, among acquaintances in several disciplines, of an increasing need for recurrent, ongoing evaluation of the rapid accretion of knowledge of cerebral function. Of particular concern is the ever-increasing tendency toward specialization not only in particular disciplines but even in specific methods of investigation, not even in certain bodily systems but even in small parts of single organs. A principal reason for the success of the first meeting was the remarkable extent to which a useful exchange was achieved among a most heterogeneous group. This group included clinical psychologists, and practicing physicians including psychiatrists, internists, child neurologists, and neurologic, otologic, and ophthalmic surgeons. All of these, it turns out, have not only a common interest in the brain generally but also in many particular, practical aspects such as treatment with learning facilitators, vasodilators, and psychoactive drugs.

We are particularly indebted to Doctors Joseph E. Bogen, Keith Conners, Hywel Davies, and Walter B. Essman for their ability to cross interdisciplinary barriers not only "popularizing" for others their own special fields but also for expediting the stimulating discussions. The excellence of the presentations by the other panel participants is evident in the papers included in this volume.

Many symposia have been organized over the years focusing on many important aspects of drugs and behavior. They have not satisfied the widespread need, however, for continuity in expanding developments, for annual review, for reporting the most recent contributions.

Drugs directly affecting cerebral functions and behavior divide themselves roughly into four categories: psychoactive drugs, neurochemical aspects, drugs which facilitate learning, and those drugs which may directly influence a body system, e.g. vasodilators. These areas are sufficiently broad to follow most recent developments in drugs and behavior and serve as a general outline for the Symposium.

A most challenging and rapidly growing segment is the one of assessing correlates of brain function and behavior. Along with continual modifications in research design and procedure, neuropsychology has become basic to psychopharmachological progress and an ongoing area in itself.

A primary purpose of the Annual Cerebral Function Symposium is to bring forth research either previously unpublished or if published brought current.

W. LYNN SMITH, PH.D., *Chairman*

Acknowledgments

I want to thank the panelists for their timely papers which are presented here as they were given. The Final Panel necessitated much editing, so for any inaccuracies in its contents I must take full responsibility.

My appreciation is extended especially to Dr. Bogen and Dr. Essman, who helped most in making this first meeting a success. Also, I want to thank my staff for their efficient handling of countless details inherent in this meeting. In addition, I would like to express my appreciation to Mr. Payne E. L. Thomas for his expertise as well as prompt and courteous assistance in making an early publication of this volume possible. Finally, my sincere gratitude goes to the seven pharmaceutical companies for their financial assistance which made this Symposium possible:

    CIBA Pharmaceutical Company
    Geigy Pharmaceuticals
    Hoffman-LaRoche, Inc.
    Ives Laboratories, Inc.
    The Lilly Research Laboratories
    Marion Laboratories, Inc.
    Merck Sharp & Dohme Postgraduate Program

                                                                     W.L.S.

Contents

	Page
Contributors	vii
Foreword	xi
Introduction	xiii
Acknowledgements	xv

PART I

ANATOMICAL CORRELATES

Chapter

1. The Corpus Callosum, the Other Side of the Brain and Pharmacologic Opportunity
   Joseph E. Bogen ... 5
2. Post-Tetanic Potentiation as a Measure of Excitability in the Hippocampus and Neocortex
   Berry Campbell and Mihai Demetrescu ... 14
3. Mechanism of Changes in Electrolyte and Water Distribution in Central Nervous Tissue
   Antonie Van Harreveld ... 29

   Concluding Discussion on Anatomical Correlates
   Joseph E. Bogen ... 36

PART II

PSYCHOACTIVE DRUGS

4. Chlorpromazine and CNS Changes in Man
   Max Pollack ... 41
5. Prediction of Response to Drugs and Placebo: the Current Frontier of Drug Research
   Solomon C. Goldberg ... 53
6. Pupillography as a Tool in the Assessment of CNS Functions and Drug Effects
   Gad Hakerem ... 59

7. Psychotropic Drugs and the Regulation of Behavioral Activation in Psychiatric Illness
   Donald F. Klein 69

PART III

LEARNING FACILITATORS

8. The Use of Stimulant Drugs in Enhancing Performance and Learning
   C. Keith Conners 85
9. Dilantin® Effect on Emotionally Disturbed Children
   William J. Turner 99
10. Effects of Sodium Diphenylhydantoinate and Pemoline Upon Concentration: A Comparative Study
    Lionel R. C. Haward 103
11. Facilitating Verbal-Symbolic Functions in Children With Learning Problems and 14-6 Positive Spike EEG Patterns with Ethosuximide (Zarontin®)
    W. Lynn Smith 121
12. Some Clinical and Laboratory Studies of Psychotropic Drugs in Children: An Overview
    John S. Werry 134
    Concluding Discussion on Learning Facilitators
    C. Keith Conners 145

PART IV

BIOCHEMICALS

13. Central Nervous System Metabolism, Drug Action, and Higher Functions
    Walter B. Essman 151
14. Drug Response Following Brain Damage
    Martin W. Adler 176
15. Effects of Flurothyl on Memory Processing
    Arthur Cherkin 187
16. Pharmacology, Limbic Regulation, and Cortical Function
    Russell C. Leaf 201
17. Hypoxia as a Model for Drug Effects on Behavior
    Stephen A. Weinstein 215
    Concluding Discussion on Biochemicals
    Walter B. Essman 231

PART V
VASODILATORS

18. Cerebral Blood Flow
    D. Hywel Davies 234
19. Clues to Cerebral Circulatory Disturbance from Ocular
    Fluorescein Angiography
    Lemuel T. Moorman 238
20. Sensorineural Hearing Loss
    Will P. Pirkey 247
21. The Effects of Vasodilators on Psychological Test
    Performance in Patients with Cerebral Vascular Insufficiency
    W. Lynn Smith 252

PART VI
FINAL PANEL

Moderator: *Joseph E. Bogen* 263

Index 273

DRUGS AND CEREBRAL FUNCTION

PART I

ANATOMICAL CORRELATES

Chapter 1

The Corpus Callosum, the Other Side of the Brain and Pharmacologic Opportunity

JOSEPH E. BOGEN

In an interdisciplinary meeting such as this, each participant tries not only to make his subject matter more understandable to the nonspecialist, but he may also offer some suggestions. I would ask the pharmacologists present to forgive a little brashness in this regard.

Among the ways in which pharmacology has advanced, one of the most important has been the introduction of drugs into systems previously investigated physiologically. A classic example was the work of Rudolph Magnus, Professor of Pharmacology at Utrecht in Holland in the early part of this century. He devoted most of his life to an analysis of postural reflexes and then used the understanding obtained therefrom to investigate certain drugs of most interest to him (1).

In more recent times, pharmacologists benefited from neurophysiological studies of the reticular formation occupying the brain stem core and exerting both descending and ascending influences on a variety of other systems (2). Beginning about 1950, the brain stem reticular formation became an increasingly attractive subject for physiologists. Some idea of this can be had from Figure 1-1 which shows a graph based on some library "research" in the Biologic Abstracts. Although the data are easily criticized on several grounds, the overall trend is clearly illustrated: the number of listings under the heading "Brain Stem" rapidly increased during the decade of the 1950's; the papers primarily concerned with the effects of drugs on the brain stem showed a similar rapid rise beginning several years later. We see that pharmacologic interest mounted rapidly as the physiologic knowledge became more available.

As the rush to the reticular formation has gradually eased, interest in the cerebral cortex has increased, particularly with respect to the commissural connections of the two cortices. We may note parenthetically that students of the cortex have tended to gravitate toward the opposing views of topism (the attempt to localize particular functions to particular places) or holism (the tendency to emphasize the emergent properties of the overall organism), just as synaptologists were at one time divided into "spark" and "soup" schools depending on whether they favored electrical or humoral transmission at one or another neuronal junction. An inclination to either topism or holism does not necessarily prescribe a particular position on another persistent division,

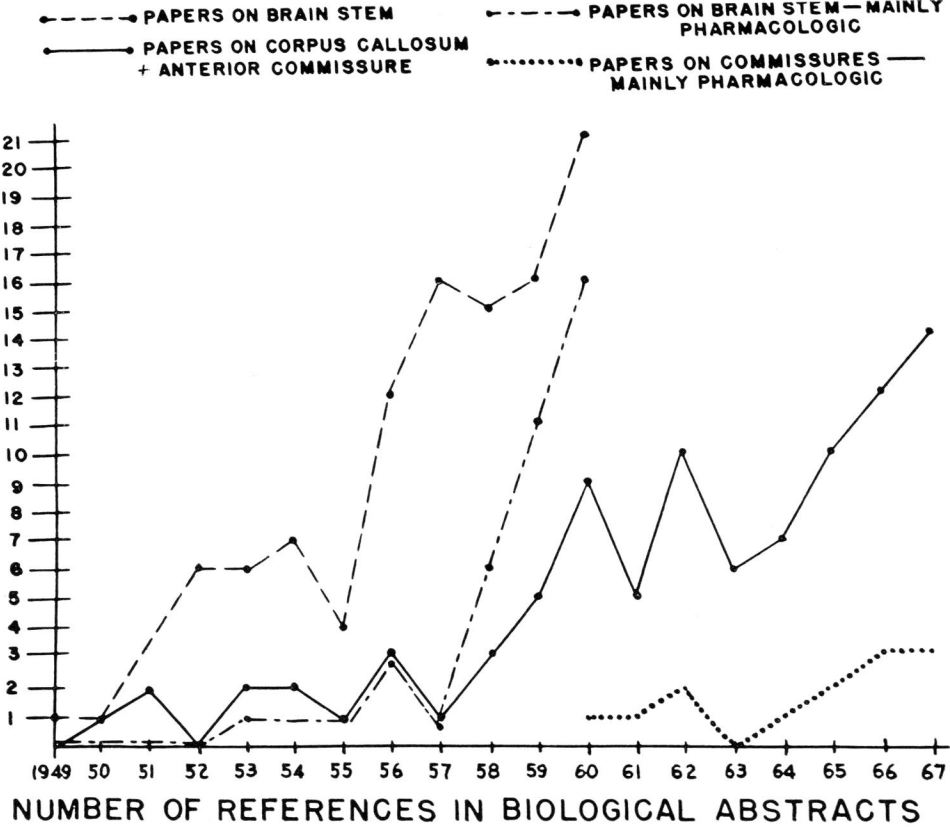

FIGURE 1-1. Pharmacologic interest in the brain stem reticular formation began to increase rapidly several years after the increase in physiological interest. A similar increase of pharmacologic interest in the cerebral commissures may be in the offing.

the one between a connectionist view in which interaction between nerve cells is likened to a wiring diagram (and the actual proximity of the elements is relatively unimportant) and on the other hand the contiguist view that the spatial configuration of the neuronal agglomerate determines how neurons work together. Much recent interest in the cerebral cortex has been stimulated by the findings of connectionists, such as R. W. Sperry, who has consistently emphasized the wiring diagram outlook (3). Sperry and his co-workers have been particularly active in investigations of the corpus callosum, a large collection of fibers whose obvious function is to connect one side of the brain with the other.

The prevailing doctrine of the 1940's and 1950's was that fiber tracts were relatively unimportant, a conclusion in large part attributable to the failure of Akelaitis (4) and Smith (5) to find significant psychological deficits after division of the corpus callosum. As Tomasch (6) said in 1954, of the studies of Akelaitis and Smith

> They showed very clearly and in accordance with some earlier authors like Dandy, Foerster, Meagher, and Barre, whose material however was not so extensive, that the corpus callosum is hardly connected with psychological functions at all.

This was all changed by the split-brain experiments of Myers and Sperry on cats and monkeys, which showed that after section of the corpus callosum, each half of the brain could be separately trained and that information acquired by one hemisphere was not transferred to the other (7, 8). Callosal section as a treatment for epilepsy has been reintroduced by P.J. Vogel and his associates (9, 10); and testing based on methods developed in the laboratory has confirmed that in man too the two hemispheres can be trained separately so that each has its own perceptions, memories, and volition. In other words, it has become progressively apparent in the past ten years that the corpus callosum does indeed have a lot to do with psychology. In testing humans with callosal section, many deficits are apparent when special tests are used, in spite of these persons' apparently normal behavior in everyday circumstances (11, 12, 13). Let me give you an example: If the human whose cerebral commissures have been divided is asked to feel (without looking at) an everyday object, with his left hand, and if the object is then jumbled up with a bunch of similar things in a bag, he can reach into the bag with his left hand and quickly retrieve by palpation alone the original test object. The same is true for retrieval with the right hand of test objects originally held in the right hand. However, if the object is felt by one hand, and retrieval is attempted with the *other* hand, the patient fails. This is an example of the lack of interhemispheric transfer which is typical of the split-brain; it is the same for the human as for the experimental animal.

The split-brain human has some additional symptoms because he can talk and because speech is largely lateralized to one hemisphere, the left one in right-handed persons. For example, the commissure-sectioned human names unseen objects held in his right hand just as would you or I. But such persons cannot name an object held unseen in the left hand, in spite of the fact that the object can be retrieved as described above and in spite of the fact that the object is manipulated by the left hand in a well-coordinated and appropriate manner. Similarly, objects seen only in the left visual field cannot be named even though the individual can retrieve the appropriate object from a bag full of objects when using his left hand. In fact, if two different objects are simultaneously flashed to the two visual fields, the individual will say that he saw the object which was in the right visual field at the same time that the left hand is retrieving the object seen in the left visual field! In other words, the talking hemisphere appears quite unaware of what the other hemisphere is thinking. (See Fig. 1-2.)

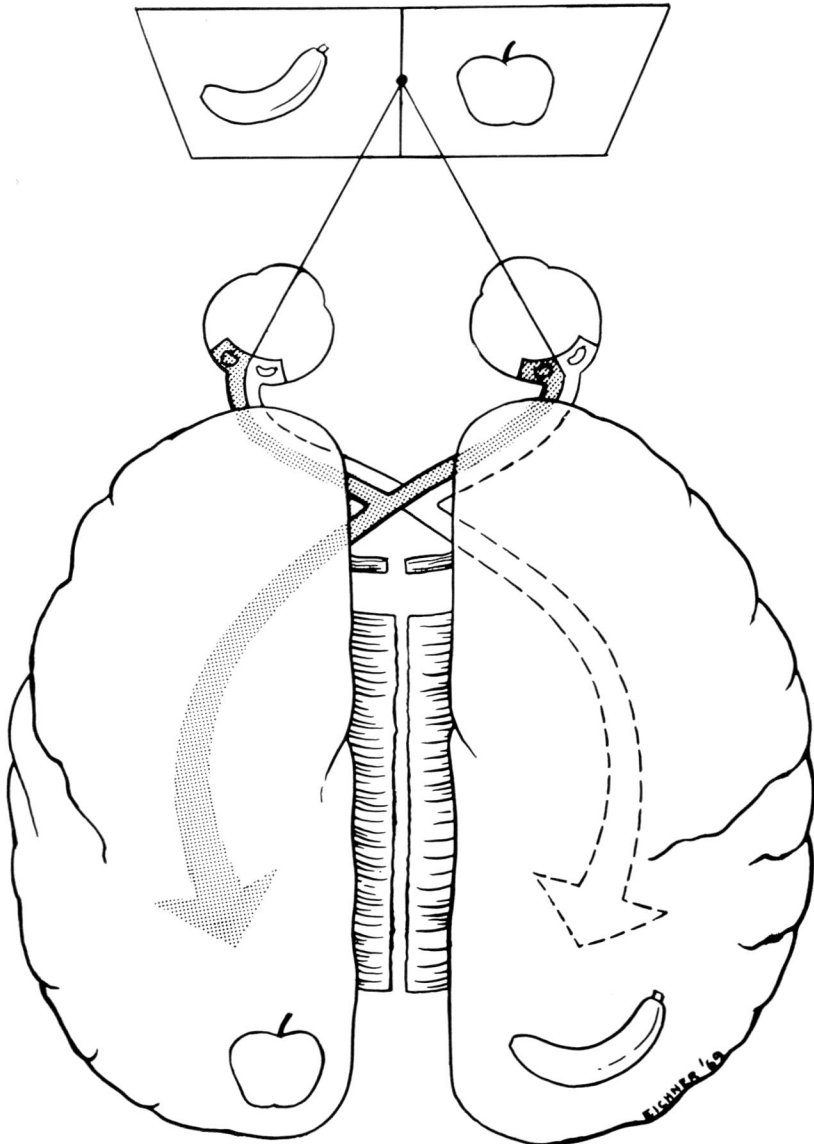

FIGURE 1–2. Diagram illustrating the duality of consciousness demonstrable by special testing techniques after complete cerebral commissurotomy. A picture of a banana is flashed into the left visual field simultaneously with an image of an apple in the right visual field, while the right-handed split-brain patient fixates on a central point. The patients' left hand will retrieve from a collection of objects (by feel alone) a banana. However, if the patient is asked (before he can look at his left hand) what he saw, he will say that he saw an apple; and his right hand will retrieve an apple if he is asked to pick out by feel alone what he saw (adapted from Sperry, 1968.)

It is not my purpose here to dwell on the evidence which the split-brain studies have provided for a belief in the duality of the minds, one propositional and the other appositional; this question has been considered at length elsewhere (14). What I should like to emphasize here is the new information which we have obtained on the special functions of the so-called "minor" hemisphere. While the left hemisphere is reading, writing, and talking, what is the other side doing?

That there is a strong association between each hand and the contralateral hemisphere has been known for two millenia, ever since Hippocrates (15). The lateralization of language capacity including speaking, reading, and writing to the left hemisphere in the right-handed has been known for about a century, ever since Broca (16) and Dax (17). Evidence for special functions of the right hemisphere has begun to appear during the past decade (18). Our studies of humans with commissurotomy have provided particularly persuasive evidence for a special right hemisphere capacity. This is based on the common observation that the right-handed person can also write, awkwardly but legibly, with his left hand. Following division of the corpus callosum and anterior commissure, the ability to write with the left hand is lost. That is, the individual has *dysgraphia* in the left hand. A reasonable explanation for this is that the right hemisphere, controlling the left hand, has been disconnected from the language function of the left hemisphere. What is more surprising is that the same person becomes disabled in the *right* hand for copying geometric figures in spite of the fact that he usually can copy with the left hand (which no longer writes)! We may say then that such a person has dysgraphia in the left hand and *dyscopia* in the right hand (19, 20, 21). An example of this is shown in Figure 1-3.

The dyscopia in the right hand can be explained in the same way as the dysgraphia in the left hand; that is, the left hemisphere which controls the right hand has evidently been disconnected from some visuospatial capacity in the right hemisphere. This lateral dissociation of dysgraphia-dyscopia does not persist unchanged. We believe that subsidence of this phenomenon is attributable not only to increased cooperation between the hemispheres, but also to the fact that each hemisphere comes to acquire a degree of control over the ipsilateral hand. In our youngest patient, the lateral dissociation of dysgraphia-dyscopia was present for only a week following operation and he has since then been able to write and draw with either hand. However, when he was given a test for the matching of spatial forms by a method which restricted the input to only one or the other hemisphere, thus minimizing contamination by ipsilateral control, the right hemisphere was again found to be superior (22).

There is an additional finding which illustrates a right hemisphere superiority for visuospatial function. The block design test may be familiar to most of

FIGURE 1-3. Following cerebral commissurotomy, this right-handed patient continued to write well with his right hand; he wrote to dictation the word "hat" as seen in the upper left. He could not write spontaneously with his left hand. Neither could he copy with his left hand (except for a small scrawl) his own right-handed writing. When the word "HAT" was printed for him in capital letters (upper right) he could copy it with his left hand just as he could copy geometric figures. His left-handed copies of the cross and cube are shown to the left of the models. His attempts with the right hand are shown to the right of the models. The dysgraphic left-handed copies are better than the right-handed copies.

us here since it is usually included in the Wechsler battery. The blocks must be assembled in imitation of a pattern presented to the patient; it is important to keep in mind that the pattern to be imitated is ordinarily presented in such a way that both hemispheres can see and react to it. Following cerebral commissurotomy, the left hand often does better on block design tests than does the right hand. As with the dysgraphia-dyscopia finding, the block design differential, therefore, appears only at the time when the patient has sufficiently recovered from the operation to cooperate well but has not yet reacquired good ipsilateral control. In some patients this time is either brief or nonexistent so that the phenomenon cannot be obtained; but in other patients the phenomenon is quite clear. An example is shown in Figure 1-4.

Once we understand that the right hemisphere has different functions from the left, it is reasonable to suppose that an important function of the corpus callosum is to facilitate and regulate an exchange of complementary information between the two hemispheres. To the extent that this postulated regulations fails in some way, aberrant thinking would emerge. For example, we could speculate that the psychedelic efforts reported by users of LSD (23-24) may depend upon an increased access to the left (speaking) hemisphere of visuospatial activity going on in the right hemisphere but ordinarily less available to the left hemisphere consciousness. Perhaps this question could be examined by the developing methods of behavioral pharmacology (25). There

R.M. JULY 31, 1966 PATTERN	BLOCK DESIGN TEST TIME IN SECONDS	
	LEFT HAND	RIGHT HAND
1.	 27	115
2.	35	>180
3.	47	65
4.	32	>180
5.	 32	125
6.	 110	160

FIGURE 1-4. Four months after operation, the Block Design Test was done fairly well by R.M. using his left hand first. The right hand required longer time and failed within the arbitrary time limit on two patterns.

is another perhaps more direct approach. That is, does the drug augment the activity of callosal fibers as recently studied with microelectrodes (26)? Or does it augment the callosal response known to be evoked by cortical stimulation in homotopic areas of the opposite cortex (27, 28, 29)? The data presented in Figure 1-1 on the number of references to the corpus callosum for each year was a by-product of a search for already existing studies of the latter question. It appears that Marazzi and Hart (30) investigated the effect of LSD on the transcallosal response. These investigators found, contrary to what might have been expected, that LSD *decreases* the transcallosal response; perhaps this is a good example of the importance of the experimental method! On the other hand, it may be possible to defend the original speculation by supposing that the transcallosal response is inhibitory. Furthermore, 5-hydroxytryptamine also causes a depression of the transcallosal response which is antagonized by LSD; and interpretation of the results is further complicated by an apparent tendency of each of these drugs to cause a cortical spreading depression; and these drugs alter the ascending reticular influences on the cortex by action at brain stem sites; and all of these and other neuronal activities are affected by an action directly on the carotid sinus (31). As of now, it appears that considerably more work is needed before we can be said to have acquired a pharmacology of the corpus callosum. As both behavioral studies and the electrophysiology of the corpus callosum continue, we may expect that pharmacology will reap the benefit of an increasing interest in this important bridge between the two sides of the brain.

REFERENCES

1. MAGNUS, R.: *Körperstellung.* Berlin, Julius Springer, 1924.
2. MAGOUN H.W.: Caudal and cephalic influences of the brainstem reticular formation. *Physiol Rev, 30*:459–474, 1950.
3. SPERRY, R.W.: Physiological plasticity and brain circuit theory. In Harlow, H.F., and Woolsey, C.N. (Eds.): *Biological and Biochemical Bases of Behavior.* Madison, University of Wisconsin Press, 1958.
4. AKELAITIS, A.J.: A study of gnosis, praxis and language following section of the corpus callosum and anterior commissure. *J Neurosurg, 1*:94–102, 1944.
5. SMITH, K.U.: Experimental analysis of the associative mechanism of the human brain in learning functions. *J Comp Physiol Psychol, 45*:66–72, 1952.
6. TOMASCH, J.: Size, distribution, and number of fibres in the human corpus callosum. *Anat Rec, 119*:7–19, 1954.
7. MYERS, R.: The neocortical commissures and interhemispheric transmission of information. In Ettlinger, E.G. (Ed.): *Functions of the Corpus Callosum.* London, Churchill, 1965.
8. SPERRY, R.W.: Cerebral organization and behavior. *Science, 133*:1749-1757, 1961.
9. BOGEN, J.E., AND VOGEL, P.J.: Cerebral commissurotomy in man. Preliminary case report. *Bull Los Angeles Neurol Soc, 27*:169–172, 1962.
10. BOGEN, J.E., SPERRY, R.W., AND VOGEL, P.J.: Commisural section and the propagation

of seizures. In Jasper, H.H., Ward, A.A., and Pope, A. (Eds.) : *Basic Mechanisms of the Epilepsies.* Boston, Little, Brown and Co., 1969.
11. GAZZANIGA, M.S.: The split brain in man. *Sci Amer, 217*:24–29, 1967.
12. SPERRY, R.W.: Mental unity following surgical disconnection of the cerebral hemispheres. In *The Harvey Lectures* (Series 62). New York, Academic Press, 1968.
13. SPERRY, R.W., GAZZANIGA, M.S., AND BOGEN, J.E.: The neocortical commissures: Syndrome of hemisphere deconnection. *Handbook of Clinical Neurology.* Amsterdam, North-Holland Publishing Co., 1969, Vol. IV, Chapt. 14.
14. BOGEN, J.E.: The other side of the brain II. An appositional mind. *Bull Los Angeles Neurol Soc. 34*:135–162, 1969.
15. CHADWICK, J., AND MANN, W.N.: *The Medical Works of Hippocrates.* Oxford, Blackwell, 1950, p. 263.
16. JOYNT, R.J., AND BENTON A.L.: The memoir of Marc Dax on aphasia. *Neurology, 14*:851–854, 1964.
17. BROCA, F.: La faculté du langage articulé. *Bull Soc Anthropologie, 6*:493–494, 1865.
18. ZANGWILL, O.L.: Asymmetry of cerebral hemisphere function. In Garland, H. (Ed.) : *Scientific Aspects of Neurology.* London, E.&S. Livingstone, 1961.
19. GAZZANIGA, M.S., BOGEN, J.E., AND SPERRY, R.W.: Some functional effects of sectioning the cerebral commissures in man. *Proc Nat Acad Sci USA, 48*:1765–1769, 1962.
20. BOGEN, J.E., AND GAZZANIGA, M.S.: Cerebral commissurotomy in man: Minor hemisphere dominance for certain visuospatial functions. *J Neurosurg, 23*:394–399, 1965.
21. BOGEN, J.E.: The other side of the brain I. Dysgraphia and dyscopia following cerebral commissurotomy. *Bull Los Angeles Neurol Soc, 34*:73–105, 1969.
22. LEVI-AGRESTI, J., AND SPERRY, R.W.: Differential perceptual capacities in major and minor hemispheres. *Proc Nat Acad Sci USA, 61*:1151, 1968.
23. CHAPMAN, L.F., AND WALTER, R.D.: Actions of lysergic acid diethylamide on averaged human cortical evoked responses to light flash. In Wortis, J. (Ed.) : *Recent Advances in Biological Psychiatry.* New York, Plenum Press, 1965, vol. VII.
24. UNGERLIEDER, J.T.: *The Problems and Prospects of LSD.* Springfield, Charles C Thomas, 1968.
25. THOMPSON, T., AND SHUSTER, C.R.: *Behavioral Pharmacology.* Englewood Cliffs, Prentice Hall, 1968.
26. BERLUCCHI, G., GAZZANIGA, M.S., AND RIZZOLATTI, G.: Microelectrode analysis of transfer of visual information by the corpus callosum. *Arch Ital Biol, 105*:583–596, 1967.
27. CURTIS, H.J.: Intercortical connections of corpus callosum as indicated by evoked potentials. *J Neurophysiol, 3*:407–413, 1940.
28. GRAFSTEIN, B.: Postnatal development of the transcallosal evoked response in the cerebral cortex of the cat. *J Neurophysiol, 26*:79–99, 1963.
29. BREMER, F.: Étude électrophysiologique d'un transfer interhémisphérique callosal. *Arch Ital Biol, 104*:1–29, 1966.
30. MARRAZZI, A.S., AND HART, E.R.: Relationship of hallucinogens to adrenergic cerebral neurohumors. *Science, 121*:365–367, 1955.
31. BOND, H.W.: Interaction of 5-hydroxytryptamine and d-lysergic acid diethylamide in the transcallosal response. *Life Sci, 7*:249–58, 1968.

Chapter 2

Post-Tetanic Potentiation as a Measure of Excitability in the Hippocampus and Neocortex

BERRY CAMPBELL and MIHAI DEMETRESCU

The excitability of the cerebral cortex is expressed variously. Limiting ourselves to electroneurophysiology, we find facilitation and inhibition of the evoked potential are to be measured in the classical ways. Even more favored, nowadays, is the study of single cell activity as shown by extracellular or intracellular electrodes. Though these are of great importance and interest in the elucidation of some particular patterns of organization and integration of the cerebral cortex, for example Hubel and Wiesel (1), an overall view of cortical function is hard to achieve in this fashion. Statistically, the single cell studies are unsatisfactory. In addition, the rules or laws which relate single cell activity to the overall function of the cortex are in the long process of being worked out. One of us (2) has reported on single cell correlates of evoked potentials and cortical inhibition.

Intracellular recordings of hypopolarization and hyperpolarization similarly give information too particular to be reliably related to cortical function in the larger sphere. These indicate the processes which occur in particular cells—or even in particular sites of these cells. They measure the milliseconds of time governing the ongoing business and traffic of the cortex. But their use is as though one were using too fine a net for the larger school of fish.

In this paper we will consider utilization of a more inclusive sign of cortical activity. This is post-tetanic potentiation. As it is best seen in that specialized portion of the cerebral cortex, Ammon's horn or the hippocampus, we will look first to that region to define the sequence of events. We will then examine its application to the generalized cortex to see if a useful transfer of this approach can be made. Certain preliminary applications of drugs which have been studied in this way will not be discussed here. Instead, the application of external polarizing currents will be used as a variable condition. The investigation of the interaction of steady applied currents to the nervous system is an old experimental approach whose scattered literature will not be reviewed here. It is of interest to us both for its promise in unravelling basic physiological mechanisms and because it stands in need of newer technical

Note: This research was made possible through donation of equipment by David Kopf Instruments and through support from a UCI research development grant.

approaches. To this end, we are presenting a new electronic circuit for the generation of currents, a current clamp in fact. This has been designed to compensate for the sudden and sizeable variations in impedance which the brain and other tissues exhibit upon polarization. It has proven to be a regulator of great stability and with the use of such current clamps it would seem that considerable functional dissection can be made of complex neurophysiological processes.

METHODS AND MATERIALS

Rabbits and cats were used in these experiments. Nembutal® was the anesthesia. Recordings were made with low impedance platinum iridium needles, electrolytically sharpened and coated with glass. Stimuli were delivered from a square wave generator by means of concentric or close dipole electrode pairs. Oscillographic recording was conventional.

Polarizing current was applied with the aid of a regulated polarizing circuit designed for this purpose (Fig. 2-1). This circuit acts as a voltage clamp in that it delivers a set current without fluctuation over wide ranges of impedance (0 to 50,000 ohms). One pole consisted of a platinum ring, 2.5 mm in diameter, backed up by a tube of insulating plastic material through which the probing needle electrode was directed. The other pole was a large steel needle placed in the ventral neck region of the animal.

THE CORTICAL STRUCTURE

Before examining the electrical records, let us look at the cells which make up the generalized cerebral cortex and its variant, the hippocampus. Figure 2-2 illustrates two typical cortical cells as visualized in a Golgi stain of the cerebral cortex of a monkey. In Figure 2-2a, we see a medium-sized pyramid of the neocortex. In Figure 2-2b, a pyramidal cell form the hippocampus is shown. The most noteworthy feature of the cortical cells is their uniformity of structure. With very few exceptions, the cortical cells are of this general pyramidal shape with long apical dendrites, with several basal dendrites and an axon. In all such cells the orientation in the cortex is the same: the apical dendrites extend toward the pial surface, the axons toward the ependymal or ventricular surface. Exception to this would total only a small fraction of one percent of the myriad of cells making up the cerebral cortex. In the illustration, the polarity of the hippocampal pyramid has been reversed—axonal end upwards—in keeping with our experimental approach. There is a considerable variation in the size of the cells of the neocortex (Fig. 2-3a). Throughout the structure, but mostly in midlayers, are cells which are small as far as nerve cells go. Because the nuclei are always relatively large in smaller cells, the cell bodies are globular, not pyramid-shaped. Nevertheless, the great majority of these so-called granule cells have dendrites which rise

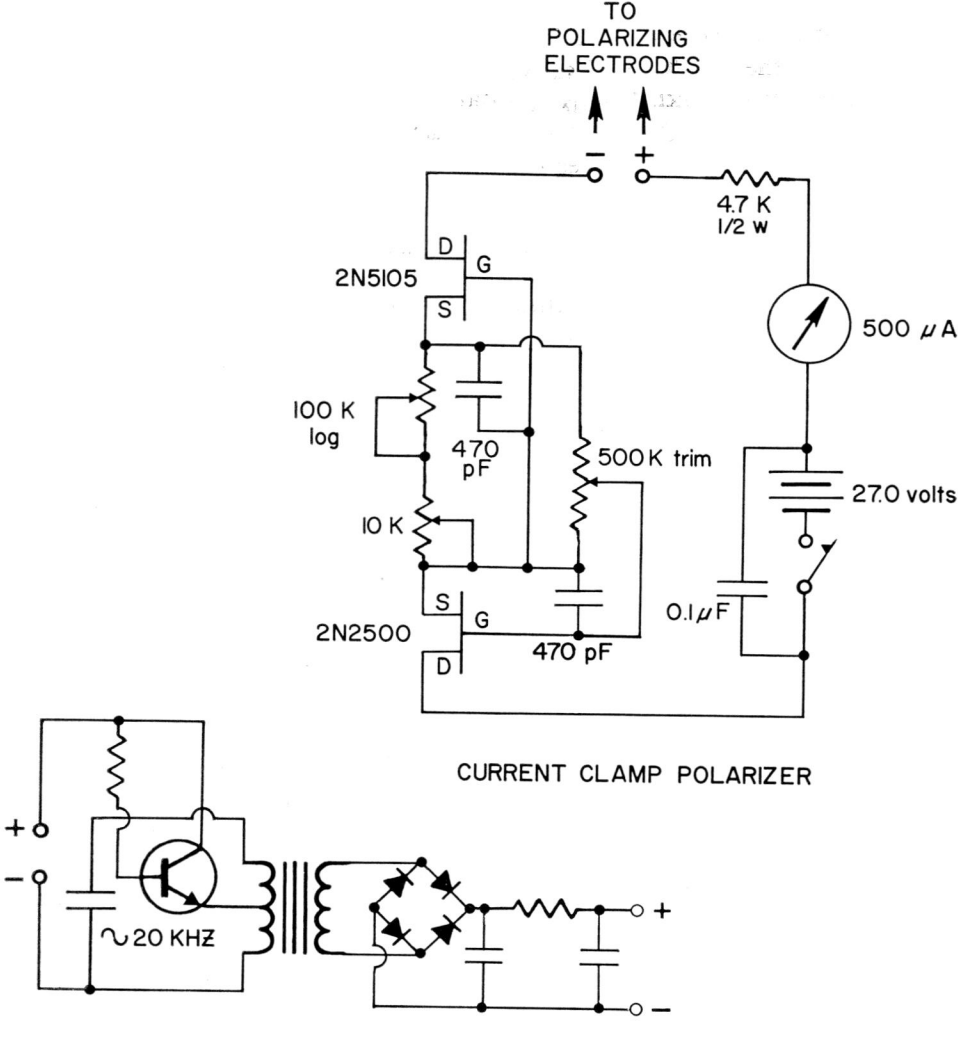

FIGURE 2-1. Electronic circuit of polarizer used in these experiments. The current output is regulated so as not to respond to changes in impedance.

toward the pial surface and axons which pass inward to the deeper layers. From these small cells, variation in size is continuous up to the really giant cells of the cerebral cortex, the apical dendrites of which may be as long as two or more millimeters and whose transverse diameter may be in excess of 75μ. In summary, the cerebral cortex has cells of many sizes with the cell bodies located throughout the cortical thickness but yet nearly all of which are oriented in the same direction.

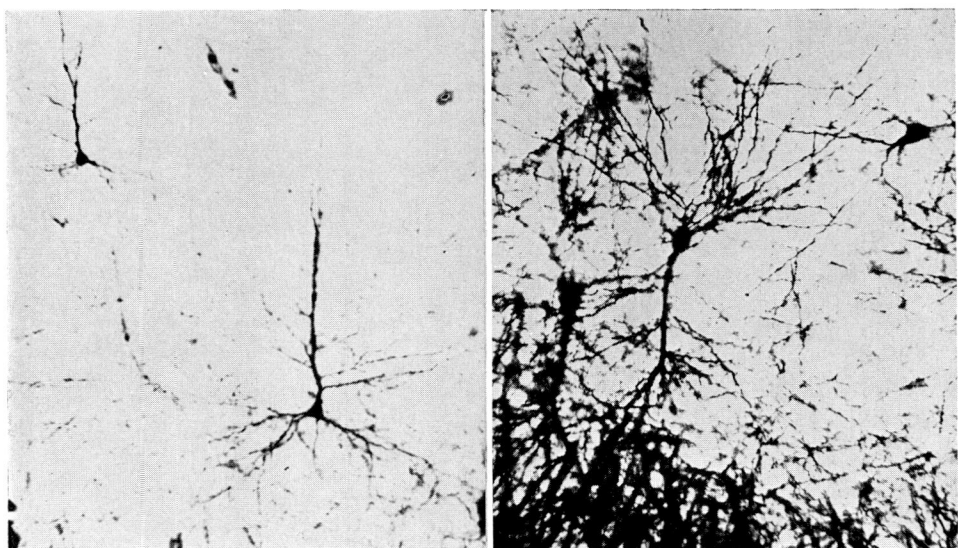

FIGURE 2–2. Pyramidal cells of brain of monkey, Golgi strain. *(Left)* Medium-sized pyramid of neocortex. *(Right)* Hippocampal pyramid.

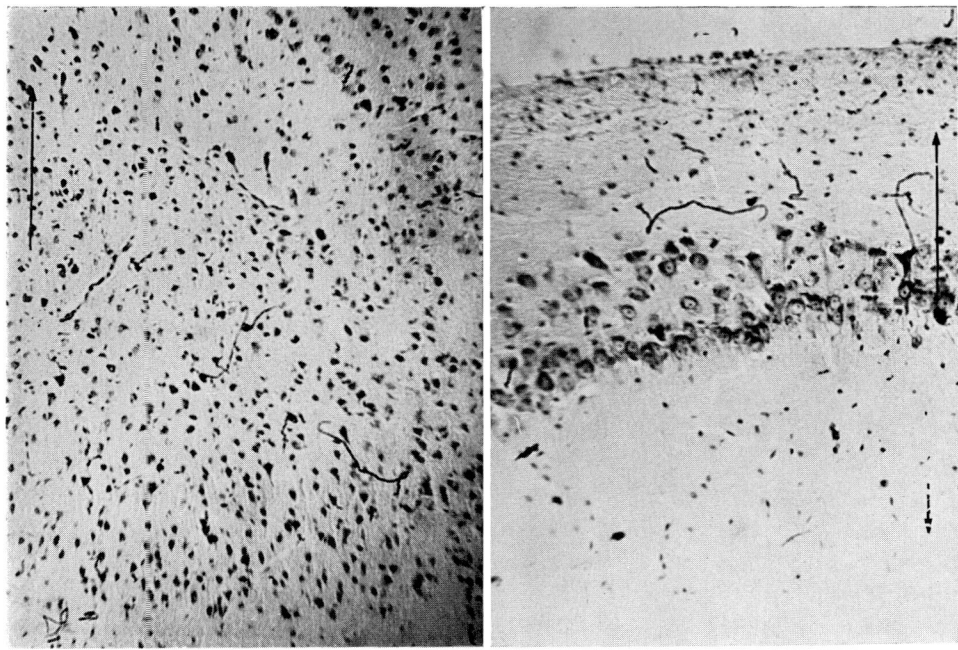

FIGURE 2–3. Sections of neocortex and hippocampus of cat, Nissal strain, to show pacing arrangements of cells. *(Left)* Neocortex. *(Right)* Pyramidal layer of hippocampus. In both figures, the pial surface is upward.

The hippocampus is of particular interest in that it presents considerable areas which crowd rather uniform, medium-sized pyramid cells into a very dense layer where the cell bodies are side by side with little space between them (Fig. 2-3b). Because of the proximity of these cells, probably, they tend to act in unison and in other ways demonstrate a close dependence upon one another. The orientation of these cells, the so-called hippocampal pyramids, is similar to those of the cerebral cortex, to the deeper cells of which they correspond. As they are customarily approached from the ventricular surface, their polarity seems reversed.

POST-TETANIC POTENTIATION IN THE HIPPOCAMPUS

The hippocampal pyramids may be stimulated by the ascending efferents in the fornix (3, 4). Single stimuli seldom bring about firing of these cells. Tetanic trains of stimuli do, however, excite their firing, resulting in a procession of potentials which are spectacular and are subject to rather detailed analysis. Figure 2-4 shows the sequence of response in two successive tetanic stimulations of the hippocampus of a cat. Each is to be read from the bottom up. Preceding the tetanus, a series of control sweeps showed little activity to be evoked by the shocks. With a repetition of the stimuli at ten per second for a number of seconds, simultaneous discharge of the cells commenced which built up to a very high level by the end of the period of rapid stimulation. Then with the sampling stimuli and sweeps much further apart, the summed action potential of the cells waxes and wanes in characteristic manner.

Most striking (and in contrast to the findings in the generalized cerebral cortex, as detailed below) is the lability of the latency of response. A *continuous* variation in the latency of the firing over a period of 10 msec. or so is found between the earliest response, which occurs at the third or fourth sampling sweep, and the last response over thirty seconds later (Fig. 2-5). Anatomical considerations suggest that no interposed cells lie between the ascending afferents and the hippocampal pyramids. This interpretation is made all the more certain by the smooth variation of the latency as one passes along the successive evocations of the potential. If a small number of interposed cells existed, some stepwise alterations in the latency would be expected. These are not seen. A large number of interposed neurons is, on anatomical grounds, out of the question. The second firing, seen best in the left-hand column, bears on this also. As the post-tetanic potentiation rises to maximum in sweeps 4 to 10 following the tetanic train, a second peak, which we take to represent a second firing to the original stimulus, shows the excitability of the cells to be too great to cease with but one discharge. The curve of the latencies of these second spikes, during their ephemeral appearance, is an exaggeration of that of the first spike. A conspicuous variation in the synchrony of the response, as shown by the width of the spike, can be similarly

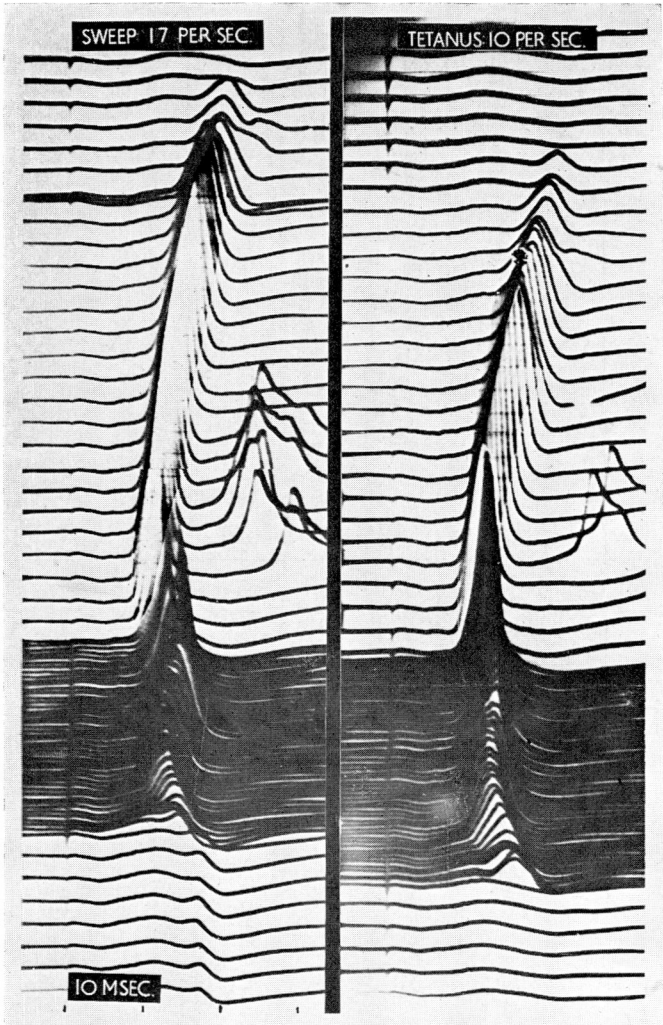

FIGURE 2–4. Post-tetanic potentiation of hippocampus. The stimulation was delivered to the ipsilateral fornix; the recording made with a needle electrode at the level of the cellular layer. To be read from bottom of columns upward.

correlated with the strong surge and ebb of excitability of the hippocampal pyramids. As the reaction begins, to die down, the spikes become wider and wider. Thus the same sequence is seen in the short train of second responses as in the first discharges. From this we conclude that the cells, lying as closely adpressed as they do, hold one another in the grip of the common external potential field during the firing state.

In the hippocampus, as probably in other parts of the nervous system, a

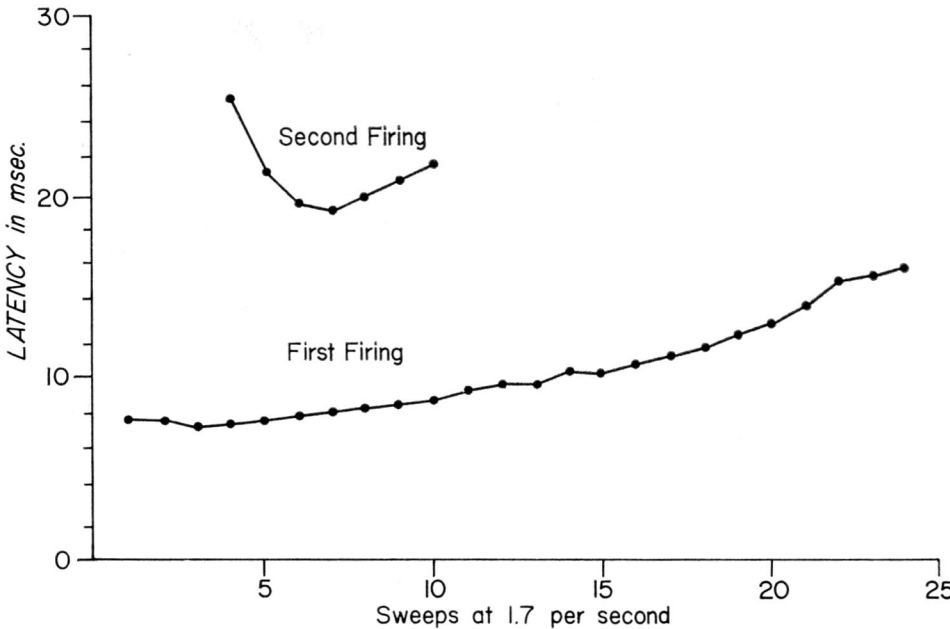

FIGURE 2-5. Graphic analysis of evolution of latencies of first and second spikes in first column of Fgure 2-4.

capacity for the dynamic expression of cell excitability can be demonstrated to have several convenient parameters. Easily measured are latency, snychrony, amplitude, and second firing. As these are readily available for drug studies, this preparation should be of particular interest to the neuropharmacologists. The method, first used by Dusser de Barenne, of applying drugs absorbed to small pieces of filter paper, here is simplified by the easy accessibility of the cells through the ventricular approach. Injection of drugs into the ventricle or even intravenously offers simple alternatives.

POLARIZATION OF THE HIPPOCAMPAL PYRAMIDS

It is not the demonstration of drug effects, however, which we wish to present here. Instead, we have concerned ourselves with the effects of polarizing currents and their interaction with post-tetanic potentiation. Figure 2-6 illustrates the effect of 400 μa current with the positive or anodal pole upward (that is, at the axonal end of the cell) in contrast to the alternative or negative up orientation. Figure 2-7 is a graphic analysis of the latency changes of the first, second, and third columns of Figure 2-6. It is seen that the application of current with the negative pole looking towards the axonal ends of the cells (the ventricular surface) and the reversed polarity displace the post-tetanic potentiation curve in opposite directions from the control. This re-

Post-Tetanic Potentiation as a Measure of Excitability

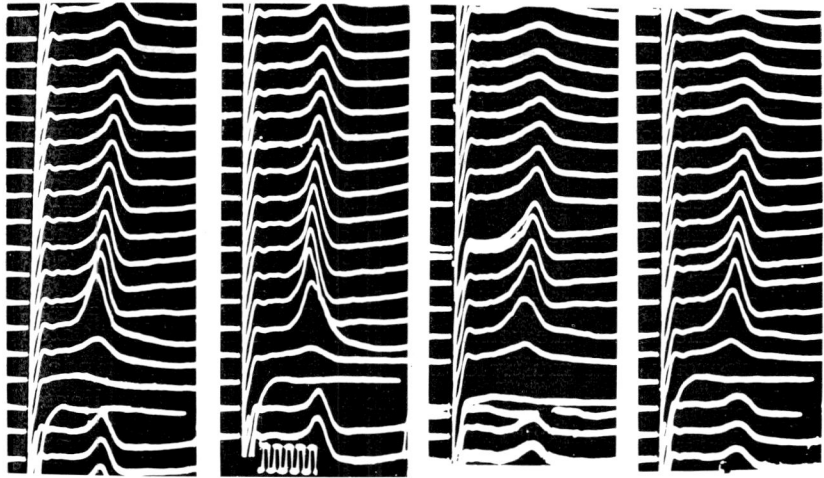

FIGURE 2–6. Records of post-teanic potentiation in hippocampus of cat following stimulation of ipsilateral fornix. *(1st column)* Control. *(2nd column)* Same with 300μa current, negative up. *(3rd column)* Same with 400μa current, positive up. *(4th column)* Control. Time: 1000 cycles; amplitude: 1 mV.

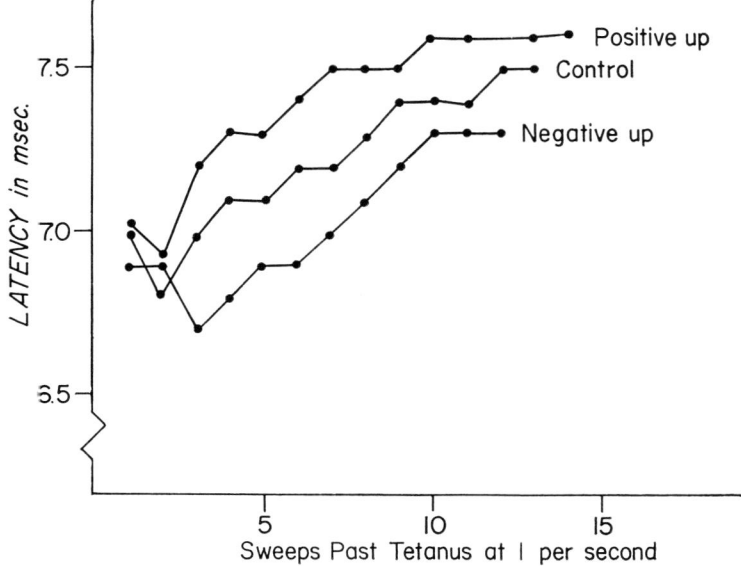

FIGURE 2–7. Graphic analysis of latencies of post-tetanic spikes of column *a*, *b*, and *c* of Figure 2–6.

lationship of the polarity to the axonal-abaxial axis of the cell will be seen below in the generalized cortex as well as in the hippocampus. It was shown by Campbell and Sutin (4) that the polarity of the external fields of pyramidal cells during firing is in the same orientation as the facilitating current, i.e. negative on the axonal end. Their figure of the depth time electroarchitectonic map of these events is reproduced here (Fig. 2-8). This corresponds also to the directional facilitatory and inhibitory effects of polarization on the firing of ventral horn cells of the spinal cord by Renshaw (5). It is also of interest that the nonfiring, activation potential of the hippocampal pyramids showed the same polarity as did the firing (4). The effects of the applied currents are reflected in the general parameters of excitability, latency, amplitude, synchrony, and multiple firing. Thus we must conclude that the threshold of the cell is related in a specific way to electrical gradients. This is an old finding and one which cannot be reviewed here. One of the other participants in this symposium, Dr. Van Harreveld, has contributed much (6).

With weaker stimuli than in the previously analyzed experiment, a shorter train of potentiated spikes were elicited in the four sequences shown (Fig. 2-9) Column 1 represents a control tetany of two hundred pulses delivered to the ipsilateral fornix in two seconds. Test sweeps 3 to 12 show some firing. This rises to a maximum in sweep 7 but shows poor synchrony and irregular progression. With the negative pole upward in column 2, much greater potentiation is shown with a strong tendency to synchrony at the maximum level. Some firing is seen in sweeps 3 to 8. Quite a different reaction is shown in column 3 where the positive pole was upward. Compared with its counterpart in column 2, the number of sweeps showing some firing is reduced in number and both the amplitude and synchrony are less. Column 4 is another control series, resembling column 1 in most respects. It is noteworthy that all four of these columns, with rapid and weak tetanic stimuli as compared with the previous experiment, show very clearly the subnormality of the first post-tetanic sweeps mentioned by Larrabee and Bronk (7) and seen by most authors who have followed them.

POST-TETANIC POTENTIATION AND POLARIZATION OF THE NEOCORTEX

The examination of the effects of post-tetanic potentiation of the neocortex, with and without polarization, offers an opportunity, in view of its somewhat different arrangement of cells, to make a correlation of the findings with these particulars. In general, we find much the same effects from tetanization and tetanization plus polarization as seen in the hippocampus, but with considerable less deviation from the simple evoked potential. Whether these differences are specifically related to the stimulation of the visual cortex via the lateral geniculate body is a possibility which must be kept in mind.

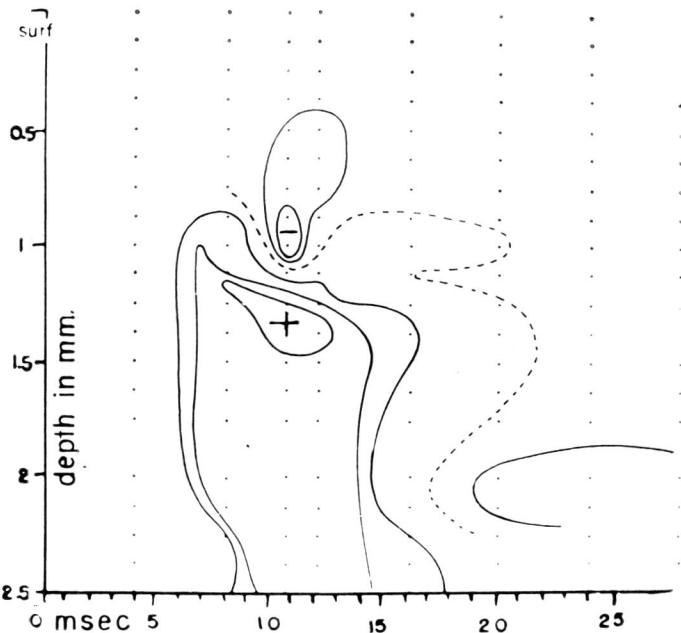

FIGURE 2–8. Electroarchitectonic map of spike discharge in hippocampus of cat. Ordinates represent depth below ventricular surface, abscissa represents time in msec. Isopotential contours delineate electric fields. From Campbell and Sutin (4).

In Figure 2-10, column 1, a sequence of potentials is shown as recorded with a microelectrode a short distance below the pial surface. The stimulus is delivered by concentric electrodes placed stereotaxically in the lateral geniculate body. Our attention is focused on the surface-positive (downward) deflection which represents the fourth wave of current authors (arrow). This component, which is obviously the sign of an intracortical process shows, in the sequence illustrated, a very definite post-tetanic potentiation insofar as its amplitude is concerned. Figure 2-11 illustrates by graph analysis the sequence following a tetanic train of one second frequency of one hundred per second. The first two sweeps reveal a rising excitability (as measured by amplitude) and the succeeding sequence shows a decline which by nine seconds has reached that of the control sweeps. This is in good agreement with the findings given above for the hippocampus. A remarkable difference is shown in the neocortex, however, in regard to the latency reaction to the tetanic train. Careful measurement has shown that in this and other such experiments, acceleration of latency is limited to about 0.4 msec. This is quite in contrast to the hippocampus. The most obvious difference between the two structures is the concentration of cells into one layer in one and the diffuse spacing in the other.

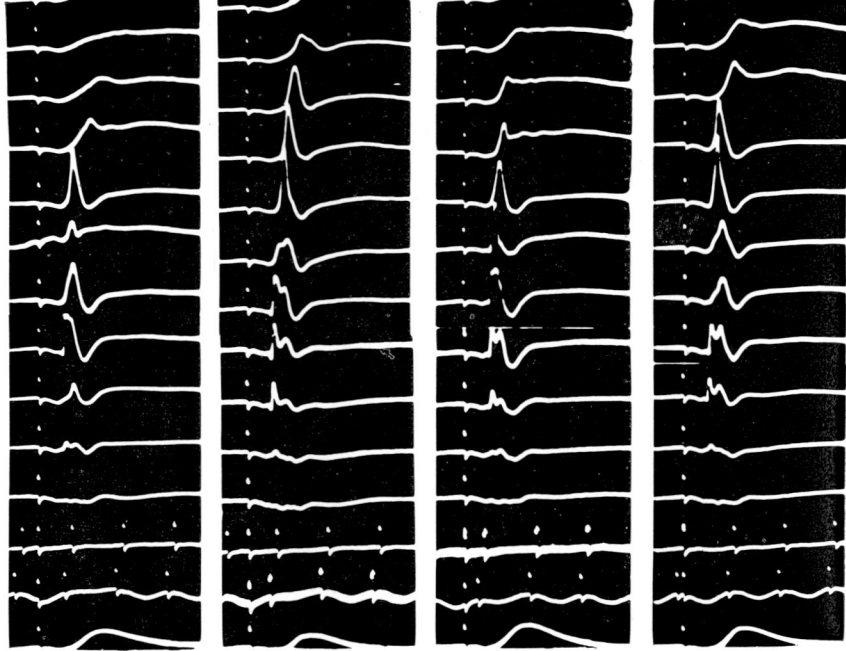

Figure 2-9. Records of four post-tetanic sequences from hippocampus of rabbit. Stimulation was at ipsilateral fornix—200 shocks in 2 seconds; recording was at layer of pyramidal cells. *(1st column)* Control. *(2nd column)* 300μa polarization negative up. *(3rd column)* Same, with positive up. *(4th column)* Control.

Here, it must be remarked that the neocortex, in spite of the diffuse spacing of its cells, is fired in a single event. The connectionists of the past, who thought that the incoming thalamic fibers set off the upper layers of the cortex which then in turn excited sequentially the deeper and deeper cells, submitted a cortical model which would have, as a necessary consequence, a trickling through of activity from the pial to the deepest layers. Bearing in mind the synaptic delays and the slow conduction of fine fibers, a speed easily measured—certainly slower than 1 mm/msec—would be apparent. This is not observed. In the model of the cortex presented by Sutin and Campbell (8), no such filtering of signal is postulated. Instead it suggests that not all cells contributing to the evoked potential actually generate conducted impulses and those which do are timed by other means than a progressive downward sweep of activity.

As our approach to the neocortex is from the pial surface rather than the ventricular, the orientation of the polarizing currents relative to the cell axes is reversed. In Figure 2-10, columns 1 and 2 show the effects of superimposition of a current of 300μa upon the post-tetanic potentials of the cortex as recorded by a microelectrode (10 to 30μ tip diameter) in a superficial though subpial locus. There is a definite and consistent displacement of the cortical components of the potential upward (negative side of electrical zero axis) where the current is applied with the positive pole on the pial surface (column 2). This displacement is shown in Figure 2-11 by the generally lesser measured amplitude of the deflections (line *b*). However, the slope of the descending line of the potentiation curve is a gentle one indicating a longer lasting excitatory state. As in the unpolarized sequences (column 3), the latency varies minimally if at all.

The results of neocortical stimulation which are presented here show the phenomenon of post-tetanic potentiation to be much less evident—and thus, perhaps less useful in drug assay—than in the hippocampus. However, it must be emphasized that only the thalamocortical responses of the visual cortex have been examined. Functionally, this is a precision system and may differ in qualities measured by lability of latency and amplitude from other cortical systems.

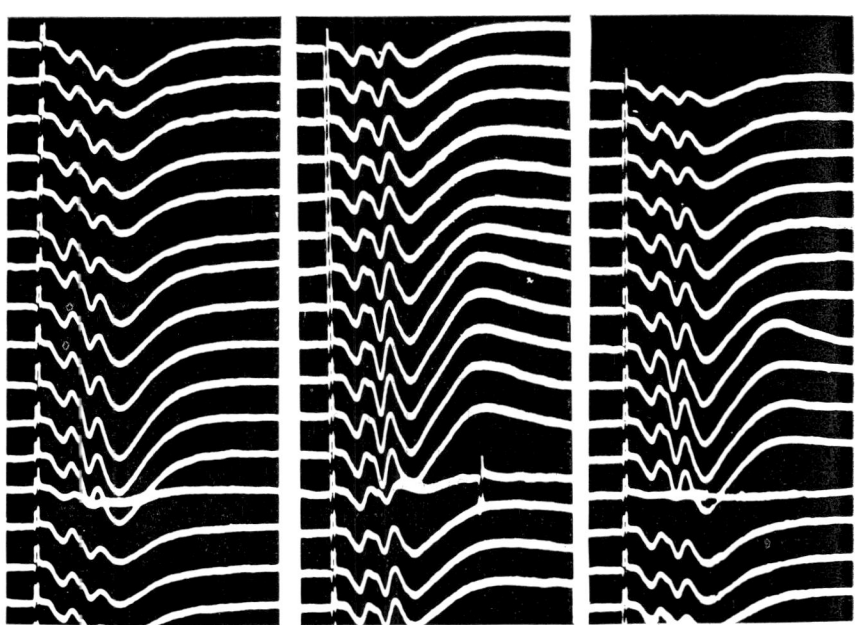

FIGURE 2–10. Post-tetanic potentiation in visual cortex of cat. Stimulus to ipsilateral lateral geniculate body; recording by needle electrode below pial surface of neocortex. Tetanus of 100 shocks in one second at fourth sweep from bottom of columns. *(1st column)* 300μa, negative up. *(2nd column)* 300μa, positive up. *(3rd column)* Control.

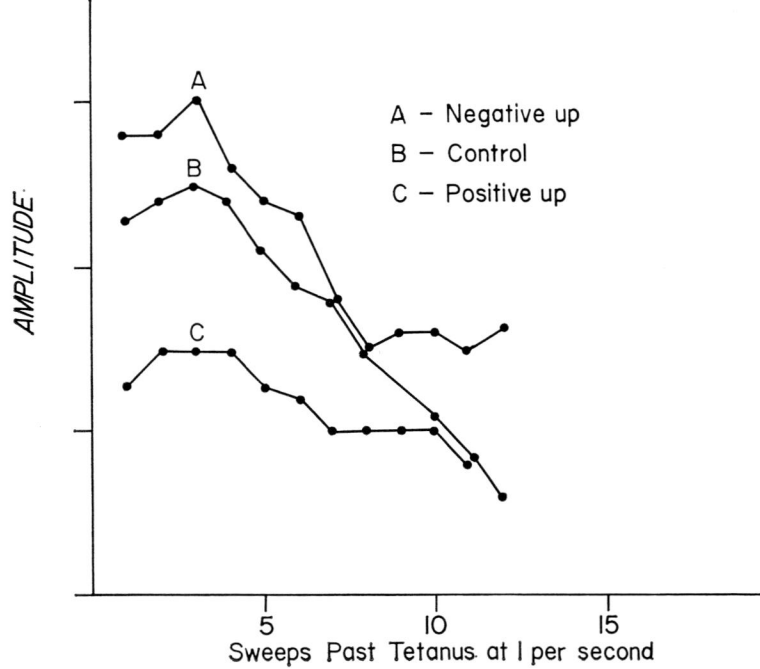

FIGURE 2–11. Graphic analysis of evolution of amplitudes in post-tetanic sequences illustrated in Figure 2–10.

DISCUSSION

If the transmission of signal in the nervous system, or in the cerebral cortex itself, is analyzed using the common neurophysiological parameters, a variation is found which seems to correlate with function or at least with our current ideas of function. Some transfer is made through mechanisms which show a long time carry-over of the states of excitation of the elements. Perhaps the most spectacular of these yet described are the post-tetanic potentiations which we have demonstrated in the hippocampus. In what is obviously a relay involving only the afferent and the efferent units, excitability changes can be demonstrated for a half minute or more. On the other hand, we have seen that in the generalized cortex, the transmittive mechanisms seem somewhat less labile in their response—or memory—to previous tetanic stimulation.

The functions served by the slow excitability phenomena are not certain. As the hippocampus is a part of the limbic system, they may play a part in the establishment and maintenance of effective states. Current thinking would lead one to relate those in the neocortex to more discriminative or engram forming functions. That such long-lasting processes are demanded by most learning theories makes the demonstration of such events fascinating to all who are interested in the neurological translation of behavior. In contradistinction to this, which we might term soft transmission, one of us pointed out in a presentation some years ago (9) that the proprioceptive component of the segmental reflex is remarkably stable under varying loads of stimulation. With tetanic trains far in excess of any used in this study, the latency of transmission of the proprioceptive spike can seldom be made to advance more than 0.2 msec. It was remarked then, and seems true now, that transmission patterns reflect not only functional needs but structural constraints as well. Thus the proprioceptive, or muscle afferent system, is seen to mediate simple rather unyielding reflexes, the knee-jerk as an example. Anatomically, these are the systems which show large synaptic junctions in the form of boutons. The transmittive apparatus of the hippocampus is quite different than this as it consists of a feltwork of neuropil on the afferent side in which the apical dendrites of the hippocampal pyramids are buried.

In the neocortex, the situation would seem to resemble somewhat the hippocampus. It is an interesting historical sidelight that Cajal, in his many illustrations of the cerebral cortex, did not indicate boutons as the synaptic junctions. These were introduced by Lorente de No. (10) in the diagram which appeared in Fulton's text on neurophysiology. However, anatomists seem now to have agreed that the synaptic terminals in the cortex are of quite a different sort and can be visualized only with the electron microscope.

For testing the effects of metabolic agents, of drugs, of physical agents such as heat, or the action of polarizing currents, the preparations and the precedures which we have described would seem to be useful. The conjoint study of the intact organism by behavior manifestations and of neurologic transmission in the post-tetanic phenomena of the cerebral cortex and hippocampus would seem to make a functional approach of great power.

REFERENCES

1. HUBEL, D.H. AND WIESEL, T.N.: Receptive fields, binocular interaction and functional architecture in the cat's visual cortex. *J Physiol, 160*:106, 1962.
2. DEMETRESCU, M.: Symposium on cortical activation and active inhibition. (Western conference of neurophysiology and brain research, Tahoe City, Calif., February 2, 1968). *Electroenceph Clin Neurophysiol, 26*:332, 1969.
3. DAITZ, H.M., AND POWELL, T.P.S.: *J Anat, 87*:456, 1953.
4. CAMPBELL, B., AND SUTIN, J.: Organization of cerebral cortex. IV. Post-tetanic potentiation of hippocampal pyramids. *Amer J Physiol, 196*:330, 1959.
5. RENSHAW, B.: Activity in the simplest spinal reflex pathways. *J Physiol, 3*:373, 1940.
6. VAN HARREVELD, A.: On galvanotropism and oscillotaxis in fish. *J Exp Biol, 15*:197, 1938.
7. LARRABEE, M.G., AND BRONK, D.W.: Prolonged facilitation of synaptic excitation in sympathetic ganglia. *J Neurophysiol, 2*:139, 1947.
8. SUTIN, J., AND CAMPBELL, B.: A model of cortical activity. *Nature, 175*:339, 1955.

9. CAMPBELL, B.: Specificity and non-specificity in neural pathways. *Trans Amer Neurol Ass, 28*:74, 1957.
10. LORENTE DE NO, R.: Cerebral cortex: Architecture, intracortical connectors, motor projects. In Fulton, J.F.: *Physiology of the Nervous System,* 3rd ed. (rev.) New York, Oxford University Press, 1949.

Chapter 3

Mechanism of Changes in Electrolyte and Water Distribution in Central Nervous Tissue

ANTONIE VAN HARREVELD

Central nervous tissue is extraordinarily sensitive to O_2 lack. Its functions are suspended after a few minutes of asphyxiation at the most. This sensitivity is not found in peripheral nerves which do not stop conducting until the O_2 supply has been arrested for twenty minutes or longer. Certain central nervous functions which normally show the usual sensitivity to O_2 lack were found to be more resistant when the nervous tissue had been asphyxiated previously for certain periods of time. Cats in which the lumbosacral spinal cord had been asphyxiated for about thirty minutes showed two weeks later an exaggerated tone and often enhanced tendon reflexes and clonus in the hind legs (33). These reflex phenomena are the expression of monosynaptic reflex activity which has been demonstrated in the asphyxiated cord (9,38). The asphyxial survival time of these reactions was in the most resistant preparations similar to that of peripheral nerve, fifteen to twenty minutes (21). These observations suggest that two mechanisms of different latency are involved in the asphyxial arrest of central nervous functions. The one with a latency of fifteen to twenty minutes or more is present both in peripheral and central nervous tissue. Its mechanism may be the lack of oxidative energy for the ion pumps which maintain the concentration gradients across the plasma membranes responsible for the membrane potentials and possibly for other mechanisms active in synaptic transmission. The arrest of the ion pumps will result in an increase in the intracellular sodium concentration and an outflow of potassium from the cells as has been observed in other tissues under anaerobic conditions (12). This mechanism would thus be due to the failure of the energy sources in the cell and would not be specific for central nervous tissue but common to all body cells.

The short latency mechanism of asphyxial arrest is found only in central nervous tissue, not in peripheral nerves and as far as known not in other organs or tissues. This mechanism produces a number of changes in the tissue which have lately been analyzed in some detail. For instance, asphyxiation of the cerebral cortex causes in addition to the arrest of the electrocorticogram

Note: These investigations were supported by grants from the National Institutes of Health, the National Science Foundation, and from the Department of the Navy, Office of Naval Research.

a surface negativity with respect to an indifferent electrode which develops after a latency of two to three minutes (14, 15). Simultaneously with this asphyxial potential the tissue impedance increases; in the cerebral cortex the latter value may double in the ensuing one to two minutes (16,34). It is generally recognized that tissue impedance is a measure of the abundance of extracellular electrolytes (5). The intracellular electrolytes are surrounded by cell membranes which in general have a high resistance, impeding participation of the intracellular ions in the transport of the current used in the impedance measurement. It has been shown that no more than a few per cent of a one thousand cycle measuring current flows through the intracellular compartment (25,34). A large change in tissue impedance as occurs during asphyxiation of the cerebral cortex can thus be taken as an indication that extracellular electrolytes have been lost. Similar asphyxial potentials and impedance increases have also been observed in the cerebellar cortex (24) and in the spinal gray matter (26). In the latter tissue the latency of these changes is often not more than ten to fifteen seconds.

Since the electrolytes lost from the extracellular compartment cannot well leave the tissue it has been postulated that they are taken up by the cellular elements in the cortex where surrounded by plasma membranes they cannot freely participate anymore in the transport of the measuring current. Considerable support has been found for this postulate. Since the extracellular electrolytes in central nervous tissue as in other tissues consist mostly of sodium chloride one has to assume a transport of this salt from the extracellular into the intracellular compartment during asphyxiation. Such a movement could indeed be demonstrated with a histochemical method for chloride (36). This method consists in rapidly freezing the cerebral cortex and substituting the ice in the tissue with alcohol at low (-20°C) temperature. The alcohol contains silver nitrate (and nitric acid), and as chloride is released from the frozen tissue during the substitution it is precipitated on the spot by the silver ions. The resulting silver chloride can later be made visible by exposure to light which reduces this material to a brown subhalide. The location of the brown material thus indicates the location of the chloride at the moment of freezing. It was found that the distribution of chloride in cortices frozen while the circulation was intact is rather uniform. However, in tissue frozen after asphyxiation for eight minutes the chloride was accumulated in cellular elements, mainly in apical dendrites (37). Similar experiments performed on the cerebellar cortex demonstrated a chloride transport into dendrites of Purkinje cells and into fibers of Bergmann (24). The latter observation is of considerable interest since these fibers are glial elements, showing that the chloride accumulation is not restricted to neuronal structures. The chloride transport is considered to be the expression of a transport of sodium chloride into the intracellular compartment. To maintain osmotic equilibrium such a transport has to be accompanied by a water movement into the same cellular elements. Indeed a rather marked swelling of apical dendrites (22) and of the fibers of Bergmann (24) during asphyxiation could be demonstrated.

It has been attempted to show the shift of extracellular material into the intracellular compartment during asphyxiation with the electron microscope. The usual chemical fixatives cannot be used for this purpose since they have been shown to produce similar impedance increases as asphyxiation and thus can be expected to cause similar movements of extracellular material into cellular elements (30). To circumvent this difficulty a method was developed in which central nervous tissue was frozen very rapidly by bringing it in contact with a polished and meticulously cleaned silver surface kept at about -205° C. The tissue was then substituted in acetone at -85° C, embedded and sectioned for electron microscopy (27). This method can be expected to preserve the water distribution in the tissue more faithfully than conventional methods of fixation (28). Electron micrographs of cerebellar cortex frozen shortly (within thirty seconds) of circulatory arrest showed rather abundant extracellular spaces, especially between the small tissue elements (thin nonmyelinated axons). The cellular elements, neuronal as well as glial, had a rather uniform electron density. When the same tissues were frozen after an eight-minute asphyxial period the extracellular space was decreased markedly. At many places the tissue elements were so closely approximated that the plasma membranes formed five layered tight junctions. Furthermore certain dendritic and glial (cerebellum) elements appeared enlarged and electron transparent, suggesting that these elements had taken up the extracellular material (28,32). The observations made with the histochemical method for chloride and the electron microscopic study of freeze substituted material thus support the conclusion derived from the increase in tissue impedance that O_2 deprivation causes a major shift of extracellular material into the intracellular compartment.

All the changes caused by O_2 deprivation of the cerebral cortex also occur during spreading depression. This phenomenon discovered by Leão (13) consists of a depression of the spontaneous cortical activity which spreads slowly (2 to 4 mm/min) in a concentric fashion from a stimulated area over the cerebral cortex. It is accompanied by a surface negativity of the cortex as observed during asphyxiation (14,15), a marked increase in cortical impedance (8, 16, 20, 35), an accumulation of chloride (37) and water (23) in apical dendrites and finally by a loss of extracellular space as observed in electron micrographs of cortex frozen at the height of spreading depression and substituted in acetone (29). All these changes are so similar to those observed during asphyxiation that they can be expected to be caused by a common mechanism.

The transport of sodium chloride and water into the intracellular compartment can be explained by the assumption of an increased sodium permeability of the neuronal (and glial) membrane during asphyxiation and spreading depression (25, 34). The neuronal membrane is normally permeable for potassium and chloride and impermeable for large intracellular, organic anions. It also has a low (functional) permeability for sodium. A greatly increased permeability for sodium would make the membrane permeable for all of the major ions but for the intracellular anions. In this situation, studied in detail by Donnan, extracellular sodium chloride can be expected to move into the cellular compartment accompanied by water to maintain osmotic equilibrium. A major increase in sodium permeability can be expected to result in a depolarization of the structure involved. Indeed during spreading depression and asphyxiation a marked depolarization of cortical cells was demonstrated with intracellular techniques (3, 6). This depolarization may be the cause of the asphyxial potentials observed.

The mechanism which causes the increased sodium permeability can now be considered. The electrophoretic application of certain amino acids such as glutamic acid to nerve cells causes a depolarization and stimulation of all cells investigated by a general increase in the ion permeability of the cell membrane (7). Assuming that the permeability for the large organic intracellular anions is not markedly enhanced then such a membrane change will not only cause the depolarization of the cellular elements (and the asphyxial potentials) but also the movement of sodium chloride and water into these elements by Donnan forces. Glutamate is abundantly present in central nervous tissue and a release of this amino acid into the extracellular space could explain all the changes observed during spreading depression and O_2 deprivation of the tissue. Attempts to demonstrate a glutamate release from the cerebral cortex during asphyxiation and spreading depression which as mentioned above are accompanied by identical tissue changes failed. Amino acids including glutamate were collected in Ringer's solution flowing over the cerebral cortex. However, they were present in such proportions that it seemed likely that they were derived from the blood in the pial vessels rather than from the cortical intracellular compartment (31).

In a recent investigation with Dr. E. Fifková, a more favorable central nervous tissue, the retina, was used. The retina can be isolated from the eye as a this membrane which remains viable *in vitro* (1). Spreading depression can be elicited in such isolated retinas (10, 18). The retinas of chickens were charged with ^{14}C labeled glutamate and place in a chamber through which Ringer's solution flowed at constant rate. One minute portions of this fluid were collected. They were subjected to paper electrophoresis and the radio activity of the amino acid spots was determined with a strip counter. After a number of control values had been collected the retina was stimulated either by increasing the potassium concentration in the perfusion fluid or by adding 1 mM/L glutamate to it. Both compounds are able to produce spreading depression. Labeled glutamate is continually released from such retinas in small quantities. During the development of spreading depression this release increased markedly, supporting the postulate that the tissue changes during spreading depression and asphyxiation are caused by a release of this amino acid.

The proposed mechanism for the tissue changes during spreading depression and asphyxiation is not inconsistent with the potassium release from the cerebral cortex observed under these circumstances (2, 11). The marked depolarization of nervous elements occurring during spreading depression and asphyxiation (3, 6) which was postulated to be caused by a glutamate release will result in a movement of intracellular potassium into the extracellular compartment. The resulting increase in the extracellular potassium concentration can be considered as an additional mechanism adversely affecting the function of nervous elements. Axons do not seem to be sensitive to glutamate, as suggested by their lack of swelling in nervous tissue freeze substituted after asphyxiation or during spreading depression. However, a sufficiently large increase of the extracellular potassium concentration will depolarize their membrane and arrest the conduction of impulses. Several authors (4, 17, 19) have suggested that during spreading depression the conduction in nerve fibers is suspended. The mechanism of potassium release discussed above may account for this effect.

REFERENCES

1. AMES, A., AND HASTINGS, A.B.: Studies in water and electrolytes in nervous tissue. I. Rabbit retina: Methods and interpretation of data. *J Neurophysiol*, 19:201, 1956.
2. BRINLEY, F.J., KANDEL, E.R., AND MARSHALL, W.R.: Potassium outflux from rabbit cortex during spreading depression. *J Neurophysiol*, 23:246, 1960.
3. BROZEK, G.: Changes in the membrane potential of cortical cells during spreading depression. *Physiol Bohemoslov*, 15:98, 1966.
4. BUREŠ, J., BUREŠOVA, O., FIFKOVÁ, E., AND RABENDING, G.: Reversible deafferentiation of the cerebral cortex by thalamic spreading depression. *Exp Neurol*, 12:55, 1965.
5. COLE, K.S.: Permeability and impermeability of cell membranes for ions. *Cold Spring Harb Symp*, 8:110, 1940.
6. COLLEWIJN, H., AND VAN HARREVELD, A.: Membrane potential of cerebral cortical cells during spreading depression and asphyxia. *Exp. Neurol*, 15:425, 1966.
7. CURTIS, D.R., PHILLIS, J.W., AND WATKINS, J.C.: The chemical excitation of spinal neurones by certain acidic amino acids. *J Physiol (London)*, 150:656, 1960.
8. FREYGANG, W.H., AND LANDAU, W.M.: Some relations between resistivity and electrical activity in the cerebral cortex of the cat. *J Cell Comp Physiol*, 45:377, 1955.
9. GELFAN, S., AND TARLOV, I.M.: Interneurones and rigidity of spinal origin. *J Physiol (London)*, 146:594, 1959.
10. GOURAS, P.: Spreading depression of activity in amphibian retina. *Amer J Physiol*, 195:28, 1958.

11. KRIVÁNEK, J., AND BUREŠ, J.: Ion shifts during Leão's spreading cortical depression. *Physiol Bohemoslov, 9*:494, 1960.
12. LEAF, A.: On the mechanism of fluid exchange of tissues *in vitro*. *Biochem J, 62*:241, 1956.
13. LEÃO, A.A.P.: Spreading depression of activity in the cerebral cortex. *J Neurophysiol, 7*:359, 1944.
14. LEÃO, A.A.P.: Further observations on the spreading depression of activity in the cerebral cortex. *J Neurophysiol, 10*:409, 1947.
15. LEÃO, A.A.P.: The slow voltage variation of cortical spreading depression of activity. *Electroenceph Clin Neurophysiol, 3*:315, 1951.
16. LEÃO, A.A.P., AND FERREIRA, H.M.: Altração da impedancia elétrica no decurso da depressão alastrante de atividade do córtex cerebral. *Anais Acad Brasil Cien, 25*:259, 1953.
17. MARSHALL, W.H.: Spreading cortical depression of Leão. *Physiol Rev, 39*:239, 1959.
18. MARTINS, FERREIRA, H., AND DE OLIVIERA CASTRO, G.: Light scattering changes accompanying spreading depression. *J Neurophysiol, 29*:715, 1966.
19. OCHS, S., HUNT, K., AND BOOKER, H.: Spreading depression using chronically implanted electrodes. *Amer J Physiol, 200*:1211, 1961.
20. RANCK, J.B.: Specific impedance of cerebral cortex during spreading depression, and an analysis of neuronal, neuroglial, and interstitial contributions. *Exp Neurol, 9*:1, 1964.
21. VAN HARREVELD, A.: The resistance of central synaptic conduction to asphyxiation. *Amer J Physiol, 133*:572, 1941.
22. VAN HARREVELD, A.: Changes in volume of cortical neuronal elements during asphyxiation. *Amer J Physiol, 191*:233, 1957.
23. VAN HARREVELD, A.: Changes in diameter of apical dendrites during spreading depression. *Amer J Physiol, 192*:457, 1958.
24. VAN HARREVELD, A.: Asphyxial changes in the cerebellar cortex. *J Cell Comp Physiol, 57*:101, 1961.
25. VAN HARREVELD, A.: *Brain Tissue Electrolytes*. Washington, Butterworth, 1966.
26. VAN HARREVELD, A., AND BIERSTEKER, P.A.: Acute asphyxiation of the spinal cord and of other sections of the nervous system. *Amer J Physiol, 206*:8, 1964.
27. VAN HARREVELD, A., AND CROWELL, J.: Electron microscopy after rapid freezing on a metal surface and substitution fixation. *Anat Rec, 149*:381, 1964.
28. VAN HARREVELD, A., CROWELL, J., AND MALHOTRA, S.K.: A study of extracellular space in central nervous tissue by freeze-substitution. *J Cell Biol, 25*:117, 1965.
29. VAN HARREVELD, A., AND KHATTAB, F.I.: Changes in cortical extracellular space during spreading depression investigated with the electron microscope. *J Neurophysiol, 30*:911, 1967.
30. VAN HARREVELD, A., AND KHATTAB, F.I.: Perfusion fixation with glutaraldehyde and postfixation with osmium tetroxide for electron microscopy. *J Cell Sci, 3*:579, 1968.
31. VAN HARREVELD, A., AND KOOIMAN, M.: Amino acid release from the cerebral cortex during spreading depression and asphyxiation. *J Neurochem, 12*:431, 1965.
32. VAN HARREVELD, A., AND MALHOTRA, S.K.: Extracellular space in the cerebral cortex of the mouse. *J Anat, 101*:197, 1967.
33. VAN HARREVELD, A., AND MARMONT, G.: The course of recovery of the spinal cord from asphyxia. *J Neurophysiol, 2*:101, 1939.
34. VAN HARREVELD, A., AND OCHS, S.: Cerebral impedance changes after circulatory arrest. *Amer J Physiol, 187*:180, 1956.

35. Van Harreveld, A., and Ochs, S.: Electrical and vascular concomitants of spreading depression. *Amer J Physiol, 189*:159, 1957.
36. Van Harreveld, A., and Potter, R.L.: Histochemical differentiation of chloride from other ions precipitated by silver nitrate in freeze-substitution fixation. *Stain Techn, 36*:185, 1961.
37. Van Harreveld, A., and Schadé, J.P.: Chloride movements in cerebral cortex after circulatory arrest and during spreading depression. *J Cell Comp Physiol, 54*:65, 1959.
38. Van Harreveld, A., and Spinelli, D.: Reflex activity in spinal cats with postasphyxial rigidity. *Arch Int. Physiol, 73*:209, 1965.

I

Concluding Discussion on Anatomical Correlates

JOSEPH E. BOGEN

We have had the pleasure of hearing from two scientists who held fast to their interest in the cerebral cortex through the past few decades in which it has fluctuated in fashion. Professor Van Harreveld is a physiologist whose early approach to the cortex was mainly electrical; but he has in recent times become an authoritative microscopist. Professor Campbell is an anatomist whose interest in the microscope has persisted, but only in spite of a recurrent tropism for electrophysiology. Of Dr. Campbell it should be said that he opposed axonology at a time when the Nobel Laureate Gasser reigned under a banner proclaiming that nerve cells function the same way in the central nervous system as they do in the nerve trunks. Nowadays, when standing waves and nonpropagated potentials populate the literature, Dr. Campbell seems to have emerged a winner! He has done well not only in this respect, for he opposed reflexology in the days when the only textbook of neurophysiology was Fulton's, when reflexology seemed almost synonomous with neurophysiology. How times have changed! One rarely hears these days, on this side of the Iron Curtain at least, attempts to explain the mind in terms of reflexes. Dr. Campbell's unorthodox opposition to contemporaneous synaptology may yet be vindicated; so far, however, he remains in a distinct minority—perhaps we can say that as of now, the evidence is not yet all in.

Another hard-fought battle on the cortex has waxed and waned somewhat more quickly than the aforementioned. In this struggle it has been Professor Van Harreveld who held the ramparts. It was only a few years ago that electron miscroscopists showed so clearly that there is practically no extracellular space in the brain and that the chemical and electrical studies of Van Harreveld and others must therefore have been incorrectly interpreted. Dr. Van Harreveld took up from the electromicroscopists their own instrument; improved their methods; and to the relief of most of us watching from the sidelines he has restored the extracellular space to the brain by showing that the electron microscopic absence was itself the result of artifacts in the preparation techniques. Having an extracellular space in the brain again is a great relief; since there is a lot of sodium in the brain, if there were no extracellular space, the sodium would have to be in the cells and therefore the internal environment and the entire biochemistry of the brain cells would have to be altogether different from all other animal cells. Happily, Dr. Van Harreveld has saved us this problem by hoisting the electron microscopists on their own pétard.

It is these ongoing issues, rather than a mélange of facts, which we have tried to emphasize in today's presentation. I should like, however, to conclude by mentioning some of our most recent data which further emphasizes the importance of the right hemisphere, not only for visuospatial function but also for certain aspects of music. We have recently had several opportunities to record the singing of right-handed patients during the time that their left limbs were paralyzed by a right carotid amytal injection. These patients could sing well before and after the testing. During the test, however, they sang in a monotone, that is without melody, whereas articulation and rhythmic sense were largely preserved. This result is in accord with the well-documented amusia without aphasia consequent to right hemisphere lesions.

PART II

PSYCHOACTIVE DRUGS

Chapter 4

Chlorpromazine and CNS Changes in Man

MAX POLLACK

This paper has a twofold purpose: one is to detail some of the neuropsychological changes associated with chlorpromazine (CPZ) and electroconvulsive therapy (ECT) usage in psychiatric patients since both psychiatric treatments have common physical and psychological characteristics. The second is much more difficult and more speculative, namely, to attempt to gain some insights into the action of these treatments in reorganizing and ameliorating cognitive derangements in severely disturbed patients. Since I will not be dealing with brain chemical and neural activity directly, but rather with the attributes of living humans as measured by psychological and electroencephalographic examinations, the CNS, I refer to is the "conceptual nervous system," a term borrowed from Hebb (10).

The clinical term "thought disorder," while loosely defined is the cardinal symptom in the schizophrenic syndrome. In a survey of over one hundred leading British psychiatrists who were asked to rank-order a large number of symptoms, thought disorder led the list. It is abundantly clear from the findings of a number of well-designed studies that an adequate dosage of many of the phenothiazines is most efficacious in reducing or eliminating the maladaptive behavior associated with thinking disorders in schizophrenic patients (20, 23). It is of interest to note that electroconvulsive therapy, although less effective than the phenothiazines is significantly superior to the psychological treatments (20). Before proceeding to a discussion of the neuropsychological changes induced by chlorpromazine and convulsive therapy the obvious should be repeated; namely, there are schizophrenic patients who do not show marked clinical improvement with either or both treatments. These are most often patients who have had long-term histories of deviant social development, often starting in childhood (13). Thus, theories relating to the physiological effects of drugs must be tempered with the realization that the predrug baseline is a most crucial factor in understanding behavioral effects. This report is concerned with the following:

    1. A comparison of the changes in perceptual, perceptual-motor, and intellectual functioning associated with two psychiatric treatments that induce different degrees of EEG slowing; severe (grand-mal convulsions) and mild (CPZ).

    2. The relation of these psychological changes to these induced EEG changes.

3. A discussion of possible mechanisms underlying the restitution of "normative" functioning in response to pharmacological treatment in severely impaired psychiatric patients.

CHLORPROMAZINE

Method

In a voluntary psychiatric hospital, 144 patients consecutively referred for psychotropic drug therapy randomly received (in a double-blind design) a course of orally administered placebo (PL), CPZ, or imipramine. Dosages were increased to 1200 mg of CPZ with 15 mg of procyclidine added to reduce "side effects." Patients were tested in the week prior to drug administration and during the sixth week of PL or CPZ (1200 mg) medication. At time of retest there were forty-three PL and forty-nine CPZ-treated patients. The mean age of the group was 31.1 years; mean education 12.6 years; mean full-scale Wechsler-Bellevue IQ was 109.3. The diagnoses were as follows: schizophrenia (58%), psychotic depressions (25%), character disorders (9%), and psychoneurosis (8%). The group was alert and cooperative; retest correlations of psychological variables under PL conditions were extremely high and did not differ from that obtained with normals (25).

Statistical Analysis

Seventeen different psychological tests and five EEG variables were investigated. (The test are outlined in Table 4-1). The CPZ group was compared with the PL group by two statistical techniques, univariate and multivariate analysis. In the univariate analysis the means for each of the variables for the CPZ and PL groups were compared by analysis of covariance in which the on-drug scores were adjusted for pretreatment level; the adjusted on-drug means were then compared by the appropriate test. Multivariate analysis was performed using a discriminant function analysis for the two groups (28).

UNIVARIATE ANALYSIS

EEG

Fink (8) in our laboratory, employed an electronic frequency analyzer to measure the changes in the frequency spectra. Twenty-four frequencies from 3 to 33 cps were recorded. When compared with PL the CPZ group showed a statistically significant increase in mean delta (3.0 to 4.5 cps) and theta (5 to 7 cps) but not in alpha (8 to 12 cps), $beta_1$ (13.5 to 20 cps) or $beta_2$ (22 to 33 cps) frequencies.

Psychological Tests

Of the seventeen tests, CPZ significantly affected performance in nine. For eight measures, there was a statistically significant impairment when the drug was compared with the PL group (Table 4-2). For one measure, the

TABLE 4-1
PSYCHOLOGICAL MEASURES

Area of Functioning	Tests	Response Measures
Perceptual	Critical Flicker Fusion	Threshold in cycles per second
	Rod and Frame	Errors in degrees from vertical
	Delayed Auditory Feedback	Difference in seconds between reading under feedback and normal conditions
Visuomotor	Tapping Rate	Taps per 10 seconds
	Hand Steadiness	Number of contacts in 15 seconds
	Two-Hand Coordination	Time on target in one minute
Cognitive	Wechsler-Bellevue, Form I	Weighted scores
	Information Subtest	
	Comprehension Subtest	
	Similarities Subtest	
	Arithmetic Subtest	
	Digit Span Subtest	
	Picture Completion Subtest	
	Block Design Subtest	
	Object Assembly Subtest	
	Digit Symbol Subtest	
	Picture Arrangement Subtest	
	Rorschach	Perceptual-analysis scores per card and memory for previous response

special Rorschach test (1), the results were in the opposite direction, i.e. an improvement of the CPZ group over the PL group. This finding will be discussed in a separate section later on.

Analysis of the results indicates that all the significant changes in visuomotor or cognitive tasks involved some aspects of timed performance or serial retention involving a time limit aspect. Of the perceptual tests only critical flicker fusion (CFF) threshold was significantly decreased, the tests of sensory distortion, the rod and frame and delayed auditory feedback, did not differ significantly from placebo. The lack of sensitivity of auditory delayed feedback to CPZ is of interest in that it is a test that was expected to be altered by cerebral dysfunction (18).

All of the visuomotor tests showed a significant change with decreased speed in digit symbol substitution and tapping speed and increased hand unsteadiness. Performance on tests requiring mental alertness, digit span, and arithmetic were also impaired. The tests involving verbal aspects such as information, comprehension, or similarities were not significantly affected.

Of the Wechsler-Bellevue subtests, digit symbol substitution was most affected. Birren has noted that this test seems most associated with "aging" (3, p. 396).

The profile of changes is consistent with that found following acute administration of CPZ in normal volunteers (5, 17). These changes are also compatible with that reported by those workers using these or similar ones to measure changes in the aged (3, 12, 19).

TABLE 4-2

SIGNIFICANT TEST CHANGES WITH CHLORPROMAZINE

Analysis of Covariance

	Mean Pre-Drug	Mean On-Drug	t values (one-tailed)	p
Critical Flicker Fusion				
Placebo	35.6	35.2	5.04	.0005
Chlorpromazine	34.9	32.5		
Digit Symbol Substitution				
Placebo	10.7	12.1	4.15	.0005
Chlorpromazine	10.3	10.1		
Hand Steadiness				
Placebo	1.1	0.8	4.06	.0005
Chlorpromazine	1.2	2.0		
Tapping Rate				
Placebo	66.0	66.5	2.85	.005
Chlorpromazine	65.6	62.7		
Digit Span				
Placebo	9.9	10.5	2.84	.005
Chlorpromazine	10.0	9.1		
Arithmetic				
Placebo	10.3	11.8	2.73	.005
Chlorpromazine	10.0	10.1		
Block Design				
Placebo	10.4	11.0	1.77	.05
Chlorpromazine	9.4	9.4		
Two-Hand Coordination				
Placebo	15.1	20.1	1.77	.05
Chlorpromazine	14.1	16.8		

Intercorrelations of Test Changes

Correlation of changes in chlorpromazine-altered psychological tests and changes in delta and theta EEG frequencies were with one exception not significant. Hand steadiness decreased with increased delta ($r = .34$, $p = .05$).

Of the psychological tests only CFF and digit symbol substitution were correlated significantly ($r = .30$, $p = .05$). The correlation of CFF and digit symbol has been reported in studies of the aged by Loranger and Misiak (19). In a factor analysis of the psychological variables for one hundred and forty-four subjects prior to drug treatment digit symbol, CFF, digit span and object assembly all loaded on one factor. (The intercorrelations and factor analysis of pretreatment variables and placebo and chlorpromazine change matrices are available on request).

MULTIVARIATE ANALYSIS

A discriminant function analysis using the Maholonobis D^2 was employed using on-drug scores. The D^2 statistic provides a means of rank-ordering all subjects along the dimension that maximally differentiates placebo from drug effects. It also determines the overlap between the two groups and gives an estimate (F value) of the likelihood that this overlap differs from chance. Therefore, it is possible to rank each patient from most placebo-like to most placebo-like to most chlorpromazine-like. For the psychological variables, only those that by covariance analysis individually differentiated CPZ from PL were used. The F value was 9.13, $p < .01$, indicating the minimal degree of overlap between groups using these tests. For the EEG variables, the F value was 2.39, $p < .05$, indicating a greater overlap than that found with psychological variables but nevertheless indicating a significant degree of discrimination.

In order to relate the psychological and EEG changes a rank-order correlation was performed for both the placebo and chlorpromazine groups employing the ranks provided by the D^2 analysis. For the CPZ group the correlation of the psychological and EEG orderings was highly significant, the rho $= .71$, $p < .01$. For the PL group it was .39 just failing significance at the .05 level. This indicates that there is an overall multivariate association between the chlorpromazine-induced EEG and psychological changes.

In summary, the pattern of psychological and EEG changes with chronic administration of a high dosage of CPZ closely resembles that found with normal-aged subjects and during "absences" in seizure patients (22). The lack of significant correlations between the changes in psychological test and EEG variables using univariate analysis in contrast to a substantial relationship between these disparate measures using multivariate analysis raises the question of the utility of using single variables as adequate indicators of change in brain function. However, no statistically significant relationship between clinical changes as measured by psychiatric scales and these neuropsychological and EEG changes were found.

I would now like to present some psychological test data that parallel some of the clinical changes observed in CPZ-treated patients (1). We used a special version of the Rorschach test, one originally designed by Birch and Belmont (2) to assay the perceptual-analytic abilities of brain-damaged adults, most often hemiplegics. We incorporated this procedure after our drug study was underway; consequently a smaller number of patients were tested. There was a positive correlation between the perceptual-analytic score as measured by the rating of the patient's "clear thinking" (4) by his psychiatrist. When compared with placebo, the CPZ-treated schizophrenic patients showed a significantly greater improvement in their ability to organize this perceptual material than did the nonschizophrenic patients. What may appear paradoxical is that there was also a significant improvement in the recall of previous Rorschach responses in the drug-treated schizophrenic as compared with nonschizophrenic patients. This discrepancy between an "impairment" in experimenter-paced time tests such as the recall of serially order digits and the improvement self-paced ideational recall has been noted also by Lehmann (16) in CPZ-treated chronic schizophrenic patients.

CONVULSIVE THERAPY

Procedure

Grand-mal convulsive treatments were administered three times a week. The patients were studied in the week prior to treatment, between the tenth and twelfth treatments and two weeks following the termination of the final treatment.

Thirty-six consecutively referred patients were studied. The mean age of the group was 37.8 years, education 11.6 years, mean IQ 104 (Verbal Scale, Wechsler-Bellevue); 42% were diagnosed as schizophrenia, 28% as psychotic depression, 14% as involutional disorder, and 16% as psychoneurosis.

Only one EEG variable was measured, the percent time occupied by waves 6 cps or less in 66 seconds of recording from the anterior temporal vertex leads. Ten psychological variables were studied. These were the recognition of tachistoscopically presented pseudo isochromatic numbers, the rod and frame, delayed auditory feedback, and five subtests of the Wechsler-Bellevue form I: information, comprehension, digit span, object assembly, and digit symbol. With exception of the tachistoscopic recognition test and reading time all have been outlined in Table 4-1.

RESULTS

EEG

The changes in slow wave activity are shown in Table 4-3. By the tenth treatment increase in slow wave activity was very pronounced and the record appeared grossly abnormal. Clinically, the patients showed marked mental changes such as memory loss (they were amnestic for the pretreatment examinations) and disorientation for time or place. Older subjects showed a greater impairment clinically and this was reflected in the EEG. The correlation between age and increased EEG slowing was .41 (p <.01).

TABLE 4–3

EFFECT OF CONVULSIVE THERAPY ON EEG SLOWING

(% 6 cps or slower)

	Pre Treatment	After 10 to 12 Treatments	Pre Treatment	Two Weeks After Last Treatment
N	36	36	25	25
Mean	5.5	54.0	5.6	16.5
SD	4.4	22.0	4.3	10.0
Mean Diff.		48.5		10.9
t		12.8†		4.8†
r		.34*		.09

*P<.05   p<.001

Psychological Performance

With treatment, performance on all tests, except the rod and frame, delayed auditory feedback, and two-hand coordination was significantly impaired when compared with pretreatment level (Table 4-4). The performance on the two-hand coordination tests was slowed significantly when compared with placebo or drug controls whereas neither the rod and frame nor the delayed auditory feedback tests differed from controls. With cessation of treatment, functioning on all tests returned to pretreatment level or showed improvement over pretreatment scores. The importance of the pretreatment level of functioning is illustrated by the high retest correlations.

Psychological Test Changes and EEG

Decrement in performance on four tests, (tachistoscopic recognition, and three Wechsler-Bellevue subtests, digit span, digit symbol and object assembly correlated significantly with increased slow wave activity. All correlations were between .4 and .6. It is of interest that although the verbal tests, information and comprehension, were significantly impaired by the convulsive therapy, these changes did not correlate significantly with EEG slowing. All of the tests that correlated significantly with EEG slowing involved functioning under time limit conditions or in the case of digit span had a time delay feature.

TABLE 4-4

EFFECT OF CONVULSIVE THERAPY (CT) ON TEST SCORES

	Pretreatment and 10-12 CTs		Pretreatment and 2 weeks after last treatment	
	Mean Diff.	r	Mean Diff.	r
Tachistoscopic—PIN	6.7†	.80†	−6.3†	.64†
Rod and Frame	−2.0*	.93†	−5.1†	.77†
Delayed Auditory Feedback	−11.1	.30	+5.4	.54*
Reading Time	+11.9†	.74†	+4.0	.79†
Two-Hand Coordination	−1.4	.76†	+4.3*	.90†
Wechsler-Bellevue Subtests				
Information	−1.9‡	.80†	−0.4	.93†
Comprehension	−1.7†	.55†	+1.0*	.72†
Digit Span	−2.3‡	.59†	−0.2	.75†
Object Assembly	−1.1*	.69†	+3.1‡	.73†
Digit Symbol	−2.2†	.76†	+0.9*	.81†

*p<.05,   †<.01   ‡p<.001

DISCUSSION

The changes in psychological test performance associated with induced mild and severe EEG slowing are similar to those found in studies of aged persons (24). The changes with chlorpromazine paralleled those reported for normal aged while those with convulsive therapy resemble those of senile patients. The correlations of intellectual tasks with EEG also resemble the results obtained with normal and cerebrally damaged aged. The high retest correlation under conditions of induced mild and severe diffuse brain dysfunction suggests the crucial importance of premorbid functioning.

Cognitive Improvements and Induced CNS Change

If I were to stop at this point, theories of behavioral change would be embedded in the concept of symbolic reorganization with diffuse brain change. Such theories have previously been postulated by Weinstein and Kahn (29), Fink (8), and (9), Fink (8) has summarized his position as follows:

> Thus, improvement in convulsive therapy in the neurophysiologic-adaptive view is based on those neurophysiological changes which are the cerebral basis for the altered behavioral adaptations, molded by personality variables and sustained by environmental tolerances. This view has been most helpful in understanding the various neurophysiological studies reported and the clinical problems of convulsive therapy. It is also helpful in providing a framework for studies in psychopharmacology. It is our view that the therapeutic process with the various classes of psychotropic agents can be best understood within a similar neurophysiological-adaptive interactive hypothesis.

While the above point of view is one in the right direction, the framework is too broad and lacks the specificity needed to obtain a more presice insight into the reparative, changes in cognitive functioning associated with somatic therapy.

Another approach would follow the theories of Kornetsky and Mirsky (15), who assume that chlorpromazine has a specific action on altering arousal mechanisms through its effect on some central subcortical structures. This hypothesis is based on the supposition that psychotic patients, particularly schizophrenics, are characterized by a state of hyperarousal. The theory may be faulty in that it would have to assume that cognitive changes in nonschizophrenics are also related to a dampening of the "arousal system." A criticism of the overarousal theory has been made by Klein (this volume), who argues against the adoption of a unidimensional physiological (e.g. rheostat) model for the action of psychotropic drugs.

Finally I want to speculate about the physiological reparative action of CPZ. According to Feinberg and his associates (6, 7) who have been studying sleep in a variety of psychiatric and neurological conditions, most drugs that produce delirium upon withdrawal suppress the activity of deep sleep as measured by EEG stages 3 and 4. Stage 4 looks something like the EEG pattern induced by ECT. CPZ increased stage 4 EEG without depressing rapid eye movement (REM) sleep. Equivalent dosages of phenobarbital had an opposite effect on stage 4 sleep. Feinberg claims that in chronic schizoprenics as in several other psychiatric conditions there is a diminution of stage 4 sleep. The selective replenishment of stage 4 sleep in psychotic patients, whether or not they be delirious, with chlorpromazine, is a new and perhaps important finding for understanding psychotic states. The action of CPZ on the "confusional delirious state" induced by an anticholinergic hallucinogen such as Ditran (9, 11) may have a link to Feinberg's results. Ditran dosages that induce confusional states are associated with the production of 2 to 5 cps EEG slow waves and 30 to 50 cps fast activity. CPZ potentiates the EEG slow activity and abolishes the very fast activity. This results in alteration of the delirium and a state of sleep stupor ensues. This proecss could be an example of Pavlovian "protective inhibition", and may account for the empirical findings of CPZ as a treatment for such conditions as alcoholic delirium.

SUMMARY

The effects of two psychiatric treatments that induce different degrees of EEG slowing, electroconvulsive therapy and chlorpromazine, on the alteration of certain psychological tests is detailed. The relation of neurophysiological alterations, as measured by sleep EEG variables, to the amelioration of cognitive confusion and the restitution of normal functioning is discussed.

REFERENCES

1. BELMONT, I., POLLACK, M., WILLNER, A., KLEIN, D.F., AND FINK, M.: The effects of imipramine and chlorpromazine on perceptual analytic ability, perceptual responsivity and memory as revealed in Rorschach responses. *J Nerv Ment Dis,* 137:42–50, 1963.
2. BIRCH, H.G., AND BELMONT, I.: Functional levels of disturbance manifested by brain-damaged (nemiplegic) patients as revealed in Rorschach responses. *J Nerv Ment Dis,* 132:410–416, 1961.
3. BIRREN, J.E.: Research on the psychologic aspects of aging. *Geriatrics,* 18:393–403, 1963.
4. CLYDE, D.J.: Manual for the Clyde Mood Scale. Biometric Laboratory, University of Miami, Coral Gables, Fla., 1963.
5. DIMASCIO, A., HAVENS, L., AND KLERMAN, G.L.: The psychopharmacology of phenothiazine compounds: A comparative study of the effects of chlorpromazine, promethazine, trifluoperazine and perphenazine in normal males. *J Nerv Ment Dis,* 136:15–28, 168–186, 1963.
6. FEINBERG, I.: Recent sleep research: Findings in schizophrenia and some possible implications for the mechanism of action of chlorpromazine and for the neurophysiology of delirium. In Siva Sanka, D.V. (Ed.): *Schizophrenia: An Appraisal,* in press.
7. FEINBERG, I., WENDER, P.H., KORESKO, R.L., GOTTLIEB, F., AND PIEHUTA, J.A.: Differen-

tial effects of chlorpromazine and phenobarbital on EEG sleep patterns. *J Psychiat Res,* in press, 1969.
8. FINK, M.: Quantitative EEG and human psychopharmacology. In Wilson, W.P. (Ed.) : *Applications of Electroencephalography in Psychiatry.* Durham, Duke University Press, 1965, pp. 226–240.
9. FINK, M., AND ITIL, T.: Anticholinergic hallucinogens and their interaction with centrally active drugs. In Brill, H. (Ed.) : *Neuro-Psycho-Pharmacology.* International Congress Series No. 129. Amsterdam, Excerpta Medica Foundation, 1967, p. 381.
10. HEBB, D.O.: Drives and the c.n.s. (conceptual nervous system) . *Psychol Rev, 62*:243–254 (b) , 1955.
11. ITIL, T.M.; *EEG "sleep" state after anti-cholinergic drugs.* In Brill, H. (Ed.) : *Neuro-Psycho-Pharmacology.* International Congress Series No. 129. Amsterdam, Excerpta Medica Foundation, 1967, p. 380.
12. JARVIK, L.F., KALLMANN, F.J., AND FALEK, A.: Intellectual changes in aged twins. *J Geront, 17*:289–294, 1962.
13. KLEIN, D.F.: Psychiatric diagnosis and a typology of clinical drug effects. *Psychopharmacologia, 13*:359–386, 1968.
14. KLEIN, D.F.: Psychotropic drugs and the regulation of behavioral activation in psychiatric illness. Presented at the First Annual Cerebral Function Symposium, Aspen, Colorado, June 6–9, 1969.
15. KORNETSKY, C., AND MIRSKY, A.F.: On certain psychopharmacological differences between schizophrenic and normal persons. *Psychopharmacologicia, 8*:309–18, 1966.
16. LEHMANN, H.E.: The influence of different psychoactive drugs on cognitive and memory tests in schizophrenic and geriatric psychotics. In Brill, H. (Ed.) : *Neuro-Psycho-Pharmacology.* International Congress Series No. 129. Amsterdam, Excerpta Medica Foundation, 1967.
17. LEHMANN, H.E., AND CSANK, J.: Differential screening of phrenotropic agents in man: Psychophysiologic test data. *J Clin Psychopath,* 18:222–235, 1957.
18. LINDSLEY, D.B.: Common factors in sensory deprivation, sensory distortion and sensory overload. In Solomon, P. *et al.* (Eds.) : Cambridge, Harvard University, 1961, p. 174–194.
19. LORANGER, A.W., AND MISIAK, H.: Critical flicker frequency and some intellectual functions in old age. *J. Geront, 14*:323–327, 1959.
20. MAY, P.R.A.: *Treatment of Schizophrenia,* New York, Science House, 1968.
21. MIRSKY A.F., AND CARDON, P.V.: A comparison of the behavioral and physiological changes accompanying sleep deprivation and chlorpromazine administration in man. *Electroenceph Clin Neurophysiol, 14*:1–10, 1962.
22. MIRSKY, A.F.; PRIMAC, D., AJMONE-MARSAN, C., ROSOVOLD, H.E., AND STEVENS, J.A.: A comparison of the psychological test performance of patients with focal and nonfocal epilepsy. *Ex Neurol, 2*:75–89, 1960.
23. NATIONAL INSTITUTE OF MENTAL HEALTH, PSYCHOPHARMACOLOGY SERVICE CENTER COLLABORATIVE STUDY GROUP: Clinical effects of three phenothiazines in "acute" schizophrenia. *Publication Rep. No. 6* US Public Health Service, Bethesda, Maryland 1966.
24. POLLACK, M.: *Physiologically induced neuropsychological changes and aging.* In Welford, A.T., and Birren, J.E. (Eds.) : *Behavior Aging and the Nervous System.* Springfield, Charles C Thomas, 1965, p. 272–283.
25. POLLACK, M., KARP, E., BELMONT, I., WILLNER, A., KLEIN, D.F., AND FINK, M.: Com-

parative studies of chlorpromazine and imipramine. II: Psychological performance profiles. In Bradley, P. (Ed.) : *Neuropsychopharmacology* 3:376–380, 1964.
26. OBRIST, W.D.: The electroencephalogram of normal aged adults. *Electroenceph Clin Neurophysiol,* 6:245–252, 1954.
27. OBRIST, W.D., BUSSE, E.W., EISDORFER, AND KLEEMEIER, R.W.: Relation of the electroencephalogram to intellectual function in senescence. *J Geront,* 17:197–206, 1962.
28. RAO, C.R.: *Advanced Statistical Methods in Biometric Research.* New York, John Wiley & Sons, 1952.
29. WEINSTEIN, E.A., AND KAHN, R.L.: Symbolic reorganization in brain injuries. In Arieti, S. (ed.) : *American Handbook of Psychiatry.* New York, Basic Books, 1959, Ch. 48, pp. 964–979.

Chapter 5

Prediction of Response to Drugs and Placebo: the Current Frontiers of Drug Research

SOLOMON C. GOLDBERG

It seems that whenever one is working intensively in any field, progress is discouragingly slow. What facts you think you know with some certainty today seem always to have been known, because once a fact is established concerning an issue which was formerly in controversy, the fact begins to make so much sense and to be so self-evident that you wonder what the controversy was all about. It is consequently of some value occasionally to stand back to review one's area with some historical perspective, in order to see how far we have gone and where the current frontiers are.

GENERAL EFFICACY OF PHENOTHIAZINES

Even after the phenothiazines had come into extensive use in the treatment of schizophrenia by the mid-1950's, there was still a large question in the minds of research workers as to whether these drugs really worked. After Congressional testimony by Nathan Kline and others, funds were earmarked by the Congress for the purpose of doing research on the efficacy and activity of drugs in schizophrenia. Understandably, however, the National Institute of Mental Health did not receive these funds with open arms because they and other experienced research workers had learned to be skeptical of all the new "cures" that were periodically touted in psychiatry, accompanied by great enthusiasm, only to be shown to be, at best, of limited value. Imagine, if you will, how ridiculous it must have sounded that a mental disorder as complex in etiology and development as schizophrenia should succumb to a pill that was stumbled upon accidentally.

The literature that ensued on the efficacy of phenothiazines was mixed; some studies showed efficacy and others did not. The early studies were done on captive populations such as chronically hospitalized schizophrenic patients and demonstrated, for example, a higher discharge rate in drug-treated groups. At the same time, however, it was disquieting to learn that the rehospitalization rate had also increased during this period, thus casting some doubt on the value of phenothiazines in the long-term treatment of schizophrenia. Eventually this question was resolved by the sheer accumulation of research and associated critical reviews. For example, Heilizer in reviewing chlorpromazine studies showed that the studies which showed no difference between drug and placebo had used smaller doses of the drug, fewer patients in the comparison samples, and a smaller study-treatment period. These cumulated studies plus the large-scale collaborative efforts by the Veterans Administration and the National Institute of Mental Health established with some certainty the fact that chlorpromazine and several other major phenothiazines were effective in reducing the symptoms of schizophrenic patients—chronic and acute. The work of Kris and the Engelhardt further established the need of these patients for maintenance medication after they had been discharged to the community. Thus what seemed be be an area of controversy as little as nine or ten years ago is no longer so and is generally resolved.

HOSPITAL DIFFERENCES IN OUTCOME

The mixed literature at that time also gave rise to another hypothesis to account for the failure of some studies to find a significant drug-placebo difference. The hypothesis stated that those institutions which had intensive nonsomatic treatment programs were so effective in the treatment of their placebo patients that the addition of drugs could produce little additional effectiveness. Only those hospitals with weak or nonexistent nonsomatic programs gave the drug a better opportunity to have an effect. This hypothesis was not born out by the data in the National Institute of Mental Health study which showed, first of all, that the *size* of the drug-placebo difference did not differ significantly among a wide variety of treatment settings even though the general level of improvement on drug and placebo did vary from one setting to the next. This variation in hospital outcome was shown to be a function almost exclusively of the prognostic value the patient brought with him to the hospital in the way of symptom pattern and background characteristics. In other words, it was common knowledge that some patients tend to improve more than others because of personal characteristics and history, and the distribution of these patients with different prognostic likelihoods was not evenly spread over all hospitals. The results seemed to confirm this common knowledge and further demonstrated that hospitals had little or no institutional effect on the outcome of the patient.

The point about the efficacy of the major phenothiazines now may be considered well established even though there was heated but honest controversy at a fairly recent point in time. We know now that phenothiazines will reduce the symptoms of schizophrenics, that the symptoms will return if phenothiazines are discontinued, and that this statement can be generalized across a wide variety of treatment settings. We also know that discharged patients who do not maintain their medication in the community are more likely to relapse.

OUTCOME RELATED TO SIDE EFFECTS

At one point in time there was the popular hypothesis that a phenothiazine will be effective only if it produces extrapyramidal and neurological side effects which were an indication to the treating physician of his administering an adequate dose. The Veterans Administration and the National Institute of Mental Health studies which employed thioridazine seemed to dispel this notion by showing that thioridazine, which produces practically no extrapyramidal symptoms, was clinically as effective as several other phenothiazines which do produce extrapyramidal symptoms. Despite these findings there are still a few practitioners who cling to the earlier belief, but sooner or later this ought to die out.

SPECIFIC ACTIVITY OF DRUGS AND PLACEBO

Once the phenothiazines were considered established as a treatment, the next logical question was concerned with the specific behavioral atcivity of these drugs as compared with placebo. Perhaps the phenothiazines were more effective in reducing some schizophrenic symptoms than others. In this regard the National Institute of Mental Health studies have shown the greater drug effects to be in those symptoms which might be labeled fundamental or core or nonparanoid or schizophrenic withdrawal. The main reason for this is that one sees virtually no improvement in these symptoms in placebo-treated patients. In paranoid and accessory symptoms one sees much improvement but most of this improvement is due to the placebo condition (which includes the effects of time and of the nonsomatic treatments given in the hospital). In viewing any single patient treated by a phenothiazine, one is likely to see more improvement in his accessory and paranoid symptoms than in his core-withdrawn symptoms; however, practically all of the change in his accessory symptoms may be attributed to the placebo condition while practically all of the change in core-withdrawn symptoms may be attributed to drug. Thus it appears that the effectiveness of drug treatment is due to its action upon a group of symptoms which, prior to the drug era, were not being affected by any known treatment. Other analyses in the NIMH study showed that drug treatment averted the development of those symptoms which patients did not have at the beginning of the study. For example, among patients who were not hallucinated at all before treatment, a significantly greater number hallucinated after treatment if assigned to placebo than if assigned to drug. This result was a further confirmation of the developmental dynamics of the schizophrenic process. It was of further interest to note that the symptoms that were averted by drug treatment were mainly the core-withdrawn symptoms and not at all the accessory paranoid symptoms. This served as further evidence that the major target symptoms for phenothiazines in schizophrenia were the core-withdrawal symptoms.

ENVIRONMENTAL INFLUENCES

As a corollary to this result, one of the analyses in the NIMH study inquired into the effect of ward atmosphere on symptom reduction. It was found that the ward to which a patient was assigned did indeed affect his outcome. It was further found that the effect of ward atmosphere was to be seen primarily in the reduction of paranoid symptoms and not at all in the reduction of withdrawn symptoms. This is all the more interesting because ward atmosphere may be conceptualized as an environmental influence. This leads us to the tentative statement that schizophrenic outcome, as we have all suspected, may be influenced by somatic therapies such as drugs and by environmental influences such as ward atmosphere. However, we go further in saying that the drugs act primarily on the withdrawn symptoms while environmental variables act primarily on the paranoid symptoms.

DIFFERENTIAL DRUG ACTIVITY

The results discussed in the last few paragraphs were concerned with the differential activity of drugs and placebo, where all the different drugs are considered of a piece. There are a number of practitioners who rightfully objected to our lumping all the phenothiazines into one group because they maintain that different phenothiazines have different effects. The clinical folklore would have it that chlorpromazine is most appropriate for the excited belligerent patient while a drug-like fluphenazine or trifluoperazine is more appropriate for the retarded apathetic patient who is in need of energizing. These contentions on the part of practitioners have given rise in the last five years or so to research which demonstrates empirically that some subtypes of schizophrenics improve more on certain phenothiazines while other subtypes improve more on others. This area of research has been popularly identified as "the right drug for the right patient" and aptly characterizes the location of the frontier of drug research in schizophrenia today. The status of that frontier is that while there seems to be fairly good evidence that there is a "right drug for the right patient," there is as yet an inability to characterize who that right patient is. Advances may come about, I hope, after several more data points have been added to rough out the total configuration.

OUTPATIENT SCHIZOPHRENIA

I would like to finish by illustrating still another "new frontier" in drug research in schizophrenia which has more to do with public mental health questions than in the theoretical issues of how the drugs work. For example, we have known for some time that drug treatment can get patients out of the hosptial and that maintenance treatment in the community can keep them out. However, follow-up studies on the level of adjustment of drug-treated patients in the community revealed that their level of adjustment leaves much to be desired. On the average, their adjustment one year after discharge is not as high as the best level they had ever achieved prior to being hospitalized.

Moreover, the best level of adjustment they had ever achieved was below that of people of like background. The obvious public health question is whether by means of drug treatment we are simply shifting the responsibility for the care of the patient to the community without his necessarily being able to live up to community demands. There are programs in a number of states, limited by availability of funds, for the social and vocational rehabilitation of former mental patients. A question which is currently being pursued inquires into the relative roles of maintenance drug treatment and social rehabilitation therapy in advancing the level of adjustment of formerly hospitalized schizophrenic patients. Our hypotheses in this research are that (a) the great majority of patients cannot be maintained at any decent level in the community without maintenance drug treatment and (b) social rehabilitation therapy will not be effective without concomitant drug therapy; thus social rehabilitation by itself should have no significantly greater value than no treatment at all, while social rehabilitation in the presence of drug treatment should show an additional effect. A further area of investigation within this research will be with what Engelhardt and his associates have referred to as the "hospital-prone" patient. It appears that some small group of community-based patients will show a better level of adjustment without drugs. Here again is an illustration of the more sophisticated kind of question that is being asked today than was the case ten years ago. In other words, while it is true that *most* schizophrenic patients in the community should be treated by drugs, there is evidence that a small group of them should not be. Engelhardt's results give us some preliminary indications as to how these may be identified. If we succeed in doing so in the next several years we will have moved still another step forward in delineating not only whether the drugs are effective, but for whom.

SUMMARY

It may be well to summarize where we have been and where we are. We know now the following facts. (1) Drugs are effective in reducing symptoms and in producing a greater discharge rate. (2) The major target symptoms for phenothiazines are the so-called schizophrenic core-withdrawal symptoms while the target symptoms for environmental influences are the accessory-paranoid symptoms. Exactly how the drugs act upon the withdrawal symptoms is a subject for research. (3) There is evidence for the differential activity of various phenothiazines in different schizophrenic patients, indicating that there might be a "right drug for the right patient." However, the power of these results is not of the same magnitude as those cited in the preceding two paragraphs, since there is still some difficulty in characterizing the kind of patient for whom any particular drug is most appropriate. (4) Studies in the prediction of response also indicate that there are some few schizophrenic patients for whom phenothiazine treatment is inappropriate. This is not true of the majority of schizophrenic patients. However, if we are ever able to specify which patients should or should not receive a phenothiazine, we will have made a considerable advance. (5) The role of drug treatment in the community adjustment of schizophrenic patients may be depicted as necessary but not sufficient. Exactly how drug treatment interacts with social rehabiliation therapy is a subject for current investigation.

Chapter 6

Pupillography as a Tool in the Assessment of CNS Functions and Drug Effects

GAD HAKEREM*

When I looked over the program for this symposium on Cerebral Functions, I was surprised to find that none of the sections seemed to deal specifically with the electrophysiology of the cortex as an indicator of its function.

I have taken the liberty to include in my paper some discussion of data obtained from recordings of the evoked cortical potentials. These data have direct relevance to the data obtained by recording of the pupil motility. It is actually because of this close relationship between data obtained from scalp electrodes and from the pupil that I dare state that the motility of the pupils does indeed reflect cortical functions.

We have come to regard the pupil of the eye as an extremely precise indicator of cerebral functions, so much so that we think of it as a "permanently implanted electrode in man." Actually this concept is not new, the pupil has been described in the literature as "the window to the soul" or as "the finest anistesiometer of the brain." The state of the pupil opening as an indicator of disease and emotions has long been known to physicians and psychiatrists. The question then arises whether the anecdotal and observational reports in the literature are based on verifiable facts and to what extent modern recording devices can help us to make use of this "window to the soul."

Let me briefly review the rationale for pupillographic studies and then discuss some of the techniques by which measurements of the pupil motility can be obtained.

The iris consists essentially of two groups of antagonistic smooth muscles, which are innervated by separate divisions of the autonomic nervous system. A group of radially located muscles is innervated by the peripheral sympathetic system via the cervical sympathetic chain. Impulses over this pathway contract the muscle and thereby dilate the pupil. A sphincter muscle forms the actual hole, called the pupil. This muscle is innervated from the Edinger-Westphal nucleus of the oculomotor center. Studies by Laties (1969) have shown that the innervation to the sphincter muscle is predominantly cholinergic.

* Assisted by Stephen Levine.

Lowenstein and Loewenfeld (12) have given a good review on the present state of knowledge on this complex innervation system.

The pupillary dilation, with which we will be mainly concerned in this paper, has at least two neural and two humoral components.

One of the neuronal components is the sympathetic activation from the hypothalamic area via the cervical sympathetic chain to the radial dilator muscles. Activation of this pathway results in a rapid, extensive pupillary dilation. The other neuronal component consists of impulses from cortex, thalamus, hypothalamus, and probably many other areas which have been shown to exert inhibitory influences in the tonic parasympathetic activity of the Edinger-Westphal nucleus. This results in a slower, less extensive dilation of the pupil. Lowenstein has called this activity "supranuclear inhibition." Studies with sympathectomized animals and Horner's syndrome patients allow us to differentiate between the dynamics of these two systems.

I will not go into the humoral elements acting on the pupil except to state that both adrenergic and cholinergic substances applied systemically and topically affect the pupillary diameter and motility.

Several recent studies have reported pupillary diameter changes to electrical stimulations of discrete areas of the brain. Ward and Reed found that electrical stimulation to parts of the frontal cortex reliably produced consensual pupillary dilation. Naquet (15) and his co-workers have shown a high correlation between cortical synchronization and pupil constriction and cortical desynchronization and pupil dilation respectively. Naquet pointed out that this correlation held whether the desynchronization was spontaneous or induced by reticular or sciatic stimulation. Delgado (1) summarized some of the stimulation work and stated that the dilation of the pupil is evoked by stimulation of cortical areas around the orbital cortex, temporal tip, cingulate gyrus, insula, rhinal fissure, and hippocampal gyrus, in addition to such deep structures as the basal telencephalon, hypothalamus, septum, midline group of thalamic nucleii, and some others.

Based on the knowledge that pupillary dilation is somehow tied into such an impressive number of major areas of the brain, it is not surprising that recent interest in the pupil has centered around its use as an indicator of the functional state of the brain. Though some people feel that the complexity of the interconnections make any meaningful interpretation of the data close to impossible, we feel that much can be learned about the functions by intelligent and creative experimental designs and procedures.

Over the centuries many efforts have been made to obtain objectives and reliable measurements of sequential changes in pupil diameter. Lupes and magnification systems have been designed to closely observe pupil changes. Ballarminof in 1885 developed a system by which the pupil diameter was recorded on photosensitive brom silver paper. In 1922 Lowenstein started to develop a cinephotographic method which photographed the pupil under dim blue light. Later, infrared sensitive film was used and it became possible to photograph the pupil in darkness. Several devices used the photocurrent produced by the visible and infrared light reflected from the iris on photo sensitive cells. Since the outer diameter of the iris does not change, any change in reflectance can be attributed to the changes in iris area. This then is inversely related to pupil diameter.

In 1956, Lowenstein and Loewenfeld developed an infrared scanning device which allowed direct electronic measurement of pupil diameter. This instrument uses a mechanical scanner which scans the eye with twelve lines of infrared light at the rate of 60 rasters per second. On each scan the infrared light spot is either reflected by the iris and sclera or absorbed in the area of the pupil opening. The reflected or nonreflected part of the scan is then directed to an infrared sensitive photomultiplier. Since the speed of the scan is calibrated, the width of the resulting square wave is proportional to the length of the sector of the pupil. Naturally, the largest sector in each raster corresponds to the pupil diameter. The level of a dc output is then made proportional to the pupil diameter at any moment in time.

Several more-recently developed devices use infrared sensitive vidicons in a television-like system (2). Except for the rather slow decay time of the presently available vidicons, these systems are very efficient. They can be made very compact. The electronics are reliable solid state circuits.

In our own laboratory we use the Lowenstein pupillograph as a basic measureing device, to which we have added a data recording and analyzing

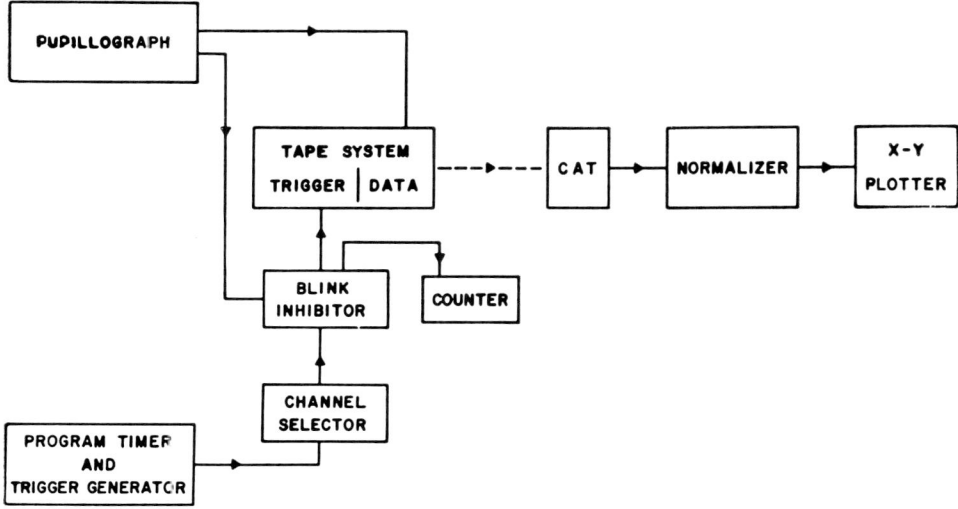

BLOCK DIAGRAM OF DATA RECORDING AND ANALYSING SYSTEM

FIGURE 6–1. Schematic bloc diagram of measuring, recording, and data analysis system.

system (3). The pupil, like other parts of the brain, is a very noisy organ. There are constant diameter changes in the pupil even at rest or when no discernible stimulus is applied. This is called "pupillary unrest" and many efforts to determine regularity in these movements have failed. Thompson (18) has traced the history of this so-called Hippus and found that it has something to do with horses but nothing to do with the eye. The term is probably a misnomer or a misunderstanding which has been carried through medical history. For all practical purposes, the unrest is random. We have therefore used average response curve techniques to pull the signal, that is, the response to our stimuli, out of the biological noise. These methods are very powerful and we have been able to detect reliable changes in pupil diameter of the order of .02 mm. Figure 6-1 shows a schematic bloc diagram of our measuring recording and data analysis system. The dc output of the pupillograph is recorded on magnetic tape. Appropriate identification and calibration pulses are added to each trial. After completion of the experiment, a tape search system identifies the code of each trial and then feeds the data into the Computer of Average Transients (CAT) The summed curves are then read out through a passive network which essentially divides each data point by N and thereby produces a true average (3).

Let us now look at some of our experiments. We have been interested in pupil motility related to rather complete conceptual events. Hess (5, 6) has recently stated that the "emotionality" of a subject and his "true" responses to specific stimulus situations can be gauged by the extent of his pupillary dilation or constrictions. Kahneman (7, 8) has reported pupillary responses to mental activity of varying difficulty, relating the amplitude of the dilation to the degree of difficulty. The phenomenon of pupillary dilation as a response to startle, fear, excitement, and interest has been described in the literature for well over one hundred years.

Our efforts were in part inspired by the work of Sutton and his co-workers (17) in our laboratories. Sutton had shown that the amplitude of the late so-called P3 component of the evoked cortical potential, as recorded from scalp, was related to such attributes of the stimulus as the certainty of its occurrence, or the value a subject might attribute to the stimulus. In Sutton's experiments the subject had to guess whether stimulus would be light or sound (uncertain), In the control experiment, the subjects were told what the stimulus would be (certain). In all subjects there was a difference between curves at 300 msec. The recordings were obtained from electrodes attached over the vertex, thus there is no doubt that they reflect cortical activity. We elaborated somewhat on Sutton's experimental design to take into consideration the somewhat slower response characteristics of the pupillary muscles. In these experiments we used a guessing situation as our experimental paradigm. We assumed that in such a guessing situation, the subject would try his best to come up with as many right guesses as possible. It is interesting to note that none of our subjects ever used a "safe" guessing strategy. They all took certain risks.

Figure 6-2 shows the stimulus situation which we presented the subjects, all normal adults. The stimuli were clicks of 50 msec duration and about 50 dB above threshold.

There was a single click, a double click, two clicks separated by 50 msec, and a triple click (a double click followed by a third click 1000 msec later). The subject was asked to guess whether the next stimulus constellation would be a triple click (yes) or a double or a single click (no). If the subject hears the single click, he has all the information about the stimulus constellation, namely that it is a single click.

In the double click constellation the subject cannot be sure whether it was a double or triple click until the 1000 msec have passed. Then, by the presence or the absence of the third click his uncertainty of the situation will be resolved. This means that the first two clicks contain only 50 per cent of the information. In a control situation the subject was informed before the stimuli were presented what constellation would appear. Thus the subjects were certain about the characteristics of the stimuli.

Averaged response curves were obtained from five subjects. In all subjects the dilation in the guess situation (uncertain) is larger than in the told or certain condition. Also in the certain condition there is no double dilation, even when the triple click is present. This seems to indicate that the dilation is related to the uncertainty of the situation and not to the occurrence of the stimulus per se. The curves also are highly characteristic for each of the subjects. This intra-individual reliability of the data and its inter-individual

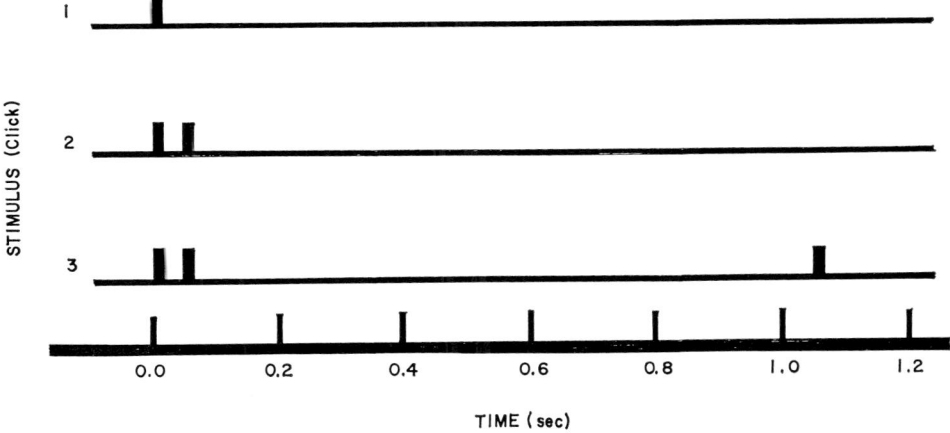

FIGURE 6–2. Stimulus constellation.

difference was one of the striking findings in our work. We superimposed all the curves from the five subjects to show the differences.

The ECP (17) data show a similar trend. We wondered whether this intra-individual consistency of the data, even over periods of several weeks, was determined by the subject's specific strategy in the stimulus situation, by the value system of the subject, or whether this was the reflection of a specific "neuronal hook-up." We attempted to study this question by using identical twins as subjects. We have tested so far only three pairs of twins, but the data show a high similarity between twins. If I might be allowed to speculate, I would tend to prefer the "neuronal hook-up" hypothesis.

In order to determine whether the larger dilation in the uncertain condition was the consequence of a higher level of vigilance, or attention, or in physiological terms, higher arousal level, we added a "report" condition to our design. In this condition the subject was asked to report after the trial what he had heard. The data from all subjects show that there is still a difference in amplitude between the guess and the report condition, indicating that although the higher attention produced a larger dilation, this "attention" alone did not account for the total amplitude in the uncertain condition.

Figure 6-3 shows the trials averaged according to trials guessed correctly (rights) and trials guessed incorrectly (wrongs). The curves are identical up to the peak of the dilation about 1200 msec after the information has been given to the subject by the occurrence or nonoccurrence of the third click. The slope of the descending curves differentiate clearly between the "rights" and the "wrongs." These data too show the very high intra-individual reliability. We might then relate the characteristics of these curves, their slopes, amplitudes, and latencies to the contributions of specific areas or pool of neurons through either increased or decreased impingement on the pupillomotor nuclei.

We make no claim of knowing the nature or locus of these contributions. What we have shown here is a method by which rather complex sequential events in the nervous system relating to conceptual and cognitive aspects of human functioning can be analyzed.

I would like to discuss briefly some data we have obtained in our studies with psychiatric patients. All the patients in this study were originally diagnosed as schizophrenics and had not received chemotherapy for at least two weeks. They were presented, after dark adaptation, with a series of 30-msec light flashes (.3 ml intensity via a Ganzfeld) at 30-sec. intervals.

Response curves were superimposed at stimulus onset to compare extent of pupillary contraction. I should point out that in this study we did not find differences between the dark-adapted diameter of the pupil of the patients and the controls as we had reported previously. Even without statistical analysis we saw that these curves neatly separated the patients and the controls. Figure

Pupillography as a Tool

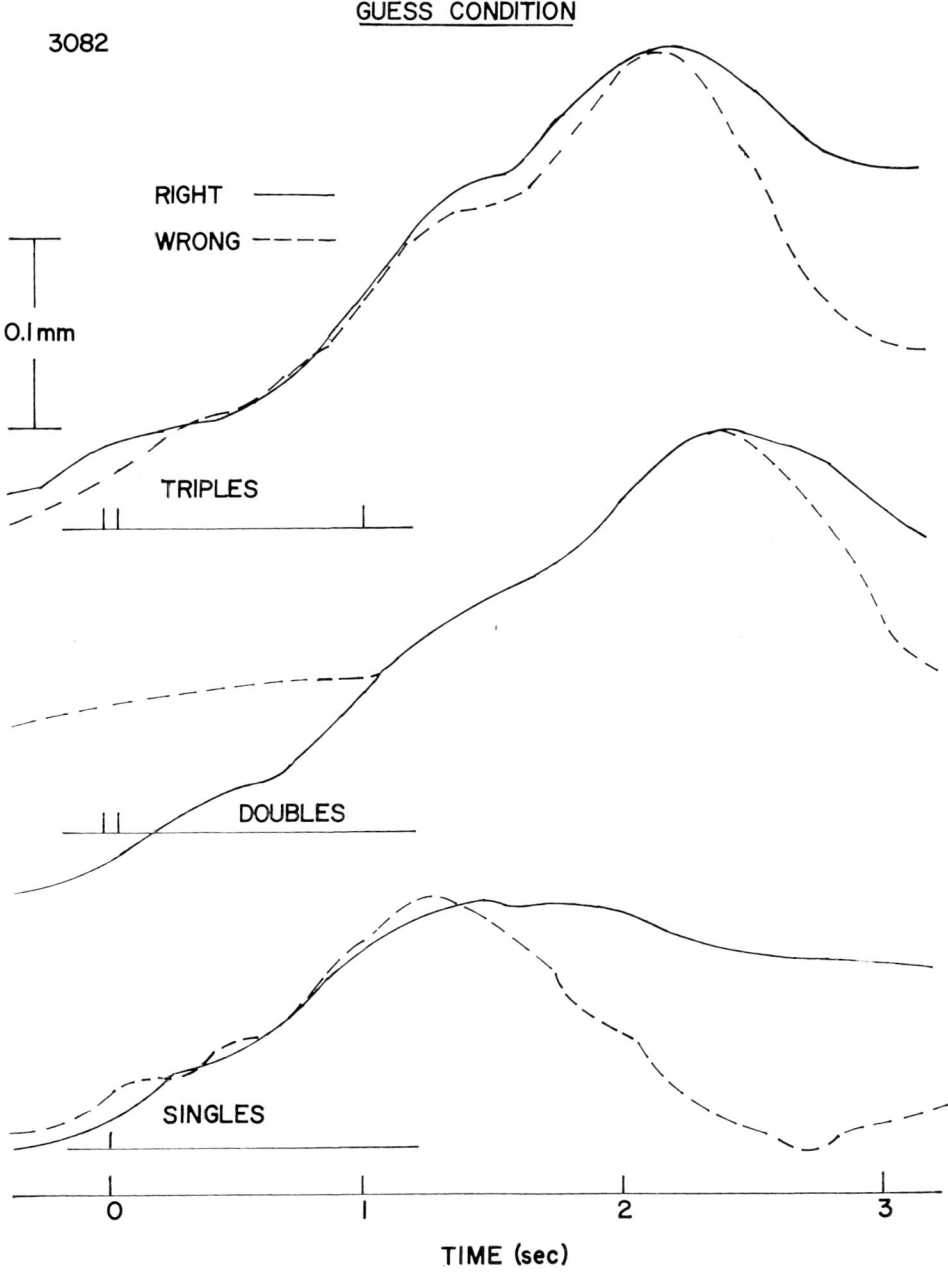

FIGURE 6-3. Averaged response curves of trials where the guess was correct or incorrect.

6-4 shows these data plotted as cumulative percentage curves. A cutoff point at 1.7 mm extent of contraction shows about 15 per cent overlap at each end.

Knopp (9) has repeated some of these experiments and essentially confirmed these findings.

Knopp has also done some interesting studies of the effect of trifluoperazine on the pupillary light response in schizophrenic patients. He reported a high correlation between extrapyramidal side effects and changes in the pupil constriction response. There were, however, large individual differences among the patients with respect to drug tolerance, relief of psychotic symptomatology, and change in the pupillary response. Knopp feels, as a clinician, that the pupillary response changes are good indications for monitoring individual patient's drug treatment. Though his data are suggestive, they do not yet warrant generalization.

Knopp also reports some interesting findings in studies of two patients with Gilles de La Tourette disease. Pupillary changes correlated well with the disappearance of the clinical symptoms during treatment with haloperidol. Knopp is now testing psychotic patients under treatment with haloperidol as well as patients with Parkinson's disease who are under treatment with l-Dopa.

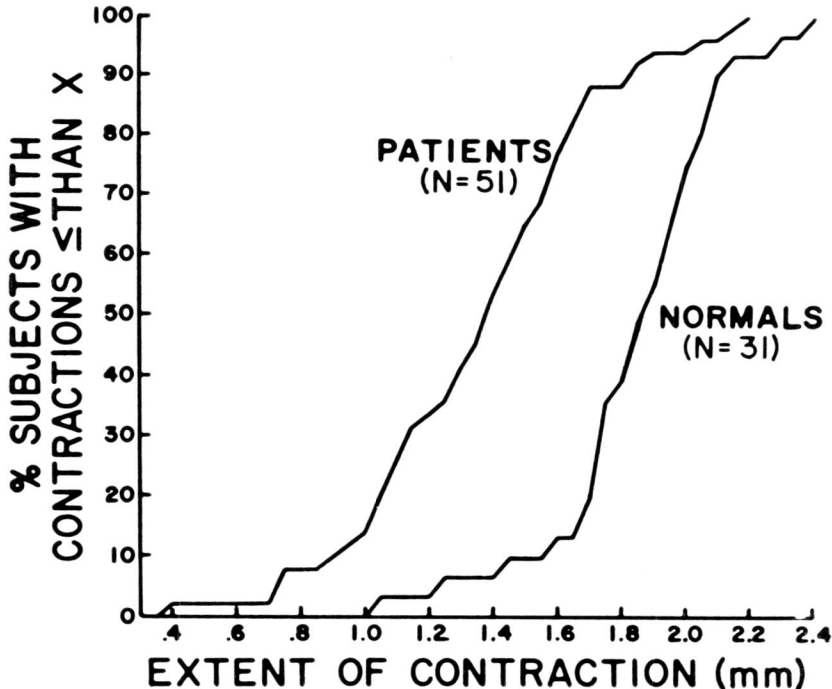

FIGURE 6–4. Cumulative percent graphs of extent of pupillary condition to single light flashes. The graphs for patients and controls are clearly separated.

Lauber (10) in Germany has studied the effects of a number of psycho-effective drugs on the pupil diameter in normal subjects. His data show different responses in pupil diameter to these drugs. More insight as to the effective loci of these drugs might be gained from studies of not only the static reactivity of the pupil, that is the diameter, but from the dynamic reactivity changes of the type I have described earlier.

We are now embarking on a project to follow psychotic patients with weekly testing sessions through their chemotherapy. We are going to use the procedures I outlined earlier. We hope to obtain data on their information processing characteristics and possible changes under proper treatment.

I should not close my presentation without mentioning Rubin's work (16) in this context. Rubin feels that psychotic patients show in their pupillary reaction either an overactivity or underactivity (or both) in either of the two sympathetic or parasympathetic systems. His 1962 paper seems to confirm such a distribution. Rubin is now engaged in a study in which the patients are given drug treatment according to the type of aberration in their pupillary reactivity. We have to wait for the results of this interesting approach.

I hope I have demonstrated to you the wide range of scientific applicability of the tool of pupillography to the study of brain functions and psychopharmacology.

REFERENCES

1. DELGADO, J.M.R., AND DIEGO, M.: Infatiagability of pupillary constriction evoked by hypothalamic stimulation in monkeys. *Neurology (Minneap) 16*:939–950, 1966.
2. GREEN, D., AND MASSEIDVAAG, F.: Closed-circuit television pupillometer, *J Opt Soc Amer, 57*:830–833, 1967.
3. HAKEREM, G.: Pupillography. In *A Manual of Psychophysiological Methods*. Amsterdam, North-Holland Publ. Co., 1967.
4. HAKEREM, G., SUTTON, S., AND ZUBIN, J.: Pupillary reactions in schizophrenic patients and normals, *Ann NY Acad Sci, 105*:820–831, 1964.
5. HESS, E. H.: Pupil size as related to interest value of visual stimuli. *Science, 132*:349–350, 1960.
6. HESS, E.H., AND POLT, J.: Pupil size in relation to mental activity during simple problem-solving. *Science, 143*:1190–1192, 1964.
7. KAHNEMAN, D., AND BEATTY, J.: Pupil diameter and load on memory. *Science, 154*: 1583–1585, 1966.
8. KAHNEMAN, D., AND BEATTY, J.: Pupil response in a pitch-discrimination task. *Percept Psychophysics, 2*: 101–104, 1967.
9. KNOPP, W. et al.: The schizophrenics individual response to trifluoperazine. *Cur Ther Res, 9*:51–59, 1967.
10. LAUBER, H.L.: Pupillometrische Versuche Bei Anwendung von Psychopharmaka. *Die Medizinische Welt, 10*:1–12, 1967.
11. LOEWENFELD, I.E., AND LOWENSTEIN, O.: Mechanisms of reflex dilation of the pupil. *Docum Ophthal Advances Ophthal, 12*:185–448, 1958.
12. LOWENSTEIN, O., AND LOEWENFELD, I.E.: Role of sympathetic and parasympathetic systems in reflex dilatation of the pupil, *Arch Neurol Psychiat, 64*:313–340, 1950.

13. LOWENSTEIN, O., AND LOEWENFELD, I.E.: Electronic pupillography; A new instrument and some clinical applications, *Arch Ophthal (Chicago), 59*:352–363, 1958.
14. LOWENSTEIN, O., AND LOWENFELD, I.E.: Basic mechanisms of pupillary movements. *Trans NY Acad Sci, 23*:579–585, 1950.
15. NAQUET, R. et al.: Variations in the responses evoked by light along the specific pathways. *Brain, 83*:52–56, 1960.
16. RUBIN, L.S.: Patterns of adrenergic-cholinergic imbalance in the functional psychosis. *Psychol Rev, 69*:501–519, 1962.
17. SUTTON, S. et al.: Information delivery and the sensory evoked potential. *Science, 155*:1436–1439, 1967.
18. THOMPSON, H.S.: Hippus. Paper delivered at the Sixth Colloqquium on the Pupil, Washington, D. C., 1969.
19. WARD, A.A., AND REED, H.L.: Mechanisms of pupillary dilatation elicited by cortical stimulation. *J Neurophysiol, 9*:329–335, 1946.

Chapter 7

Psychotropic Drugs and the Regulation of Behavioral Activation in Psychiatric Illness

DONALD F. KLEIN

The postulation of central dispositional states that exert governing, facilitating, or inhibiting influences over a wide repertoire of behaviors has had slow acceptance in the development of twentieth century behavioral analysis, although belief in "temperaments" dates from the Greeks. Early learning theory, following Hull, conceived of each specific behavior as the resultant of drive and habit. Both of these constructs were tied to rather narrow sets of antecedents. Drives were considered to be largely the result of tissue needs and therefore were closely identifiable with states of water, food, air deprivation, and so forth. Habits also were the result of a particular chain of stimuli and responses, leading to a specific learning experience and habit formation. Therefore, increments in response strength had to be explained in terms of specific response antecedents; i.e. either a relevant drive had become activated by the press of increasing tissue deficit or the response had received some special habituation training.

Interestingly this formulation of psychic activity bears many resemblances to the early psychoanalytic explanations of human behavior in general and symptomatic behavior in particular. When asked to explain a specific behavior an id-oriented psychoanalyst first thinks of the specific drive state that has instigated this behavior and second of the ego mechanisms that modify drive expression. For instance, an oral drive may heighten the likelihood of oral activity. The particular activity, e.g. chewing gum, would be considered the outcome of an oral drive that had been domesticated via upbringing in a society that provided both gum and the relevant learning experiences that increased the ego's adaptive consummatory repertoire. The fact that under conditions of neurotic development the manifest behavior may be the antithesis of the usual drive consummatory response can be accounted for by hypothesizing intervening defensive mechanisms attributed to specific learning contingencies. For instance, an oral drive whose expressions had been aversively conditioned could conceivably lead to chronically tightened masticatory muscles; the drive would be discharged via muscular contraction, al-

Note: This study was supported, in part, by USPHS Grant MH 12273. Parts of this paper were adapted from *Diagnosis and Drug Treatment of Psychiatric Disorders* by Donald F. Klein and John M. Davis. Baltimore, Williams and Wilkins, 1969.

though the usual oral consummatory activity would be held to a minimum.

Academic psychology has expanded the early Hullian model by broadening the concepts of the leading participant variables. It is now often postulated that behavior can be understood as the interaction of response selective and action instigational mechanisms rather than habit and drive. Tolman pointed out that habit is simply one rather low grade response selection mechanism, fit primarily for rote response development during overtraining in an environment that prevents higher level cognition. He demonstrated, in lower animals, the development of cognitive maps, hypotheses, and plans that allowed adaptive behavior without preliminary habits or even in opposition to preexisting habits. The Gestalt theoreticians also broadened the response-chained view of behavior by emphasizing nativistic perceptual organization and reorganization via "insight."

More recently, the still controversial ethologists have emphasized that response selection can often be due to specific species equipment that releases certain responses under certain stimulus conditions and that determines the very course of the learning experience. The cowering response of naive chicks to an appropriately moving hawk silhouette has been convincingly described. Similarly imprinting and the occurrence of critical social attachment periods indicates species structuring of learning. Therefore, under the impact of both the cognitional and the ethological school, the close tying of response selection to specific learned stimulus-response chains has diminished as a central theoretical presumption.

The cognitivist emphasis has its parallels in modern psychiatric and psychoanalytic theory. For instance, concepts such as self-image, identity, social role, and life space are obviously analogous to cognitive maps produced in relationship to oneself, one's social position, and the world in general. They do not necessarily derive from any specific sequence of learning experiences, in that a broad range of different experiences may lead people to quite similar self-images, social roles, and so forth, and vice versa. It is true that these broad ranges of experience often have certain common features from which these cognitive maps may be abstracted. However, this is the very point; the development of these cognitive maps requires a creative act of abstraction and inference and is not simply the outcome of mechanical stimulus-response linkage and habit production.

Ethological theory has also had its impact on psychoanalysis. One example is Bowlby's (4) recent revision of Freud's (10) contiguity learning theory of separation anxiety. Freud stated that separation anxiety occurs when the infant, plagued by mounting instinctual tensions, finds that his discomforts are relieved in the presence of the mothering object and worsen in her absence. Separation anxiety, then, is the learned anticipation of tension and pain under certain environmental conditions. However, animal observations indicate states of distress after separation from the mother in animals who could not have learned that separation entails lack of relief for instinctual tension. Two examples are the "lost piping" of chicks separated from the nest and the whining of puppies separated from the mother. These retrieval evocative responses occur long before any actual drive tension could conceivably have arisen. Bowlby, who has extensively studied the problems arising on the separation of children from their mother, has come to the conclusion that there is a species specific innate instinctual tie between infant and mothering object and that separation anxiety is triggered by an innate releasing mechanism in a fashion quite analogous to the above ethological demonstrations. The evolutionary value of such a mechanism is self-evident.

Another psychoanalytic parallel to the broadened concept of response selection is the development of modern ego psychology (largely identified with Hartmann) in which more attention is paid to the issue of innate ego structures, dispensing with the idea that all psychological structures are necessarily the precipitate of a conflictual interaction of the id with reality (i.e. drive and experience).

These developments in academic psychology, psychiatry, and psychoanalysis have once again emphasized the necessity for considering the constitutional elements in human development, the organisms's abilities to develop cognitive maps via nativistic imprinting and inferential processes, as well as the possibility of constitutional intellectual and affective vulnerabilities or talents influencing the response selection aspect of developmental course.

The other key aspect of the Hullian formulation, i.e. drive, has also been markedly modified. Duffy (6), Moruzzi and Magoun (25), and Olds and Milner (26) led in developing the present concerns about arousal and activation as action instigational factors, in contradistinction to the old concept of a tissue deficiency drive. Action instigational factors are now believed to determine the probability and the vigor of a broad variety of response occurrences and are linked to a wider range of antecedent organismic variables such as tissue needs, sensory deprivation, innate releasing mechanisms, fatigue, hormones, or drugs. Even more recently it has been emphasized that certain stimuli, associated with positive or negative reinforcement, acquire and incentive-motivation function for the organism and thereby acquire the property of regulating, arcusing, and inhibiting activity. Both Bindra (3) and Routtenberg (28) have emphasized the distinction between drive and incentive motivation and have presented complex neuropsychological schema to attempt to integrate the welter of confusing experimental findings in this area. They find it necessary to hypothesize at least two central arousal systems. Routtenberg specifically hypothesizes an arousal system that simply increases the possibility of response occurrence and is predominantly concerned with drive and organization of response. The second arousal system is considered as an aspect of the limbic system and is primarily concerned with behavior related to incentive-reward, or more subjectively pleasure and pain.

The question of the existence of a multiplicity of arousal systems is thorny. Duffy (6) considers that there is only one activation system and that apparently different activation states are due to organismal evaluation and direction during undifferentiated activation. She believes that when the organism is either angry or fearful the same activation is occurring, but in anger the organism evaluates the situation as attack appropriate and in fear as flight appropriate. This is a difficult issue to resolve and would require complex comparative multiple analyses of autonomic functioning, endocrine response, cardiovascular performance, skeletal muscle tension patterns, and the proneness to develop specific appetitive, consummatory, and defensive activities. Subjectively, I feel that fear, anger, and the anxious excitation prior to a threatening situation are different, but this is shoddy evidence. Similarly, the states of pleasurable anticipation and arousal prior to eating, sexual activity, defecation, urination, etcetera, also seem to have quite distinct feeling tones and patterns of internal cues associated with them. The specificity theory of activation states has been contributed to by such psychophysiologists as Ax (2) and Wenger (32). Nonetheless, it must be admitted that the issue is not scientifically resolved.

Clinically, it appears wiser to maintain a working hypothesis of multiple activating and deactivating systems. Also, from an *a priori* evolutionary viewpoint it seems hard to believe that an undifferentiated activated state would be the most survival-prone device. Rather, a differentiated repertoire of activations would seem to maximize survival potential. Further, it has been amply demonstrated that certain biological releasers result in quite complex and specific patterns of appetitive and consummatory behavior.

A striking example is in the field of pheromones, where a physical substance emitted by one organism controls the behavior of another organism. This has been clearly demonstrated in the mating behavior of moths, where the scent of a female moth directs the behavior of male moths at fantastic distances. A wide array of pheromone controlled behavior, in particular olfactory pheromones, have been demonstrated, with some evidence that such agents may control reproductive and gestational behavior in mammals. The relevance of this to human psychology and psychopathology is quite obscure, however these facts illustrate the possibility of highly differentiated arousal and response systems.

These academic developments concerning drive and activation have their parallels in psychiatry, most particularly in attempts to explain the phenomenology of psychotic states and the effects of modern psychopharmacological agents. One of the most striking features of psychotic behavior is the marked bipolarity in level of activation that many psychotic individuals show, both among diagnostic groups, as well as over time. We shall review this area so as to outline the array of drug-induced behavioral effects that an adequate pathology-relevant activation model must encompass.

Every factorial analysis of psychiatric patient behavior has demonstrated a large bipolar factor accounting for much of the range of behaviors. This bipolar factor, usually labeled "excitation-retardation," is variously defined. However, the core behavioral elements appear to be persistent hyperactivity accompanied by euphoria, belligerence, low frustration tolerance, erotomania, sleep disturbance, psychomotor acceleration, grandiosity and expansiveness versus retardation accompanied by depression, suicidal preoccupation, apathy, early morning awakening, inability to concentrate, make decisions, anticipate or experience pleasure, and losses of appetite, weight, sex drive, and humor. In our discussions of behavioral activation and deactivation we will refer primarily to this dimension. However, other behaviors might reasonably be considered relevant to the concepts of activation and deactivation; for instance, states of marked anticipatory and panic anxiety are often accompanied by wildly excited and demanding behavior. States of sullen withdrawal and the anticipation of reproach may be accompanied by relative behavioral inactivity. Confusingly, states of suicidal depression may accompany both agitation and depressive vegetative signs. We shall attempt to encompass descriptions of drug effects throughout this range of behavioral states. However, for the moment we will emphasize the excitation-retardation dimension that is particularly a feature of manic-depressive disease, schizo-affective psychosis, and the group of ill-defined psychoses referred to by Fish (9) as cycloid. Such variations in behavioral activation have naturally led to speculation concerning states of CNS excitation and inhibition underlying the psychiatric phenomena. Attempts to classify psychotropic drug effects also require a model that deals with the obvious, although complex, effects on behavioral activation.

The initial descriptions of psychotropic drug effect emphasized a unidirectional activation effect. Therefore, phenothiazines were described as "tranquilizers" and antidepressants as "energizers," paralleling the widely accepted description of barbiturates as "sedatives" and amphetamines as "stimulants." The implicit model underlying these descriptions can be economically referred to as the "rheostat" model (a variable resistor that directly raises or lowers the flow of current). It is noteworthy that a popular and well-documented theory of activation control, the catecholamine hypothesis, is a simple rheostat theory, i.e. excessive functional noradrenaline causes mania, whereas insufficient functional noradrenaline causes depression. Imipramine and MAO inhibitors are believed to increase the availability of functional noradrenaline, whereas phenothiazines and lithium do the opposite, thus respectively benefiting depression and mania.

However, broader experience is inconsistent with this model. We have attempted to outline our present knowledge in this area in Table 7-1. The clearest inconsistency is demonstrated by phenothiazine effects in schizo-affective disease; it is clearly evident that patients at both the excited and retarded poles of this disorder are normalized by phenothiazine treatment. The *a priori* belief, derived from the rheostat model, that these drugs exacerbate depression or induce retardation is supported anecdotally; however controlled studies clearly contradict these expectations and indicate that phenothiazines are markedly effective in the treatment of both retarded and agitated states.

In line with this normalizing effect is the finding that adolescent patients characterized by marked incessant mood swings (emotionally unstable character disorders) are also normalized by phenothiazines. Finally the initial rheostat model that phenothiazines are simply extremely effective sedatives and anxiety reducers is contradicted by their ineffectiveness in severe anticipatory anxiety states, in anxiety as a component of schizophrenia and in panic anxiety under conditions of separation and bereavement.

Other inconsistencies with the rheostat model are the effectiveness of imipramine in agitated depressions, separation panics, and perhaps in occasional manic states; of MAO inhibitors in retarded and agitated depression and separation panic, and the probably beneficial effects of lithium in some depressions and emotional instability.

A final deadly inconsistency with the rheostat model is the conspicuous lack of behavioral activation effect of phenothiazines (particularly the piperazine phenothiazines), imipramine, MAO inhibitors, and lithium on normal human subjects. Therefore, it appears that the activation effects of the major psychotropic agents depend upon a preexisting state of activation dysregulation, and that beneficial drug effects cannot be understood as simply excitatory or inhibiting.

An alternative to the "rheostat" is the "thermostat" model of drug action. Thus the major psychotropic drugs are postulated to specifically affect pathological disturbances in a normalizing, reparative manner rather than a compensatory one. Compensatory drugs affect normal physiology in a direction similar to their effect on pathophysiological states. That is, antacids will decrease the acidity both of normal and hyperacid gastric contents. Reparative drugs, in contrast, have an effect on pathophysiology only. For instance, aspirin lowers the temperature in febrile people but does not lower the temperature of normals; it is antipyretic, not hypothermic. It is our contention that the major antipsychotics, antidepressants, and lithium act to normalize deranged control mechanisms and are therefore reparative, whereas the sedatives, minor tranquilizers, and stimulant drugs usually have compensatory actions. The distinction between reparative and compensatory actions follows naturally from a simple negative feedback model. This model is also

TABLE 7-1
PREDOMINANT PSYCHOTROPIC DRUG EFFECTS ON BEHAVIORAL ACTIVATION IN PSYCHIATRIC DISORDERS

	Manic-Depressive Retarded	Manic-Depressive agitated	Schizo-Affective Retarded	Schizo-Affective agitated	Emotionally Unstable	Agitated Depression	Separation Panic	Anticipatory Anxiety	Pre-Puberty Hyperactive Impulse Disorder
Phenothiazines	Normalize (27)*	Normalize (17, 18)	Normalize (17, 18)	Normalize (17, 18)	Normalize (17, 18)	Normalize (17, 18)	Exacerbate (23)	No Effect (23)	Probably Normalize†
Lithium	Occasionally Normalize (7, 8)	Normalize (30)	No Data	Occasionally Normalize (11)	Normalize (21)	Occasionally Normalize (7, 8, 21)	No Data	No Data	Probably Normalize†
Imipramine (Tricyclic Antidepressants)	Normalize; Occasionally Excite (17, 18)	Occasionally Normalize (1)	Occasionally Normalize (18)	Occasionally Normalize (18)	Occasionally Normalize or Excite (17, 18)	Normalize (17, 18)	Normalize (16, 17, 18, 23)	No Effect (16, 17, 18, 23)	Probably Normalize (14, 22)
MAO Inhibitors	Normalize; Occasionally Excite (12)	No Data	No Data	No Data	Possibly Excite (19)	Normalize (12)	Normalize (12)	Controversial (29)†	No Data
Barbiturates	Acute Temporary Normalization on IV Admin.†	Only Hypnotic†	Acute Temporary Normalization on IV Admin.†	Only Hypnotic (15)	Only Hypnotic†	Sedation	No Effect (16)	Decrease but not complete normalization (20)	Occasionally Decrease and Occasionally Excite†
Minor Tranquilizers	No Data	No Data	No Data	No Data	No Data	Occasionally Normalize (20)	No Effect (16)	Decrease but not complete normalization (20)	Occasionally Decrease and Occasionally Excite†
Stimulants	Agitate†	No Data	Agitate†	No Data	Probably Agitate	Agitate†	No Data	Probably Variable†	Normalize (5, 24)

† Anecdotal reports.
* Numbers refer to references.

capable of demonstrating one remedial drug effect associated with two opposing behavioral manifestations.

The thermostat may be taken as an example of a simple cybernetic regulator. It consists of a detector, a bimetal band that acts as a thermometer, bending and unbending with fluctuations in temperature. An increase in temperature causes the detector to bend sufficiently to contact a switch that turns off the furnace. Subsequent decreases in temperature cause the band to unbend, release the switch, and turn the furnace back on, raising the temperature to a point at which the detector will again inactivate the furnace. It can easily be seen that this will result in an ambient temperature that oscillates about a mean level. The exact mean level frequency, and amplitude of these oscillations will depend on several physical factors, such as the sensitivity of the detector, the position of the switch, the efficiency of the furnace, the volume to be heated, and fluctuations in external temperature, insulation, and so forth.

The thermal regulatory system described, however, would be helpless against a rise in temperature that was not due to furnace output (e.g. summer). Under these circumstances the addition of another switch connected to a refrigerating system would allow for control of this source of temperature fluctuation. Now if the temperature (read "level of activation") remained in a specified normal range, neither furnace ("activation center") nor refrigerator ("deactivation center") would be in operation. If the temperature dropped, the furnace would be turned on; if the temperature then rose, the furnace would be turned off. If the temperature continued to rise, the refrigerating system would be turned on, and so on.

One cybernetic hypothesis would implicate a defect in a key element in this system—the detector. The existence of neural detectors assaying component levels in the bloodstream (electrolytes, osmolarity, glucose, blood pressure, etcetera) has been generally accepted. These detectors have the advantage of continually sampling from the circulation and therefore gain an integrated picture of the conditions throughout the vascular compartment. Detectors relating to general behaviorally relevant states, such as arousal, would require a data-collecting and integrating device for input. The nonspecific afferent system may fulfill this function.

If the detector became inoperative, temperature aberrations resulting from external circumstances would be entirely uncompensated, and very high or low temperatures could ensue. If, at that point, the efficacy of the detector were restored by some adjustment (i.e. medication), the system would return to normal regardless of whether it had been either too hot or too cold. If the detector were only partially repaired, so that it lacked sensitivity, the possibility of marked overshoot would exist. That is, if the patient were in a state of uncorrected marked underactivation as a result of external circumstances coupled with an inactive detector, a partial repair of the detector, resulting in a change from inoperative to low sensitivity, would lead to a delayed "switching on" of the activation mechanism. However, the activation mechanism would then stay on past the level of normal arousal and would turn off only after prolonged activation. This maladaptive overshoot may be analogous to acute psychotic exacerbation. Disease-induced partial detector defects would result either in severe oscillations or overshoots analogous to affective lability or acute psychotic states.

One useful aspect of this model is that one process (repair of the detector) will return the entire system to normal, regardless of the direction or degree of its deviation from normal. However, an even more parsimonious cybernetic hypothesis is possible. In the previous hypothesis there were two preconditions for a state of pathological activation: an insensitive activation detector and a state of externally-induced hyperactivation or deactivation. Essentially the same results could be obtained on the basis of one hypothesized defect, that is, an illness-induced change from a negative feedback regulatory circuit to a positive feedback circuit. Under these circumstances the normal reparative tendencies of the system would do exactly the wrong thing; if there was a swing towards activation the system would push towards even more activation. The usual self-regulatory alternations of mood and activation states would be replaced by dizzying surges of hyperactivation or deadening plunges of deactivation.

If drugs could reverse a positive into a negative feedback there would be a drug-induced normalizing effect regardless of the particular level of behavioral pathology. Inspection of the table suggests even more refined speculations, i.e. phenothiazines may be capable of reversing positive feedback circuits that may maintain either pole of activation level, but imipramine and the MAO inhibitors are particularly, although not exclusively, useful in reversing a positive feedback circuit that maintains deactivation. In contradistinction, lithium may be particularly, although not exclusively, useful in reversing positive feedback circuits that maintain hyperactivation. Such a method of drug effect on activation is conceivable, since control mechanism theory states that altering timing or the level of amplification within a feedback circuit may convert it from negative to positive and vice versa.

Still another cybernetic hypothesis postulates that normally the activation and deactivation brain centers have a reciprocal inhibiting effect upon each other. Therefore, when the activation center is operating, the deactivation center is not and vice versa. It is conceivable that this negative feedback circuit could also be so damaged as to produce a positive feedback. Under these circumstances both activation and deactivation mechanisms would be in operation simultaneously.

What clinical conditions would correspond to such a state of affairs? I propose that agitated depression fulfills this role. It is noteworthy that Kraepelin referred to manic-depressive mixed states, wherein signs of both mania and depression were simultaneously present. In agitated depression, both motor facilitation and psychomotor acceleration are combined with vegetative signs of depression and the characteristic depressive mood. Interestingly, the agitated depressive state responds well to ECT, phenothiazines, imipramine, MAO inhibitors, and possibly lithium. Other forms of somatic treatment such as ECT and leukotomy have had their beneficial effects attributed to the interruption of pathological positive feedback reverberatory circuits, so that this drug action hypothesis is compatible with these prior hypotheses.

The resemblance of such normalizing ameliorative patterns to imipramine, MAO inhibitor, lithium, and phenothiazine effects seems sufficiently close to warrant further investigation. Other parallels may be extended. For instance, the actions of dextroamphetamine and barbiturates or the sedative effect of chlorpromazine may depend on changing the location of the on-off switches in a related "alerting" system involved in sleep-waking regulation, thus stabilizing the alertness-vigilance-psychomotor integration level in a different range. Under normal conditions of fluctuating need for alertness and activation (e.g. sleep-waking cycle, changes in stress), other parts of the CNS concerned with environmental evaluation can be seen as regulating the position of the "on-off" switches and therefore the activation level. However, it is difficult to conceive of any value to a control operating via fluctuations in detector sensitivity or by positive feedback as this can only lead to oscillatory inefficiency or extreme derangements. Therefore, fluctuations in detector sensitivity or the development of positive feedback are presumed to be pathological. It will be seen that repair of the detector is equivalent to remedying a pathological situation; whereas, moving the switch position is analogous to affecting an normally variable control mechanism (or rheostat).

This type of theorizing implies that behavioral drugs act on control mechanisms rather than at levels often considered in energy, libidinal, or drive terminology. This model bears some resemblance to that proposed by Stein (31). However, his theorizing remains within the rheostat, stimulation-inhibition framework, thus resembling the other theories presented in Himwich's review (13), although it is applicable to a higher level of neural integration.

It is clear that this presentation makes no contributions to the issue of the etiology or nature of the hypothesized detector and/or feedback defect nor does it claim that all psychotropic agents act identically or that all manic-depressives and schizo-affectives have the same neurophysiological defect. Also this model does not imply that there is a unitary activation system. Rather, clinical evidence as well as the work of Bindra (3) and Routtenberg (28) would indicate a network of activation systems, wherein the level set by one becomes part of the input to the others and may also have effects in setting the "range switches."

Clinically, barbiturates and dextroamphetamine would seem active in setting the activation level range switches in a sleep-waking-vigilance-anticipatory anxiety-alertness center. Phenothiazines normalize excitation-retardation activation regulators, and antidepressants normalize activation regulators responsive to pleasure-pain as well as separation anxiety, rejection sensitivity, and object gain or loss. Further, the minor tranquilizer-barbiturates seem to deactivate the secondary painful anxiety effects of pain anticipation, the opiates the effects of pain experience and anticipation processing, whereas the amphetamines lower the activation threshold for the anticipation of pleasure. Obviously, this is all quite speculative.

In this view, major psychotropic drug effect and diagnosis are closely tied to each other in that a specific reparative ameliorative effect implies a specific regulatory defect, although the specific cybernetic defects hypothesized here may well be incorrect. These views of drug effect, i.e. compensatory and reparative, are not mutually exclusive. It is possible that specific physiological drug effects are compensatory for certain pathological conditions, reparative for others, and irrelevant or toxic for still others. For instance, dextroamphetamine and methylphenidate seem to compensate for adult fatigue states but normalize reparatively the prepubertal patient with hyperactive impulse disorder.

There is distinct heuristic value in this emphasis on the possibility of reparative drug action since it fosters the use of clinical drug effects as the basis for a drug-relevant psychiatric typology. That is patients would be grouped on the basis of pattern of drug-induced changes in behavioral activation symptoms, patterns of communication, participation in psychotherapy and social activity. Responses to medication would be used as dissecting tools to distinguish various subpopulations and to permit the determination of specific developmental, physiological, and psychosocial commonalities within each subpopulation. Hopefully, these commonalities may shed light on the question of the etiology and pathogenesis of psychiatric disorder, as well as serve the practical purpose of providing rational indications and contraindications for drug therapy.

REFERENCES

1. AKIMOTO, H., NAKAKUKI, M. HONDA, Y., TAKAHASHI, Y., AND TOYODA, J.: Clinical evaluation of the effect of central stimulants, MAO inhibitors, and imipramine in the treatment of affective disorders. *Proceedings of the Third World Congress of Psychiatry,* 2:958, 1961.
2. Ax, A.F.: Psychophysiology of fear and anger. *Psychiat Res Rep Amer Psychiat Ass,* 12:167–175, 1960.

3. BINDRA, D.: Neurophysiological interpretation of the effects of drive and incentive-motivation on general activity and instrumental behavior. *Psychol Rev, 75*:1–22, 1968.
4. BOWLBY, J.: Separation anxiety. *Int J Psychoanal, 41*:89, 1960.
5. CONNORS, C.K., EISENBERG, L. AND BARCAI, A.: Effects of dextroamphetamine on children. *Arch Gen Psychiat, 17*: 478–485, 1967.
6. DUFFY, E.: *Activation and Behavior.* New York, John Wiley & Sons, 1962.
7. DYSON, W.L., AND MENDELS, J.: Lithium and depression. *Curr Ther Res, 10*:601–608, 1968.
8. FIEVE, R.R., PLATMAN, S.R., AND PLUTCHIK, R.R.: The use of lithium in affective disorders. *Amer J Psychiat, 125*:492–498, 1968.
9. FISH, F.J.: *Outline of Psychiatry.* Baltimore, Williams & Wilkins, 1964.
10. FREUD, S.: Analysis of a phobia in a five-year-old boy. *Standard Editions, 10*:3–149, London, Hogarth Press, 1955.
11. GERSHON, S.: Personal communication, 1969.
12. GREENBLATT, M., GROSSER, G.H., AND WECHSLER, H.: Differential response of hospitalized depressed patients to somatic therapy. *Amer J Psychiat, 120*:935–943, 1964.
13. HIMWICH, H.E.: Biochemical and neurophysiological action of psychoactive drugs. In Uhr, L., and Miller, G. (Eds.) : *Drugs and Behavior.* New York, John Wiley & Sons, 1960.
14. HUSSEY, H.R. AND WRIGHT, A.L.: Use of imipramine in children's behavior disorder. Paper presented at the 122nd Meeting of the American Psychiatric Association, Miami, May 1969.
15. KALINOWSKI, L.B., AND HOCH, P.H.: *Somatic Treatments in Psychiatry.* New York, Grune & Stratton, 1961.
16. KLEIN, D.F.: Delineation of two drug-responsive anxiety syndromes. *Psychopharmacologia (Berlin), 5*:397–408, 1964.
17. KLEIN, D.F.: Importance of psychiatric diagnosis in prediction of clinical drug effects. *Arch Gen Psychiat, 16*:118–126, 1967.
18. KLEIN, D.F.: Psychiatric diagnosis and a typology of clinical drug effects. *Psychopharmacologia (Berlin), 13*:359–386, 1968.
19. KLEIN, D.F., AND CARRILLO, C.: Unpublished data, 1968.
20. KLEIN, D.F., AND DAVIS, J.M.: *Diagnosis and Drug Treatment of Psychiatric Disorders.* Baltimore, Williams & Wilkins, 1969.
21. KLEIN, D.F.; RIFKIN, A., AND QUITKIN F.: Unpublished data, 1969.
22. KRAKOWSKI, A.J.: Amitriptyline in treatment of hyperkinetic children. A double-blind study. *Psychosomatics, 6*:355–360, 1965.
23. KRAMER, J.C., KLEIN, D.F., AND FINK, M.: Imipramine as an adjunct to phenothiazine therapy. *Compr Psychiat, 3*:377–380, 1962.
24. MILLICHAP, J.G.: Drugs in management of hyperkinetic and perceptually handicapped children. *JAMA, 206*:, 1968.
25. MORUZZI, G., AND MAGOUN, H.W.: Brain stem reticular formation and activation of the EEG. *Electroenceph Clin Neurophysiol, 1*:455–473, 1949.
26. OLDS, J., AND MILNER, P.: Positive reinforcement produced by electrical stimulation of septal area and other regions of rat brain. *J Comp Physiol Psychol, 47*:419–427, 1954.
27. RASKIN, A., SCHULTERBRANDT, J., BOOTHE, H., REATIG, N., AND MCKEON, J.J.: Treatment, social and psychiatric history variables related to symptom reduction in hospitalized depressions. National Institute of Mental Health. Unpublished manuscript.

28. ROUTTENBERG, A.: The two-arousal hypothesis: Reticular formation and limbic system. *Psychol Rev, 75*:51–80, 1968.
29. SARGANT, W.: The treatment of anxiety states and atypical depression by the monoamine oxidase inhibitor drugs. *J Neuropsychiat, 3* (Suppl. 1) :96–103, 1962.
30. SCHOU, M.: Lithium in psychiatric therapy. Stock-taking after ten years. *Psychopharmacologia (Berlin), 1*:65–78, 1959.
31. STEIN, L.: Effects and interactions of imipramine, chlorpromazine, reserpine and amphetamine on self-stimulation: Possible neurophysiological basis of depression. *Recent Advances Biol Psychiat, 4*:288–308, 1962.
32. WENGER, M.A.: Studies of autonomic balance: A summary. *Psychophysiology, 2*:173–186, 1966.

PART III

LEARNING FACILITATORS

Chapter 8

The Use of Stimulant Drugs in Enhancing Performance and Learning

C. KEITH CONNERS

The word "stimulant" as applied to central nervous system acting drugs is a loose term usually implying certain behavioral changes (restlessness, insomnia, excitement) and, in humans, also implying euphoric mood and heightening of awareness or consciousness. Some of these effects are related to the peripheral actions of the drugs on the autonomic nervous system. The amphetamines, for example, are classed as sympathomimetic amines because of the similarity of structure and action to catecholamines (epinephrine and norephinephrine). Effector organs innervated by adrenergic nerves are affected by the amphetamines, raising blood pressure, constricting peripheral blood vessels, stimulating heart muscle, relaxing bronchial and intestinal muscle, and dilating pupils. While there is usually an electrophysiological activation from stimulant drugs (48), the behavioral effects may not be congruent with the electrophysiological ones (10). It is thought that the amphetamines have direct effects on the tonic midbrain activating system which is similar to that of epinephrine, though the duration of effects for the drug are longer and the peripheral effects less marked.

Another stimulant, methylphenidate (Ritalin®) has effects very similar to the amphetamines but appears to act more as a diencephalic or thalamic *phasic* stimulant rather than acting on the tonic midbrain portion (30). It causes cortical activation in cats which is not abolished by lesions of the reticular formation at the level of the red nucleus but is abolished by lesions of the diffuse thalamic projection (26).

Deanol acetamidobenzoate (deanol) is a CNS stimulant thought to be a precursor of acetylcholine which crosses the blood-brain barrier and is converted intracellularly to acetylcholine, thus enhancing synaptic transmission.

The present paper will review some of the psychological effects of these three stimulants on human behavior, particularly on behavior of children.

The amphetamines and methylphenidate will be considered together in terms of effects on cognition, motivation, motor behavior, and other factors since no adequate contrast studies on behavior have been done between the two drugs.

EFFECTS ON BEHAVIOR DISORDERS

Inasmuch as the use of drugs with children is always in a context of treatment being carried out for specific psychiatric or medical indications, it is natural that the bulk of the available literature should reflect an emphasis on clinical symptomatology rather than more general variables as they are affected by drugs. While it is usually difficult to maintain appropriate scientific controls within a treatment-oriented study, such studies can identify and point to important variables for subsequent investigation under more refined circumstances. Most of the phenomena resulting from stimulant drug treatment of children were noted by Bradley and his co-workers in a series of studies carried out on institutionalized emotionally disturbed children (4 to 10).

A typical finding was that the majority of the behaviorally disturbed children became calmer, more organized, less aggressive and disruptive and took an immediate interest in schoolwork (7). Bradley concluded that these effects were secondary to an improvement of the "emotional attitude" or mood of the child which seemed to be more optimistic and euphoric. Bradley (5) summarized work of a decade with 275 children with behavior disorders and reported that approximately 60 to 75 per cent were improved, 15 to 25 per cent showed no change, and 10 to 15 per cent showed unfavorable effects of Benzedrine® and Dexedrine®. A variety of symptoms, social behaviors, and school performances were noted to have definitely improved. These studies were carried out under excellent conditions for observation inasmuch as the children were well known to highly trained observers in a controlled environment. Formal controls and statistical analyses of the data are not always satisfactory in these studies, but the data are presented in sufficient detail and with a critical approach that gives considerable confidence in the results.

Other clinicians soon followed these observations on Benzedrine with reports of positive effects on children with psychoneurotic and psychopathic features (2), post-encephalitic behavior disorders (39, 40), sexual preoccupations (23), and hyperkinetic impulse disorders (12, 25, 32, 33).

Most of these studies lack placebo controls, double-blind conditions, and appropriate statistical analyses. Either clinical judgments or unstandardized instruments of questionable reliability and validity are employed as dependent variables. It is interesting to note, however, that a very early study of Benzedrine (44) employed randomly assigned, with double-blind treatment conditions, should be and a number of objective performance tests with ninety-three delinquent boys, and found positive results (although the statistics of the day leave a great deal to be desired).

Eisenberg and his colleagues (21) studied the effects of dextroamphetamine on twenty-one delinquent boys in three cottages selected as having the worst behavior problems. The three sets of matched groups of children were rated weekly on a symptom checklist by the cottage parents over a six-week period, consisting of drug, placebo, or no-treatment to which the cottage parents and investigators were blind. Dosage was increased from 5 mg to 40 mg per day, with the children in the drug and placebo cottages taking the medication in a syrup containing 10% alcohol in the form of muscatel wine and sucrose. Three pretreatment, three treatment and one post-treatment rating was recorded for each subject. Analyses of variance showed that there was both a rater effect (between cottages) and a drug effect which became significant during the last week of treatment. One complication of this study was the six-pound average weight loss in the drug group, which raises the possibility of influences on rater judgment due to side effects and expectation of finding improvement. It was also of interest to note that the variance due to raters was greater than that due to drug, showing the desirability of controlling and minimizing rater effects in this type of study and the need for objective measures of performance.

The foregoing study also included a rather unique measure of drug effect, namely peer perceptions of behavior (sociometric ratings). It was found that the Dexedrine-treated subjects were given significantly more positive role assignments for a fictitious class play after drug than before drug, while the placebo and control subjects showed no change. An earlier controlled study of Benzedrine (34) also used a delinquent population and reported positive

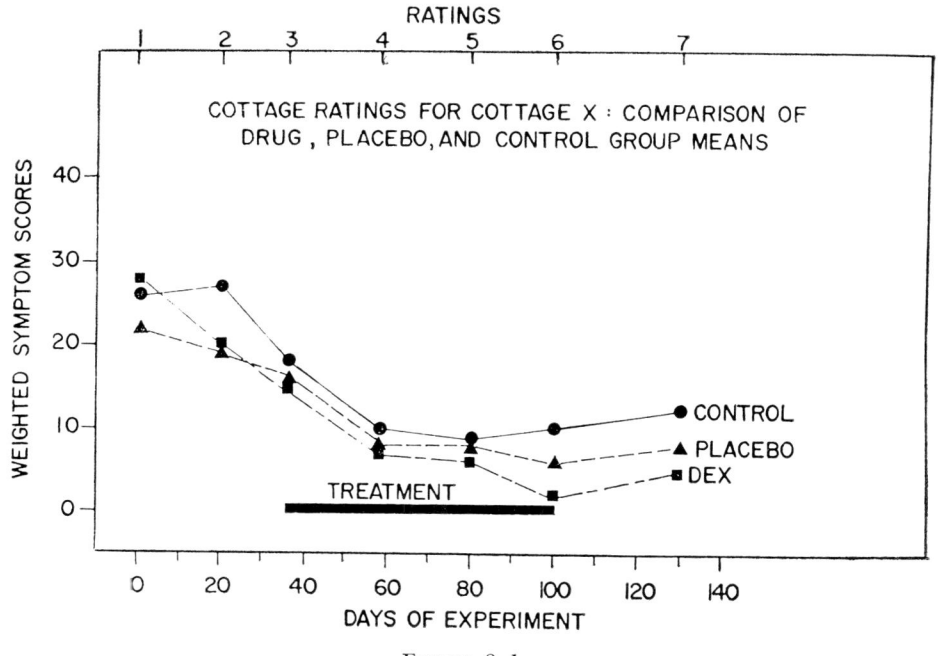

FIGURE 8-1.

effects on ratings of discipline, work, and general behavior. However, the data are presented in insufficient detail to determine whether the conclusions of positive benefit are warranted.

Conners and Eisenberg (15) reported similar findings with cottage parents' ratings of behavior in eighty-one institutionalized children. Approximately half of the children were inpatients at a residential treatment facility, and half were foster children in a city welfare institution. A double-blind trial of ten days' duration with methylphenidate (Ritalin) was carried out, with two shifts of cottage parents (day and night) each making ratings before and after drug (the final dose was 30 mg, twice daily). Behavior such as "leading others into trouble," "demanding," disobedient," and "lying" were significantly improved in the drug as compared with the placebo group, with the overall symptom score also being improved. Several other controlled studies with either Dexedrine or Ritalin have shown improvements in behavioral symptomatology as rated by parents, teachers, or clinicians (14, 16, 18, 19, 31, 54).

One development of interest in these rating studies is the use of factored scales which evaluate the effect of drugs on separate dimensions or factors in the array of manifest symptoms. Figure 8-2, for example, shows the effects of Dexedrine on two symptom clusters obtained from factor analysis of parental ratings. The two major factors, labeled "hyperkinetic" and "neurotic" show differential drug effect. The findings accord with the many clinical reports indicating better response of hyperkinetic symptoms than neurotic symptoms to the stimulants.

Table 8-1 presents the effects of Dexedrine and placebo on five scales derived from a factor analysis of teacher's ratings. Here the drug has significantly reduced all five clusters of symptoms as rated by teachers. These findings, while emphasizing the value of teacher and parent as monitors of drug effects, also raise an important methodological issue in rating methods: any signs of change, including side effects, can be a clue to the rater that some improvement should be rated in all areas; that is, a "halo" rating bias may spuriously indicate a ubiquitous drug effect. Such clues as slight behavior change or side effects, coupled with the raters' hope for improvement or knowledge of the experimenters' hypotheses, can lead to apparent improvement in the ratings. Figure 8-1 indicates quite clearly how sharply symptoms may be reduced due to rater bias alone *before* the drug is administered. Therefore, global rating methods, by themselves, are insufficient to adequately document behavioral improvement and must be supplemented by other methods of observation, or controlled systematically.

EFFECTS ON COGNITIVE FUNCTIONING

The question of whether the stimulant drugs actually enhance human

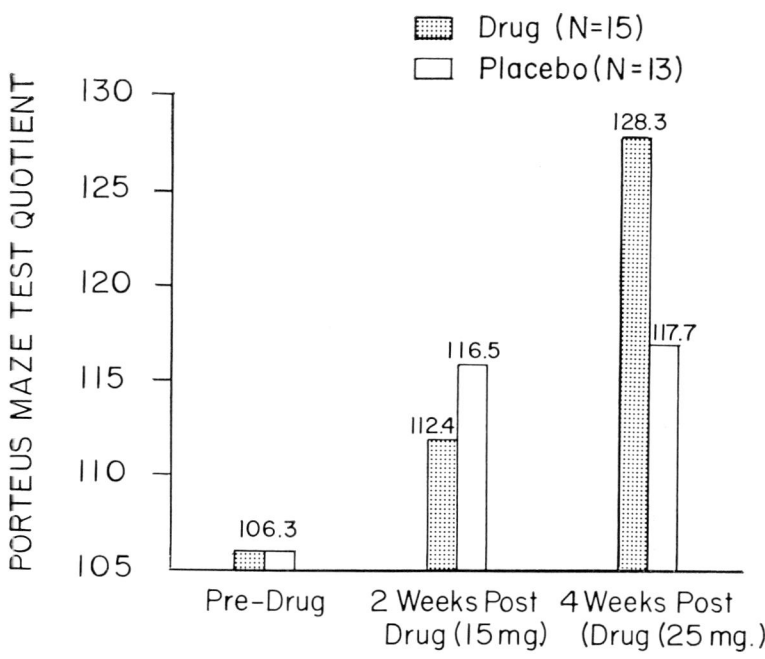

FIGURE 8-2.

cognitive performance, or simply offset the effects of fatigue, sleep, or other deficit states has not been adequately answered. In their most recent review of the effects of amphetamines, Laties and Weiss (36) remark that "It seems clear that under some circumstances, amphetamine can improve performance on simple arithmetic . . . (but) it appears that more complex intellectual performance is not affected by amphetamine." Various studies of behavior with adults lend support to this conclusion. It is of interest that in his early studies, Bradley (9) found that arithemetic performance in children was most reliably enhanced on the achievement scores but that regarding standard tests of intellectual function he found that "In general there was no striking change in intelligence quotient when amphetamine sulfate was used." Molitch and Eccles (44) found improvements on various intelligence tests but examination of the tests suggests that most of the improvement may have been in motor components of the tests. A study of Zimmerman and Burgemeister (55) showed significant effects of Ritalin on performance IQ as did Knights and Hinton (31) and Epstein *et al.* (22). Weiss *et al.* (54) found no individual tests improved in a study with Dexedrine and twenty-six hyperactive chilren, though the *number* of tests showing a positive change as compared with placebo was significant.

TABLE 8-1
FACTOR SCORES BEFORE AND AFTER DRUG OR PLACEBO TREATMENT

	Drug Group				Placebo Group				
	Before Treatment		After Treatment		Before Treatment		After Treatment		
Factor	Mean	SD	Mean	SD	Mean	SD	Mean	SD	t*
I	10.8	12.9	5.4	8.1	12.9	12.5	12.4	12.3	2.28†
II	10.98	3.9	7.2	3.7	10.2	4.4	8.7	4.6	3.43§
III	8.4	4.4	5.7	3.2	6.8	4.6	7.0	5.0	3.17‡
IV	11.9	6.3	7.0	4.6	11.3	5.5	10.2	6.2	4.59§
V	−3.4	3.4	−2.4	2.6	−3.6	3.5	−3.8	3.4	2.18+

* All t tests are for net differences between placebo and drug, with df = 75, 73, 73, 85, and 83 respectively.

†p<.03 ‡p<.002 §p<.001

This latter finding, of a small but consistent improvement across a variety of test measures, is suggestive of some more general feature of behavior which is altered by the drugs, which then leads to apparent intellectual improvement. Bradley had concluded that any improvements on intelligence tests were likely to be a function of the child's improved attitude towards the testing situation and his zest for achievement. Such a conclusion is supported by our finding (17) that a large battery of personality tests shows a general achievement factor (need for achievement) improving with Dexedrine treatment, while intellectual measures when freed of this source of variance, do not show a drug effect.

On the other hand, there are still interesting questions of possible specific enhancement of intellectual performance which are raised by certain kinds of data. For example, amphetamine injections usually produce no effect on memory in normal animals, but enhancement occurs in avoidance training when the drug is given four hours after each training session (20). Barondes and Cohen (1) recently reported that when amphetamine is injected during a period when the effects of a protein-inhibiting substance (which normally interferes with long-term memory) are slight, the resulting "arousal" leads to enhanced long-term memory. Various analeptic drugs enhance long-term memory if given during the so-called consolidation-phase of learning (41). This type of evidence suggests that "Cognitive information, an intact capacity for cerebral protein synthesis, and an appropriate degree of 'arousal' are all apparently necessary for the establishment of long-term memory' " (1).

Moreover, as in adult performance, tasks requiring vigilance and alertness usually show marked improvements in children treated with stimulants. For example, Figure 8-3 shows the effect of amphetamine on errors of omission in a continuous performance task (18, 19). Improvement of simple motor speed or motor control is not the basis of such improvements in signal detection since sheer speed may actually decrease on trials in which a signal or target occurs.

Perhaps the most interesting of our findings of stimulant effects with children is the consistent and rather dramatic effects of Ritalin and Dexedrine on Porteus Maze Performance. This test, it will be recalled, was virtually the only test to show a significant decline in scores after prefrontal lobotomies (47) and has shown considerable sensitivity to phenothiazines (46). The test requires careful planning and forethought and places a premium on the executive, decision-making function of intelligence. Figure 8-4 shows a typical result with amphetamine treatment (19). In earlier studies we found that the degree of Porteus Maze improvement was related to initial levels of IQ, with children of lower IQ showing increases in Maze scores that brought their test quotients to approximately the same level as the brighter children. These results suggest that functional impairment of planning ability can be offset by

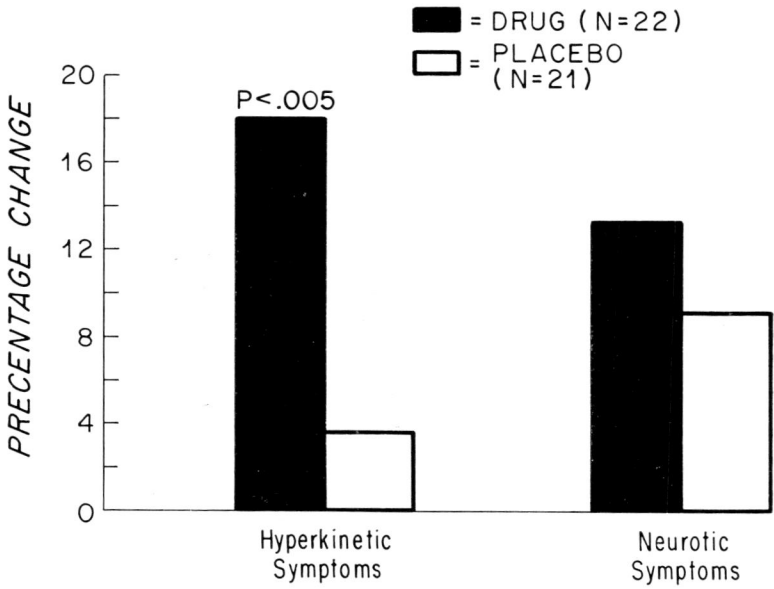

FIGURE 8-3.

the stimulant drugs. It is perhaps reasonable to suppose that the combined effects of a greater level of central arousal and less impulsivity of response will account for many other types of performance enhancement.

For example, it has been shown that aspects of visual and auditory perception (particularly figure-ground analysis and synthesis of speech elements), paired-associate learning are all enhanced in children taking stimulants* but activity level may actually increase at the same time that behavior becomes more organized (43), showing that activity level per se probably does not account for the generalized enhancement of test performances.

As pointed out by Weiss and Laties (53) one of the most consistent effects of amphetamine on human performance is the enhancement of vigilance, particularly in deficit states, though the evidence seems to suggest that actual enhancement above normal levels may also take place. This fact, of enhanced vigilance, together with various findings in children with hyperkinetic impulse disorders, in which enhanced selective attention and regulation of impulsivity occurs, suggests that central arousal level may be involved in some important way in the action of the stimulants. It is, of course, well-known that amphetamine acts directly on the reticular system. But the question as to the role of the arousal system in the hyperkinetic disorders and the way the stimulants

* See references 13, 16, 18, 19, 22, 31, 42, and 51.

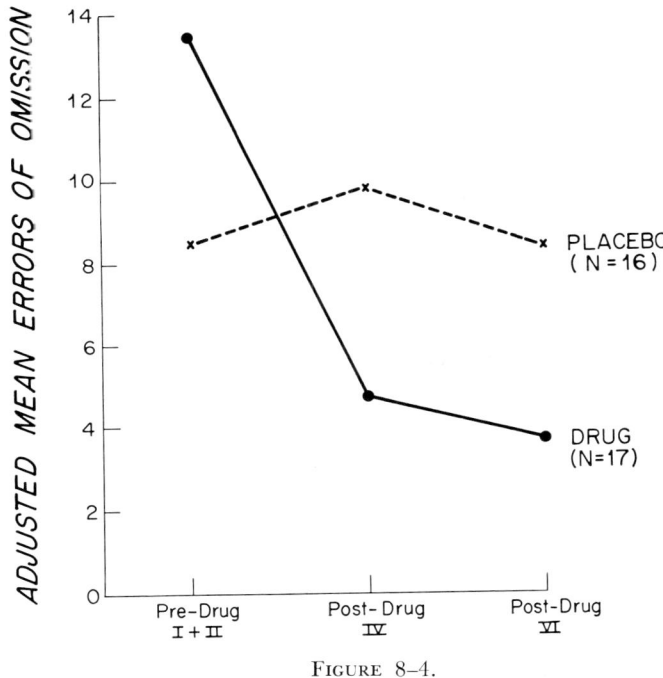

FIGURE 8-4.

alter behavior is not at all clear from available evidence. Few physiological studies have been done to clarify the neurophysiologic action of these drugs in children's behavior disorders.

In the study by Laufer and co-workers (37), it was found that amphetamines raise the photo-Metrazol® threshold in hyperkinetic children to a normal level which they interpreted as evidence for disturbance of diencephalic function. Epstein *et al.* (22) found differences in effect of the drug on certain variables. A recent study by Satterfield (49) found that hyperkinetic children have lower skin conductance levels and longer GSR recovery times than normal children of the same age, who in turn have lower conductance and longer recovery times than normal college students. This finding suggests that the hyperkinetic children have a lower central arousal level and less autonomic recovery capacity. After treatment with Ritalin or Dexedrine these children showed shifts of conductance levels towards normal values. Moreover, spontaneous GSR activity increased in the stimulant-treated subjects.

Silverman *et al.* (50) have reported that the number of spontaneous GSR increases with level of arousal and that the amplitude of the GSR response to stimulation increases with alerting but decreases in a hyperaroused state, while Burch and Greiner (11) have shown that fatigue states result in decline of nonspecific GSR occurrence. The rather surprising finding that hyperkinetic children have lower autonomic arousal thresholds and slower recovery partially explains the "paradoxical" effect of the stimulants with this group, since presumably the action of the drugs is to increase arousal levels. It must be admitted, however, that our knowledge of the variables involved in these drug effects is still primitive. Even in animals there are inconsistent effects of amphetamine on response rates (27, 29) depending on dosage, species, and stimulus parameters.

(DEANOL) ACETAMIDOBENZOATE

Some clinicians (45) describe the effects of deanol as superior clinically to the amphetamines because of fewer anorexic and sleep interference effects. Oettinger described a study with 125 previously refractory drug-treated patients who were given 50 mg of deanol for periods of one to nine months daily. He rated 48 per cent as having good improvement, 20 per cent fair improvement, and 20 per cent showing no change. Twelve per cent became worse. His measures included parent and school reports, human figure drawings, and Bender-Gestalt tests. Behavioral improvement included improved schoolwork, decreased enuresis, decrease in overactivity and lengthening of attention span. Similar findings were reported by Tobias (52) of 174 private pediatric behavior problem patients between three and eighteen years of age. Positive results for psychoneurotic patients were reported by Bostock and Shackleton (3). These studies all lacked appropriate controls.

A controlled study by Geller employed random assignments, double-blind conditions and pretesting and post-testing on seventy-five children between five and twelve years of age who were aggressive or hyperactive. Deanol produced the same degree of improvement (23 of 25 subjects) as a mild sedative (trimeglamide), with no improvement in the placebo group. However, despite the fact that he employed objective measures, data were not reported, and improvement was simply described in subjective terms. Time working on puzzle solutions were obtained, but not reported, as measures of span of attention. The possibility that deanol might offset performance decrement in repeated testing of reaction times was indicated in a study by Fleming and Orlando (24). Drug and placebo conditions were well-matched on age, IQ, sex, and diagnosis and appropriate statistical design and analysis were employed. However, there was no facilitatory effect of the drug above initial performance levels.

In perhaps the best-controlled study, Kugle and Alexander (35) studied the effect of a single daily dose of 100 mg of deanol on forty-two private pediatric patients, age six to thirteen with behavior disorders. Intelligence tests, "behavioral complexity test," Vineland Social Maturity scales, parent interviews, and direct play observations were employed before and after drug and placebo treatment in a crossover design, using counterbalanced orders of treatment. No significant drug effects were found on any variable. Despite the fact that this is perhaps the only adequate study from a methodologic point of view, one serious defect is the single, low dose employed. Moreover, as is so often the case in this literature, only change scores were reported, and no means, variances, analysis, or covariance analysis was done, which might have clarified the results.

Another carefully controlled double-blind trial on fifty retarded patients with behavior disorders by LaVeck and Buckley (38), using dosages up to 150 mg daily, found no effects on experimentally produced distractibility, narrative reports of behavior, or a checklist of behavior from ward attendants. A good baseline of observation, matching of drug and placebo groups, and appropriate analysis were carried out.

One positive effect on clerical accuracy in retarded readers of normal intelligence was reported by Huddleston *et al.* (28), but without associated improvement in reading ability.

In summary, there is no adequate controlled data to indicate that the earlier clinical reports of deanol have been substantiated. However, an important difference between the clinical studies and the controlled studies is that the latter have typically used a single fixed dose, or a small dose range of the drug, while the clinical studies typically use somewhat higher doses. It is hard to determine whether this factor alone might account for the negative results of the controlled studies. This same criticism applies to much of the controlled work done in pediatric psychopharmacology, and it is important that future studies should include dosage as a variable or use dosages sufficient to produce side effects before concluding that beneficial action has been ruled out.

REFERENCES

1. BARONDES, S.H., AND COHEN, H.D.: Arousal and the conversion of "short term" to "long-term" memory. *Proc Nat Acad Sci USA, 61*:923–929, 1968.
2. BENDER, L., AND COTTINGTON, F.: The use of amphetamine sulfate (Benzedrine) in child psychiatry. *Amer J Psychiat, 99*:116–121, 1942.
3. BOSTOCK, J., AND SHACKLETON, M.: The use of DMAE (Deaner) in behavior states. *Med J Aust, 2*:337–339, 1962.
4. BRADLEY, C.: The behavior of children receiving Benzedrine. *Amer J Orthopsychiat, 94*:577–585, 1937–38.
5. BRADLEY, C.: Benzedrine and Dexedrine in the treatment of children's behavior disorders. *Pediatrics, 5*:24–36, 1950.
6. BRADLEY, C.: Tranquilizing drugs in pediatrics. *Pediatrics, 21*:325–336, 1958.

7. BRADLEY, C., AND BOWEN, M.: School performance of children receiving amphetamine (Benzedrine) sulfate. *Amer J Orthopsychiat, 10*:782–788, 1940.
8. BRADLEY, C., AND BOWEN, M.: Amphetamine (Benzedrine) therapy of children's behavior disorders. *Amer J Orthopsychiat, 11*:92–103, 1941.
9. BRADLEY, C., AND GREEN, E.: Psychometric performance of children receiving amphetamine (Benzedrine) sulfate. *Amer J Orthopsychiat, 97*:388–394, 1940–41.
10. BRADLEY, P.B., AND ELKES, J.: The effects of some drugs on the electrical activity of the brain. *Brain, 80*:77–117, 1957.
11. BURCH, N.R., AND GREINER, T.H.: Drugs and human fatigue: GSR parameters. *J Psychol, 45*:3–10, 1958.
12. BURKS, H.F.: Effects of amphetamine therapy on hyperkinetic children. *Arch Gen Psychiat, 11*:604–609, 1964.
13. CONNERS, C.K.: The effect of Dexedrine on rapid discrimination and motor control of hyperkinetic children under mild stress. (Pending)
14. CONNERS, C.K.: A teacher rating scale for use in drug studies with children. *Amer J Psychiat,* in press.
15. CONNERS, C.K., AND EISENBERG, L.: The effects of methylphenidate on symptomatology and learning in disturbed children. *Amer J Psychiat, 120*:458–464, 1963.
16. CONNERS, C.K., EISENBERG, L., AND SHARPE, L.: Effect of methylphenidate (Ritalin) on paired-associate learning and Porteus maze performance in emotionally disturbed children. *J Consult Psychol, 28*:14–22, 1964.
17. CONNERS, C.K., EISENBERG, L., AND BARCAI, A.: Effect of dextroamphetamine on children. *Arch Gen Psychiat, 17*:478–485, 1967.
18. CONNERS, C.K., AND ROTHSCHILD, G.H.: Drugs and learning in children. In *Learning Disorders.* Seattle (Washington), Special Child Publications, 1968, vol. III, pp. 191–224.
19. CONNERS, C.K., ROTHSCHILD, G.H., EISENBERG, L., STONE, L., AND ROBINSON, E.: Dextroamphetamine in children with learning disorders: Effects on perception, learning, and achievement. *Arch Gen Psychiat,* in press.
20. DOTY, B.A., AND DOTY, L.A.: Facilitative effects of amphetamine on avoidance conditioning in relation to age and problem difficulty. *Psychopharmacologia, 9*:234–241, 1966.
21. EISENBERG, L., LACHMAN, R., MOLLING, P., LOCKNER, A., MIZELLE, J., AND CONNERS, C.K.: A psychopharmacologic experiment in a training school for delinquent boys. *Amer J Orthopsychiat, 33*:431–447, 1963.
22. EPSTEIN, L., LASAGNA, L., CONNERS, C.K., AND RODRIGUEZ, A.: Correlation of dextroamphetamine excretion and drug response in hyperkinetic children. *J Nerv Ment Dis, 146*:136–146, 1968.
23. FISH, B.: Drug therapy in child psychiatry: Pharmacological aspects. *Compr Psychiat, 1*:212–227, 1960.
24. FLEMING, J.W., AND ORLANDO, R.: Effect of deanol on attention in the mentally retarded: A reaction time method. *J New Drugs, 2*:239–244, 1962.
25. GINN, S., AND HOH?AN, L.: The use of dextrod-amphetamine in severe behavior problems of children.*Southern Med J, 46*:1124–1127, 1953.
26. GOOCH, R.N.: The influence of stimulant and depressant drugs on the central nervous system. In Eysenck, H.J. (Ed.): *Experiments With Drugs.* New York, The MacMillan Co., 1963, pp. 353–380.
27. HAUDE, R.H., AND RAY, O.S.: The visual exploration method. In Vagtborg, H. (Ed.): *Use of Nonhuman Primates in Drug Evaluation.* Austin, University of Texas Press, 1968, pp. 265–282.

28. HUDDLESTON, W., STAIGER, R., FRYE, R., MUSGRAVE, R., AND STRITCH, T.: Deanol as aid in overcoming reading retardation. *Clin Med, 8*:1340–1342, 1961.
29. JARVIK, M.E., AND DABROWSKA, J.: Effects of drugs and brain lesions upon learning and memory in monkeys. In Vagtborg, H. (Ed.): *Use of Nonhuman Primates in Drug Evaluation.* Austin, University of Texas Press, 1968, pp. 357–368.
30. JOUVET, M., AND COURZON, J.: Etude neurophysiologique de l'action centrale du chloralhydrate de l'ester methylique de l'acide phenyl piperidyl acetique (Ritaline). *Arch Int Pharmacodyn, 119*:189–193, 1959.
31. KNIGHTS, R.M., AND HINTON, G.: The effects of methylphenidate (Ritalin) on the motor skills and behavior of children with learning problems. *Research Bulletin No. 102,* University of Western Ontario, October 1968.
32. KNOBEL, M.: Psychopharmacology for the hyperkinetic child—dynamic considerations. *Arch Gen Psychiat, 6*:198–202, 1962.
33. KNOBEL, M., WOLMAN, M., AND MASON, E.: Hyperkinesis and organicity in children. *Arch Gen Psychiat, 1*:310–321, 1959.
34. KOREY, S.R.: The effects of Benzedrine sufate on the behavior of psychopathic and neurotic juvenile delinquents. *Psychiat Quart, 18*:127–137, 1944.
35. KUGEL, R.B., AND ALEXANDER, T.: The effect of a central nervous stimulant (deanol) on behavior. *Pediatrics, 31*:651–655,, 1963.
36. LATIES, V.G., AND WEISS, B.: Performance enhancement by the amphetamines: A new appraisal. In Brill, H. et al. (Eds.): *Neuropsychopharmacology.* Amsterdam, Excerpta Medica Foundation, 1967.
37. LAUFER, M.W., AND DENHOFF, E.: Hyperkinetic behavior syndrome in children. *J Pediat, 50*:463–474, 1957.
38. LAVECK, G.D., AND BUCKLEY, P.: The use of psychopharmacologic agents in retarded children with behavior disorders. *J Chronic Dis, 13*:174, 1961.
39. LEVY, S.: Post-encephalitic behavior disorder—a forgotten entity: A report of 100 cases. *Amer J Psychiat, 115*:1062–1067, 1959.
40. LEVY, S.: The hyperkinetic child—a forgotten entity: Its diagnosis and treatment. *Int J Neuropsychiat, 2*:330–336, 1966.
41. MCGAUGH, J.L.: Time dependent processes in memory storage. *Science, 153*:1351–1358, 1966.
42. MILLICHAP, J.G., AYMAT, F., STURGIS, L.H., LARSEN, K., AND WHITTLE, R.: Hyperkinetic behavior and learning disorders III: Battery of neuropsychological tests in controlled trial of methylphenidate. *Amer J Dis Child, 116*:235–244, 1968.
43. MILLICHAP, J.G., AND BOLDREY, E.E.: Studies in hyperkinetic behavior. *Neurology, 17*:467–471, 1967.
44. MOLITCH, M., AND ECCLES, A.: The effect of Benzedrine sulfate on the intelligence scores of children. *Amer J Psychiat, 94*:587–590, 1937.
45. OETTINGER, L.: The use of deanol in the treatment of behavior in children. *J Pediat, 53*:671, 1958.
46. PORTEUS, S.D.: Mental changes in psychopharmacology. In Uhr L., and Miller, J.G. (Eds.): *Drugs and behavior.* New York, John Wiley & Son, 1960, pp. 372–374.
47. PORTEUS, S.D., AND DIAMOND, A.L.: Porteus maze changes after psychosurgery. *J Ment Sci, 108*:53–58, 1962.
48. ROTHBALLER, A.B.: Studies on the adrenaline-sedative component of the reticular activating system. *Electroenceph Clin Neurophysiol, 8*:603–621, 1956.
49. SATTERFIELD, J.: Personal communication.
50. SILVERMAN, A.J., COHEN, S.I., AND SHMAVONIAN, B.M.: Investigation of psychophysiologic relationships with skin resistance measures. *J Psychosom Res, 4*:65–87, 1959.

51. SPRAGUE, R., BARNES, K., AND WERRY, J.: Methylphenidate and thioridazine: Learning, activity and behavior in emotionally disturbed boys. *Arch Gen Psychiat,* in press.
52. TOBIAS, M.: The disturbed child: A concept—usefulness of deanol in management. *American Practice and Digest of Treatment, 10*:1759–1765, 1959.
53. WEISS, B., AND LATIES, V.G.: Enhancement of human performance by caffeine and the amphetamines. *Pharmacol Rev, 14*:1–36, 1962.
54. WEISS, G., WERRY, J., MINDE, K., DOUGLAS, V., AND SYKER, D.: Studies on the hyperactive child V: The effects of dextroamphetamine and chlorpromazine on behavior and intellectual functioning. *J Child Psychol Psychiat,* in press.
55. ZIMMERMAN, F.T., AND BURGEMEISTER, B.: Action of methyl-phenidylacetate (Ritalin) and reserpine in behavior disorders in children and adults. *Amer J Psychiat, 115*: 323–328, 1958.

Chapter 9

Dilantin® Effect on Emotionally Disturbed Children

WILLIAM J. TURNER*

During the past four years, we at the Dreyfus Medical Foundation have observed an astonishing variety of conditions in human beings which are benefitted by diphenylhydantoin (DPH). Among these are behavioral disturbances in children for whom DPH has hitherto been administered only if there was a thought that the condition was of an epileptic nature. Our observations are in agreement with those of Baldwin, of Greenberg and Kurland, and of Boelhouwer, Gluek and Bernard, among others: DPH is at least as effective for children whose emotional and behavioral disturbances have no relationship to epilepsy.

We have become so accustomed to meeting with improved relations with peers, lessening of hyperkinesis, decrease in hostility and destructiveness, better school adjustment and work that we have almost begun to take it for granted that everyone knows of these effects and prescribes the medicine accordingly. I would like to describe to you some observations made on nine children, sixteen or younger, who were among the latest forty-one seen at the Foundation. Each of these nine had been given various subtests of the WISC or WAIS before and at least one month after daily administration of DPH. (See Table 9-1.)

Six of these children showed increased raw scores on Block Design after one month of Dilantin therapy. Four of the six had a rise greater than the "learning rise" of five points. All of these, and one of the two others rose beyond the expected top for their age. The accompanying table presents these data in condensed form. The dose of DPH, the pretreatment and post-treatment EEG and presenting symptoms are included in the table. The clinical changes noted cover a minimum of one month and in several the improvement held for at least three months.

DISCUSSION

Instead of beginning the discussion on the Dilantin effect on the Block Design Test, I would like first of all to call attention to the variety of ways in which improvement occurred under DPH therapy. Because the improvement always relates to the individual and his environment, we have found it impossible to find a few rubrics under which to codify the changes for purposes

* Assisted by Rita Kaplan.

TABLE 9-1

Pat #	Age	Block Design Raw Score for			EEG	DPH Dosage	Presenting Symptom Pre-DPH	Changes Post-DPH
		Pre	Post	this Age				
305*	10	14	24	16-20	Pre-abn Post-norm	150 mg daily	School behavior disorder, overactive, assaultive, short attention span, psychotherapy—7 months	Less overactive, less assaultive 1 to 2 months, then return to symptoms.
319*	13½	19	39	32-33	Pre-norm Post-norm	200 mg daily	Temper tantrums, irritability, ummotivated, resistive, assaultive, no friends, petulant, psychotherapy—18 months.	Marked improvement, cheerful, improved in school, less violence, converses, "young lady," less resistive.
326	6	No Attempt made	Two good trials	4-5	Pre-abn Post-abn	100 mg	Verbose, perseverative, restless, rote memory astonishing, late speech (3 years), extreme fears, separation anxiety, cry-baby socially, possible genetic defeat.	Less verbose, less perseverative, reduced fears, tolerates separation, maintains peer relationships.
329*	15	7	18	36-39	Pre-norm Post-norm	150 mg daily	Suspected narcolepsy, oscillating suppression & denial-overt hostility, poor school work, focus of fathers abuse. Psychotherapy-9 months.	Alert, increase of 10 pts. in school grades, standing up to brother, less hostile, friendlier.
334*†	16	20	24	16-20	Pre-norm Post-norm	200 mg daily incr to 250 mg	Cutting school, bravado, poor peer relationships, negativitic, belligerent, angry blow ups, impatient.	Remains in school, communicative, cooperative, less impatient, tolerant.
335*	8	6	15	8-9	Pre-norm Post-norm but poorly regulated	100 mg daily	Overactivity, temper tantrums, disorganized thought. Previous Dexedrine and Librium with no effect. Psychotherapy—1 year.	Less tension, possible lessening of disorganization.

337	8	9	8-9	Pre-quest. norm Post-norm	125 mg daily	School behavior problem, threatens peers, overactivity, impulsivity, clownlike. Previous Dexedrine with no effect.	Less impulsivity, easier to manage, less resistant, aware of surroundings, more communicative on mature level, less clownish.
338	9	4	5	11-15	Pre-norm Post-norm	150 mg daily	Though disorder, perseveration, overactivity, emotional immaturity, negativistic and resistant. Previous Dexedrine with increased overactivity. Psychotherapy—2½ years.	No change in behavior.
339*†	8	5	10	8-9	Pre-abn Post-abn but not as great as pre-abn	100 mg daily	Stomach pains, dizzy spells, erratic behavior, fighting, screaming, forgetful of commands but rote learning good, nightmares.	No stomach pains, dizziness, or nightmares, less anger, less resistant, smiling.

Of the last 41 patients of a total of 345 seen, nine were given various subtests of one WISC or WAIS. Six of these* showed increased raw scores on Block Design as see from pre, to one month post, drug evaluation. Two of these six† show an increase within the expected change of + 5 points.

of statistical computation. The improvements do in part bear a relationship to the environmental pressures, of course, and, in subject #305, we found that the adults who cared for this child simply had to defeat him again to preserve their own status. He then presented the picture of a schizophrenic child. Patient # 338, the only other one who showed no change in behavior, was thought to be a schizophrenic. Patient #326 has two schizophrenic close relatives on the father's side and this child has some of the qualities of an idiot savant. When he was taken off of DPH, he reverted to his previous state, a state strongly reinforced by his symbiotic relationship with his mother.

Aside from these three, the improvements in the other children have been moderate to marked and have been persistent. In view of the changes in Block Design, even in the presence of a normal EEG, we wondered whether there has not been an improvement in function of the right hemisphere attributable to the DPH which bears close relationship to the change in Block Design.

I wonder whether behavioral disturbances in these and many other youngsters could result from a sort of out-of-phase relationship between the two hemispheres. Perhaps those who have access to equipment for correlation analysis of EEG can throw light on this possibility.

REFERENCES

1. Symposium on Diphenylhydantoin, American College of Neuropsychopharmacology, Dec. 1967. In *Int J Neuropsychiat, 3* (Suppl. 2) :   , Dec. 1967.
2. BALDWIN, R., AND KENNY, T.J.: Treatment of learning disabilities in children. In Hellmeuth, J. (Ed.) : *Special Child Publications of the Seattle Seguin School, Inc.,* 2:313–327, 1966, Seattle, Washington.
3. GREENBURG, J., AND KURLAND, A.: Dilantin in Treatment of Pseudo-Retardates in an Institutional Setting. Presented at the Symposium on Diphenylhydantoin, Dreyfus Medical Foundation, Miami, Nov. 1968, unpublished.
4. BOELHOUWER, C., HENRY, C.E., AND GLUECK, C., JR.: Positive spiking: A double-blind control study on its significance in behavior disorders, both diagnostically and therapeutically. *Amer J Psychiat, 125*:473–81, Oct. 1968.

Chapter 10

Effects of Sodium Diphenylhydantoinate and Pemoline Upon Concentration: A Comparative Study

LIONEL R. C. HAWARD

This report concerns two experiments into the effects of drugs upon concentration, undertaken for two entirely different purposes. The fact that both experiments shared the same methodology and technique and that the two samples were relatively similar enabled the effects of the two drugs to be compared within the limits of the variables evaluated. Both studies were problem-orientated rather than drug-orientated, and although the problem in each case was that of impaired concentration, the cause of the impairment was different in the two cases. For this reason, each experiment will be discussed separately, and the comparison between the two conditions and the two drugs will be summarized at the end.

THE EFFECTS OF PEMOLINE ON CONCENTRATION

An increasing problem of vigilance occurs in air traffic control where peak periods of air activity produce aircraft movements of less than one minute separation. If the aircraft spends only ten minutes in the control zone this represents ten separate space and time problems all interacting in the one situation, but in some control zones the situation becomes even more complicated. Moreover, the substantial increase in air traffic has not been met by a corresponding increase in staff numbers, while at the same time the task grows increasingly complex each year due to changes in the major parameters. Many air traffic control officers, because of the earlier requirement for previous flight command experience, are generally older than men in other industries performing tasks of comparable stress and complexity. This means that age itself is also a factor to which fatigue is related, and the question of mental fatigue in air traffic control therefore becomes a serious issue demanding consideration. Following an incident in which two aircraft collided on the same runway due to an error in air traffic control, the author with the special experience of Air Traffic Control staff, who required psychiatric support as a result of operational stress, was asked to direct an intensive study of mental fatigue and loss of vigilance in air traffic control tasks, the primary concern being preventive or prophylactic measures.

Note: This study was supported by the Dreyfus Medical Foundation.

The Cambridge Cockpit

Before describing this study, perhaps it would be useful to consider one of the basic problems of fatigue and vigilance. A quarter century ago one of the most famous experiments in British aviation psychology was completed. It involved the use of what became known as the Cambridge Cockpit (19), which must have been one of the earliest recording flight simulators ever made. Designed for the study of flying efficiency under varying conditions, it consisted of the cockpit and part fuselage of a Spitfire Mark 1 aircraft.

The experimental work, organized by Sir Frederick Bartlett, Professor Russell Davis, and Professor Drew, continued throughout the war and for some time afterwards. Many of the results had an immediate and practical application to contemporary problems of wartime flying for one of the central behavioral changes observed at this time was the gradual breakdown of flying efficiency as a function of time. It was at this point that a difference of opinion emerged regarding causal factors concerned in the deterioration of flying skill.

Fatigue v Anxiety

Bartlett (4, 5), following considerable experimental work on output under varying conditions, attributed the time-correlated disorder of skill to fatigue. In his Ferrier Lecture to the Royal Society, London, in 1943, he made his position unequivocally clear. Russell Davis (17, 18) and Yates (85), on the other hand, concluded that the breakdown in cockpit skill was not so much due to fatigue but to anticipatory tension. The thesis is that skill becomes disorganized in conditions in which the outcome is in doubt. Doubt arouses anxiety and later fear, and the emergency reaction of the autonomic nervous system then produces the resulting decrement in efficiency. Casteneda (13) has since shown how anxiety affects performance, and Cattell (14) shows anxiety to be always dysfunctional. The nature of anxiety is still open to question, however, as Berger (8) has shown. One cannot dispute that doubt in this context causes anxiety and Venables (82), using a modified form of the Davis apparatus, showed that anxious psychiatric patients made more relatively extensive responses. Drew (24), on the other hand, regarded this breakdown in flying skill to be due primarily to fatigue and not to anxiety. Bartley and Chute (6) have shown that fatigue is only a semi-independent variable, however, and Drew did postulate the existence of an intermediate affective state—usually irritation—as the precursor, if not the producer, of the actual impediment to maximal efficiency. Since then Russell Davis has been at some pains to replicate these early studies in order to elicit clear evidence of the anxiety he believed to be present. In his later work he has used psychiatric patients in place of pilots and simplified the apparatus considerably from the sophisticated level of the Cambridge Cockpit. In this new context he has shown that acute anxiety heralds the onset of breakdown in skill in the unstable mental patient and that the magnitude and number of errors made are proportional to the degree of anxiety existing (19 to 22, 82).

Choice of Drugs

It is not the concern of this paper to deal with the relative merits of these two arguments, which have not been presented here with sufficient evidence on which the respective merits could be judged. The purpose in mentioning them has been to draw attention to the practical implication which this issue has for any study of fatigue-reducing medication. If impairment of work efficiency is really due to anxiety, however engendered, then work efficiency should be sustained by tranquillizing drugs of the meprobamate type, which have a specific effect upon anxiety and which modify disruption of performance produced by stress (46). On the other hand, if the loss of efficiency stems from fatigue, then one would prescribe a stimulant drug of the amphetamine type to combat its effects (42, 44, 69). If one prescribes medication from the wrong end of the stimulant-relaxant continuum, efficiency will be impaired to an even greater extent, since the alerting effect of a stimulant could in some circumstances increase anxiety, while the sedating effect of a tranquillizer may reduce mental alertness already impaired by fatigue. Kornetsky (49) has shown, for example, that meprobamate significantly impairs motor coordination, reaction time, and learning, while Loomis and West (52) reported a 10 per cent decrement in proficiency. Payne (68) has also demonstrated experimentally that certain drugs can have deleterious effects on perceptual motor skills.

Modern concepts of aerospace medicine favor the belief that operating efficiency can be maintained against the onset of mental fatigue by the administration of amphetamine-like drugs which enhance conduction in the brain stem (1); these have been shown to enhance flying performance of jet pilots (56). A recent survey of two hundred service pilots showed that no less than 64 per cent had been prescribed amphetamine and that 25 per cent took this drug after four hours flying (54). To many flight surgeons, the use of stimulant drugs in such a widespread way is viewed with some degree of disfavor, partly because of the consequences attendant upon their misuse, but chiefly because the aftereffects impair complex behavioral skills long after the beneficial effects have been exhausted. Air traffic controllers, like people performing other intellectually taxing complex tasks, resort to over-the-counter and prescription medicants in their desire to maintain working capacity, sometimes to the detriment of their efficiency. There are inherent dangers in pharmacological support; recent work in America has shown that pilots show residual difficulties in mental function twenty hours after ingesting amphetamine, while the unpleasant reactions following too much caffeine are already well known. Nevertheless, in a highly complex society such as ours, the need to combat fatigue and maintain vigilance is a real one. In many of the situations which obtain in space flight, in civil and military aviation, in active service, and in industry, the vigilance necessary at critical phases cannot always be procured without the aid of suitable drugs. For some years there has been a need for a centrally acting stimulant which can improve the cognitive processes yet be free of the undesirable side effects which accompany the ingestion of amphetamine and caffeine. A drug considered at the time to be worthy of further investigation in this respect was 5-phenyl-2-imino-4-oxo-oxazolidin, known in the United Kingdom as Pemoline and elsewhere in Europe as PIO (51, 53, 74), which has been shown to have a stimulating effect (26, 51). This drug has been synthesized to produce an effect midway in the range of present stimulants; it is claimed to be more potent than caffeine, less euphoric than amphetamine, and provides an optimum effect devoid of addiction or dysphoric reactions (32 to 39).

Methodology

It was decided to assess Pemoline's usefulness in air traffic control by means of a simulated air traffic control situation, since a real situation would not enable sufficient variables to be controlled. A blacked-out room was equipped and furnished to simulate the Air Traffic Control room at London Gatwick Airport; it consisted principally of a radar display on which aircraft movements could be portrayed and a multiple switch response system to limit behavior into a clearly defined and quantifiable unit. Auditory information was provided by a prerecorded tape of two hours' duration which gave position reports, ETA, and fuel position limits, and these were synchronized with the radar screen display by means of an eleven-channel event marker. A series of colored lights showed the clearance state of runways or indicated a state of emergency, and the task of the subject was to land, stack, or divert the simulated aircraft according to the needs of the moment. His instructions were communicated by means of the switch system, on which he identified the aircraft, gave its stacking height or other instructions, or initiated a series of priorities. The system was vetted by an experienced Air Traffic Control officer who was also used to provide a sample record, obtained by monitoring responses in terms of time and switch positions in a multichannel recorder. This technique possesses the same basic characteristics as the one described by Pearson *et al.* (70) differing from the latter in the presence of emergencies and the degree of stress imposed by the program. The attention and short-term memory required in the task have been shown to be sensitive to centrally acting drugs (48).

Program

Twenty male adults aged thirty or over and of superior intelligence (IQ 130 or over, on the Wechsler scale) received individual training on the simulator until each had achieved approximately the same level of proficiency, since Crissman (15) has shown information capacity to increase with practice. After the training, which extended over six weeks and required 20 ± 4.6 hours in the simulator, a control run of two hours without medication was undertaken. The scores were taken as the base line for each individual, although these were substantially below their final training scores because the stimulus pattern had been changed randomly. Two further runs of two hours' duration were then undertaken at the same time of day, since fatigue effects show a diurnal variation (43, 62), with at least a week's interval between trials and again with a change in stimuuls pattern. A double-blind crossover design was used, so that neither the subject nor the experimenter knew whether Pemoline or a placebo had been given. The subject was told that the drug prescribed could be either an active or an inert agent on both occasions, that is, he might receive a stimulant on both trials, or a placebo both times, or one of each. This prevented any subjective effects on the first trial from being used to deduce the nature of the drug used in the second trial. The experimenter knew, however, the subject would receive one of each although he did not know until after the conclusion of the experiment which the subject had received first. The active tablet was matched by a glucose tablet of identical appearance, and the key to the nature of each tablet was held by the pharmacist who prepared the tables and the code. A 20-mg dose was used, administered one hour before the commencement of trial, so that the active drug would have its optimum effect in the second hour of the testing session, when fatigue effects would be more pronounced.

Results

Marked individual differences occurred in the performance of these subjects (Fig. 10-1). Some showed progressive deterioration in performance, others seemed to improve towards the end of the session. All curves possessed three common characteristics: (1) little impairment in the first hour, (2) a marked rapid increase in errors during the first fifteen minutes of the second hour, and (3) a final score significantly below the interim score of the first hour (33, 34). If we take the mean curve for the sample as a whole, in each of the three trials (Fig. 10-2), we see the general pattern emerges in which the control and placebo trials show no significant difference, while performance under Pemoline, though worse than at the beginning, is not half as bad as it would be without the drug. The difference here is significant at the 5% level, but since over 70 per cent of the errors occur in the last half hour, if we compare the means for this period only we find a difference at the 1% level, that is, the probability of these differences occurring by chance is less than 1 in 100. The effect of different dosage levels was investigated during further trials when 20, 40, and 60 mg. doses of Pemoline were administered. The results

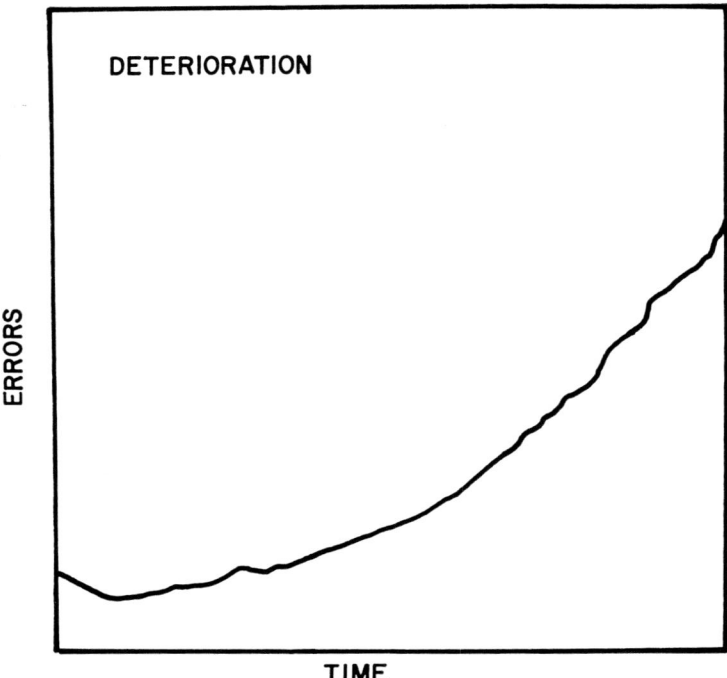

Figure 10-1.

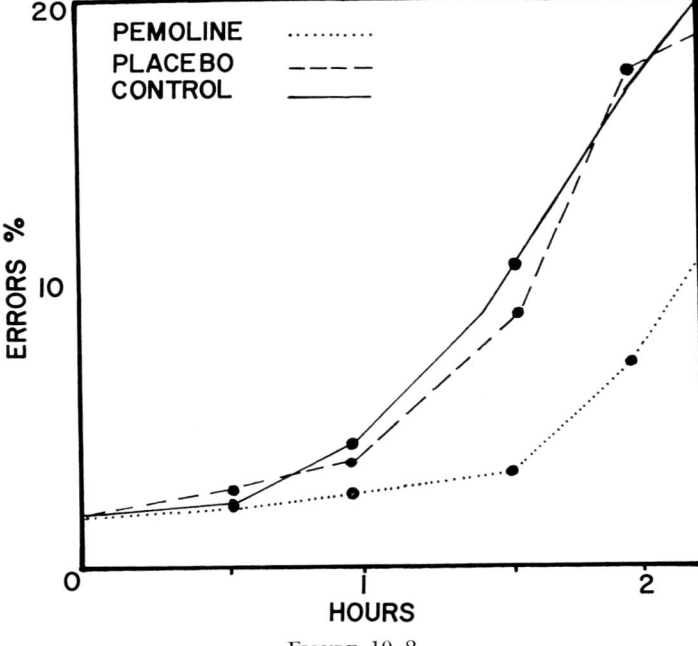

Figure 10-2.

show a dosage paradox exists, similar to that found in other drugs (64, 71). The optimum dose of 20 mg produces a significant decrease in errors, but increasing the strength of the stimulant gradually reduces this effect and finally produces more errors than no drug at all (Fig. 10-3). There are no differences in the side effects produced by single doses of the placebo and the 20-mg tablet, but at higher doses the subjects complained of muzziness. Sustained medication, even on the 20-mg dosage level has been found to produce minor side effects.

Perceptual Disorganization

It seems clear that the anxiety reaction of Davis is something different than what we experienced in this simulated Air Traffic Control situation. As in Drew's study, performance is progressively impaired, with excessive impairment occurring after ninety minutes on the task. Russell Davis's subjects showed their anxiety breakdown after some fifteen minutes. Characteristic

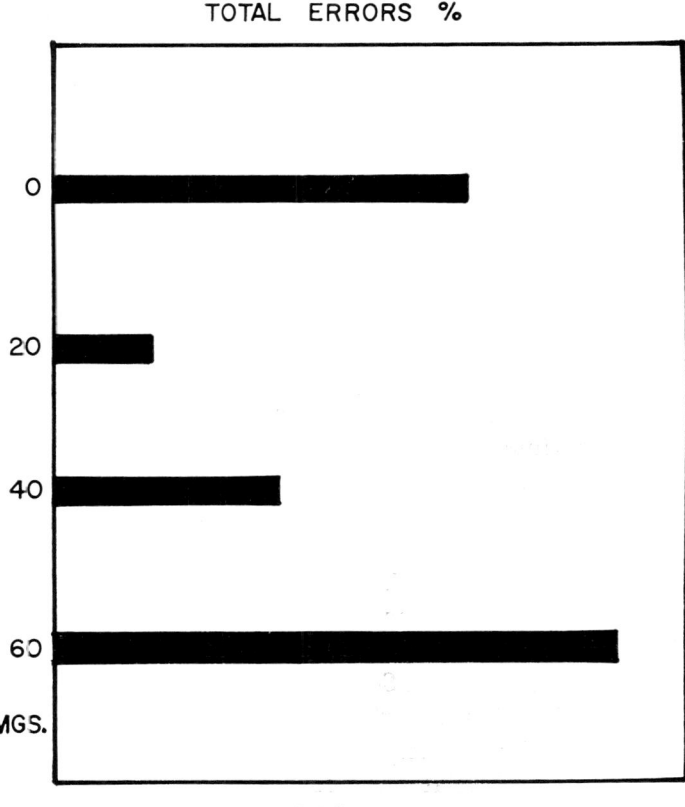

FIGURE 10-3.

of the errors in the present study was the perceptual disorganization described by Bartlet, shown by the inability to handle multiple factors at the same time. The subjects made decisions on isolated pieces of data without reference to the whole situation, and Bartlet and Drew reported pilots doing the same thing under conditions of fatigue. These and other forms of incorrect behavior occurred less often after the administration of Pemoline than in the control situation or with a placebo. Moreover, this stimulant appeared to work without any of the side effects associated with the traditional stimulants. Caffeine, as Weiss and Caties (84) have shown, produces nervousness, irritability, feverishness, and tremor which are absent from Pemoline medication; amphetamine produces more serious effects, such as hypervigilance, which causes gross perseveration (58, 59), verbal incontinence, which impairs the efficiency of verbal communication (10), and various autonomic disturbances (79) which in turn interfere with intellectual processes. These also are absent from subjects on a Pemoline regimen, which would thus appear to have a number of advantages over conventional stimulants (26). Can we extrapolate these findings to a real life Air Traffic Control situation? According to the work of Seashore using drugs and aircraft simulators, such an extrapolation would be valid. Helbing (45), who has been closely concerned with the selection of Air Traffic Control officers, has found that simulation tasks rank high as predictors of success in air traffic control. Parry (63), who has done so much work on proficiency in aircrew, has also shown that tasks involving spatial relations and complex instructions (such as the one described here) correlate higher than any other type of test with complex skills of this sort.

The Mackworth Curve

Some mention should be made of the curve shape, since the delay in efficiency decrement is later than that found by Mackworth. Mackworth (55) is probably the foremost authority on the psychology of radar screen surveillance, and many of his experiments were based on a two-hour watch period. Two possible reasons can be advanced for the difference between the conventional Mackworth Curve and the air traffic control curve obtained in this study. Mackworth found that the drop in efficiency experienced in the second half hour could be postponed by providing an immediate knowledge of results. In the present situation the subject had continuous feedback of data, and one would therefore predict a substantial delay in onset of fatigue decrement compared with Mackworth's situation. Secondly, Baker (3) and Broadbent (11) have shown that deterioration in performance is related to the stimulus interval and to the degree of variability (a finding which well accords with the theory that mental fatigue is related to boredom) and in the present study the stimulus intervals were both short and highly variable. This again would delay the onset of deterioration. The final proof of fatigue in living matter must rest in its power of spontaneous regeneration. If we provide a fifteen-minute rest period towards the end of the two-hour session we find that performance improves on resumption of the task to the level it originally started at two hours earlier, as shown also by Hauty and Payne (30).

EFFECTS OF DPH ON CONCENTRATION

Surveys carried out at both Durham University in 1953 and Sussex University in 1966 showed that impaired concentration was the most common mental symptom found in undergraduates. An analysis of the students complaining of impaired concentration was made by conventional psychometric methods, supported where more serious symptoms also existed by psychiatric investigation. It was found that the student's psychiatric conditions could be classified into one of four categories:

1. Some students concomitant symptomatology was indicative of incipient schizophrenia. The cluster of psychotic disorders subsumed under this title includes some which have a relatively high incidence in the undergraduate age group (77) so that it is not surprising that those students with low stress thresholds who are predisposed to develop schizophrenia should begin to breakdown under the stresses of academic life. Concentration is often impaired in this type of mental illness when the processes of thinking become disordered or when perception is distorted.

2. Some students showed depressive symptoms. Endogenous depression was rather more common than schizophrenia in this sample. In slowing down thinking and lowering the student's motivation to study, it caused the student to become more distractible and hence lose his ability to concentrate. Another type of depressive state was generally reactive to realistic events, such as examination failure, perceived by reason of neurotic processes to be more ego-threatening than was actually the case. In this type of depression, concentration appears to be impaired by the affective processes.

3. Most commonly, anxiety was seen as a concomitant and, in all probability, as a cause of impairment of concentration. The level of anxiety increases as examination time approaches, and by making concentration more difficult at a time when most needed, sows the seeds for yet more anxiety and so sets up a spiralling process of interaction which in some students leads to complete breakdown of intellectual efficiency requiring their withdrawal from the stressful situation.

4. One other cause of concentration difficulties is anancastia (76). In this condition concentration and its concomitant cognitive processes are often impaired by a ruminative preoccupation with irrelevant thought content. The anancastia syndrome is seen in the rather rigid obsessional type of personality. This student is often of rather lower intellectual calibre than his peers but one who, by intense drive, hardwork, and single mindedness of purpose, has achieved his place in college and obtains a good class of degree. Lucas and Knowles (53) have described how overstudy in the obsessional student leads to strain and fatigue and subsequent loss of intellectual efficiency and this in turn creates the need for even larger periods of studying and so promotes the typical spiralling effect. Academic success is important to this student and anything which impedes his progress is therefore more threatening than it is to less anancastic individuals.

Chemotherapeutic Effects

The first three conditions mentioned above are all clearly psychiatric conditions which respond to treatment: the psychotic's thinking is likely to improve with neuroleptic drugs, such as chlorpromazine and haloperidol (32) and the depressed student normally responds to the so-called psychic energizers such as the mono-amine oxidase inhibitors. In the anxiety states, tranquillizers, especially meprobamate (which has specific anxiety-reducing properties), prove effective in reducing the experimential components of the anxiety.

Unfortunately, anancastia, being a developmental characteristic of the personality rather than an illness as such, has proved to be resistant to treatment with medication. Moreover, psychotropic drugs more often impair concentration than improve it. For example, DiMascio *et al.* (23) have shown cognitive decrements to be reported with chlorpromazine and promethazine; and other reports of drug-impaired performance have been cited earlier. Such a drug-induced impairment occurs even when the psychiatric condition of the student is obviously improved. This point is not always appreciated by those responsible for the psychiatric care of the university student, and the result is that the latter has an additional burden of scholastic stress during treatment which may well delay or even prevent a satisfactory response to the therapeutic program.

Although trials of drugs to improve concentration have taken place over the past pentade, the possibility that the forced circling of ruminative thinking, or the "turned-on mind" could be treated chemotherapeutically was first proposed by Dreyfus (25). In a number of preliminary uncontrolled trials Dreyfus found that sodium diphenylhydantoinate, a preparation which under the United Kingdom generic name of phenytoin has been in use for thirty years as an anticonvulsant, has a number of remarkably beneficial effects, among which improvement in concentration and clarity of thought were prominent. Since then controlled trials (37 to 40, 72) and extended clinical trials (80) have confirmed the original reports of the usefulness of the drug. An investigation into the effect of phenytoin upon concentration in anancastic personalities was therefore undertaken.

Methodology

Twelve college students were selected for this trial. They were all males, aged nineteen to twenty-one years of age, mean age 20.2 years, all complained of difficulties in concentration and scored between 53 and 88 per cent, mean 79 per cent on a special form of the Tavistock obsessional scale (61). The subjects were introduced to the air traffic control task previously described. Each subject received two hours tuition in the simulator; on two subsequent trials of two hours' duration he received either 150 mgms of phenytoin or a placebo in a matched capsule, on a crossover basis, six students receiving the placebo first and six receiving the active preparation first. Full double-blind procedure was adopted, neither subject or experimenter knowing which was the active drug and which the inert placebo until the code was broken after the completion of the study. The scores on the second hour of the training period were compared with those obtained during the second hour of each experimental period. The difference between mean scores for the group was computed and the level of statistical significance detrmined.

Results

The results are shown in Table 10-1. No significant difference existed between the group means during the training period and on placebo, but differences between the mean score for the active drug session and those from the training period and the placebo session were significant at the 1% and 5% level respectively. Taking the two placebo sessions (first and second) separately, there was a progressive reduction in errors obtained relative to the training period baseline. While the differences between the mean scores were not statistically significant, the direction of change for the individual scores was significant at p less than 0.02.

TABLE 10-1
RESULTS

Session	Training	Active Drug	Placebo
Mean error scores	119±21	64±19	95±25

SIGNIFICANCE

Comparison	Training v Placebo	Training v Active Drug	Active Drug v Placebo	Training v ½ (P+AD)
P value	N.S.	0.01	0.05	0.05

TRAINING EFFECT

Placebo in 2nd sessions v Placebo in 3rd sessions (direction of change)	$P<0.02$

DISCUSSION

Although concentration is assumed to be measured by a number of cognitive and psychomotor tests, most of these are measuring something else as well. Asher *et al.* (2) have published a list of the subjective and objective factors in concentration, but Guthrie (28) has pointed out that attention is an intervening variable which is not reducible to simple terms, despite Hebb's attempt to clarify its meaning (47). There is obviously both a physical and a psychological component involved, since Laird (50) has shown concentration in a noisy environment requires more energy in the form of O_2, while Morgan (57) demonstrated that an unfavorable condition often improves performance possibly by preventing additional distraction. Digit span, which is considered to be a sensitive measure of concentration (48) is also well known as a test of intelligence (83). If one equates subjects for IQ, concentration test scores will be found to vary in a normal distribution; conversely if concentration scores are equated, a range of intelligence ratings is present. Furthermore, the positive correlations found to exist between various measures of concentration are not particularly high.

If one provides a test of concentration occupying only a small area of the visual field to a group of subjects and at the same time provides visual stimuli in the periphery of their visual field, or additional stimuli via other modalities, for example sounds, it will be found that some, but not all, of the group will be able to recall certain of the irrelevant stimuli. Moreover, the number of extraneous stimuli recalled by subjects obtaining identical scores on the specific concentration task will vary considerably. This can only mean that the scores conventionally chosen for concentration tasks, namely time or performance, are not accurately reflecting the subject's concentration, but merely one aspect of his cognitive performance. Of two subjects obtaining identical scores on the concentration test, the one who in addition observed and registered, albeit unconsciously, additional information, obviously has a higher level of cognitive functioning than the one who has not noted any extraneous environmental stimuli. On the other hand, the latter may be said in one sense to have the better concentration.

This aspect of congnitive functioning introduces the need to use the concept of channel capacity used by information theorists. Seifert (75) has shown that channel capacity, defined as the ratio of usable to supplied information in bits per second is unity up to a certain rate of information flow after which it falls off rapidly (see Fig. 10-4). Maximum usable information is therefore received at the acme of the curve of channel capacity, A. It is at this point that concentration must also be at its maximum. Since during so-called concentration tests, most subjects are still capable of taking in extraneous information from the periphery of vision, it follows that concentration is not a its maximum but at some point B of the channel capacity curve. For the most accurate measurement of concentration the information supplied should be at point C. Channel capacity for the individual subject can be measured successfully using any device which presents information with a variable but controlled rate of flow and which produces a rate of accurate digital response.

However, such devices, whilst admirable for measuring channel capacity and maximum concentration in unit time, are not suitable for measuring concentration over a realistic time base. Channel capacity tests are, by their very

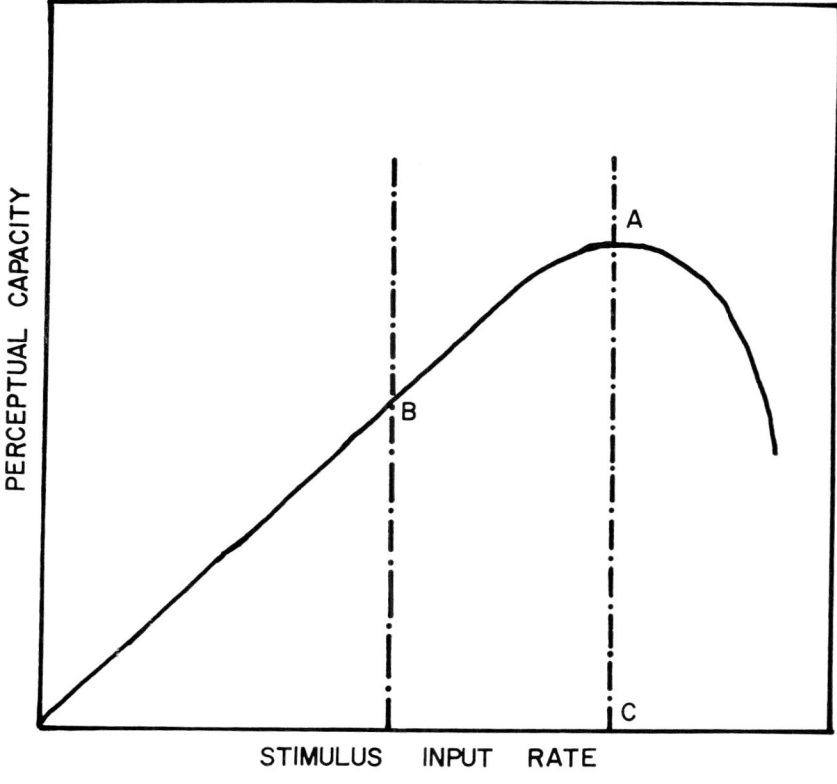

FIGURE 10-4.

nature, boring at the lower end of the curve and stress-producing at the upper end. At any given rate of information flow either condition quickly leads to loss of vigilance with reduction in cognitive efficiency. For this reason tests of concentration on a relatively long time base need to stimulate and maintain interest without imposing a disruptive degree of stress on the subject. This is particularly important in the case of highly intelligent individuals and is the reason why an air traffic control task was selected for measuring concentration in the present sample. Weiss and Caties (84) point out that task complexity may be a differential factor which has been rarely studied explicitly, and they consider whether drugs actually improve performance or merely combat decrement.

The effects of learning are clearly seen in the reduction of errors incurred during the training period to the mean score of those incurred in the combined experimental period, emphasizing the importance of a crossover design in this type of trial. Although Beecher (7) has emphasized the power of the placebo in clinical medicine the value of using a double-blind trial incorporating a placebo is by no means evident. The improvement recorded during the use of a placebo was insignificant, possibly because none of the students had received previous psychotropic medication, for Rickels *et al.* (73) have shown that the patient's previous response to drugs influences his later response to a placebo. An increasing number of studies (16, 29, 81) have shown the double-blind trial on occasion to be irrelevant, inefficient, or even misleading. The effect of the active drug in this trial was clearly demonstrated. The subtlety of the action of the drug was evident from the fact that on questioning, no subject reported noticing any difference in his feeling, thinking, or performance. This is a common experience in the clinical use of the drug; very often the patient's relatives or colleagues at work notice the improvement in behavior and working efficiency while the patient himself is still unaware of it. This is because the drug has a stabilizing effect upon the nervous system, acting neither as a stimulant nor as a depressant but as what had been called a normalizer. Many people are now taking phenytoin to assist concentration, some for special periods of intense mental activity, for example, when preparing for an examination; others, especially those working at executive level and under continuous stress, find a regular maintenance dose both beneficial and necessary if they are not to succumb to one of the stress disorders. This is but one of the many new uses for an old drug, which are regarded as among the most exciting pharmacological developments in recent years. The high level of safety, nonaddictive character, and specific action of reducing neuronal signal redundancy, give it clear advantages over the amphetamine type of stimulants which previously might have been prescribed for this purpose.

SUMMARY

Fatigue-impared performance on a real life complex task was used to evaluate two psychotropic drugs. It is argued that the task chosen, that of simulated air traffic control, is a more valid method of measuring concentration per se than many traditional tests of attention and is more sensitive to both mental fatigue and to the effects of psychotropic drugs (78). The results showed that efficiency in an air traffic control task becomes progressively impaired as a function of time, and excessively so after ninety minutes "on watch." An inert substance proved to have no significant effect upon fatigue-impaired efficiency, but a significant recovery in efficiency is provided by fifteen minutes rest intervals. Pemoline in 20-mg doses significantly reduced the impairment due to fatigue, but higher doses had less effect and at 150 mg actually exacerbated the impairment. DPH, on the other hand, while producing in high doses a smaller improvement than Pemoline 50 mg nevertheless produced a more significant improvement than Pemoline in large doses. At the lower levels Pemoline was more effective than a rest period in reducing both the cumulative errors and the peak level of inefficiency, but less so at higher levels. Moreover, Pemoline produced no side effects at the optimal single dose of 20 mg, but side effects were noted at all doses higher than the optimal one. Conversely, DPH produced no side effects, even at triple dosage levels.

The results suggest that the action of the two drugs is different. Pemoline acts as a true stimulant, with optimal dosage effects but increased impairment at dosage levels outside the optimal range. DPH, on the other hand, while improving concentration significantly, produces none of the effects characteristic of a stimulant. It could be hypothesized that the difference essentially lies in the action of Pemoline on the physical components of mental fatigue, acting as a psychic energizer, while DPH acts on the psychological components producing a "normalizing" effect which enables the subject to make more-efficient use of his physical potential. Experiments to test this hypothesis are required. The effects of long-term medication on concentration need to be examined in more detail but extended clinical trials with both preparations leave no doubt of the overall superiority of DPH for this purpose.

REFERENCES

1. ARDUINI, A., AND M.G.: Effects of drugs and metabolic alterations on brain stem arousal mechanisms. *J Pharmacol Exp Ther, 110*:76–85, 1954.
2. ASHER, E.J., TIFFIN, J., AND KNIGHT, F.B.: *Introduction of General Psychology*. Boston, D.C. Heath 1953.
3. BAKER, C. H.: Effect of stimulus interval on performance, *Brit J Psychol, 50*:30, 1959.
4. BARTLETT, F.C.: Fatigue following highly skilled work. *Proc Roy Soc [Biol], 131*:247, 1943.
5. BARTLETT, F.C.: Current problems in visual function and visual perception. *Proc Phys Soc, 55*:417, 1944.
6. BARTLEY, S.H., AND CHUTE, E.: *Fatigue and Impairment in Man*. New York, McGraw-Hill, 1947.
7. BEECHER, H.K.: The powerful placebo. *JAMA, 159*:1602, 1955.
8. BERGER, F.M.: Treatment of anxiety: A critical review. *J Neuropsychiat, 4*:98–103, 1962.
9. BEXTON, W.H. et al.: Effects of decreased variation in sensory environment. *Canad J Psychol, 8*:70, 1954.
10. BROOMBERG, W.: In the interrelationship of mind and body. *Res Publ Ass Res Nerv Ment Dis, 19*:112–143, 1939.
11. BROADBENT, D.E.: Vigilance. *Brit Med Bull, 20*:17–20, 1964.
12. CASS, W., AND FREDERECK, W.S.: Experimental and statistical problems in study of new drugs. *Canad Med Ass J, 83*:887, 1960.
13. CASTENEDA, A.: Reaction time and response amplitude as a function of anxiety and stimulus intensity. *J Abnorm Soc Psychol, 53*: 1956.
14. CARRELL, R.B., AND SCHEIER, I.H.: Nature of anxiety. *Psychol Rep (Supple. No. 5)*, 1958.
15. CROSSMAN, E.R.F.W.: Information processes in human skill. *Brit Med Bull, 20*:32–37, 1964.
16. CROMIE, B.W.: The feet of clay of the double-blind trial. *Lancet, 2*:997, 1958.

17. DAVIS, D.R.: Disorganisation of behavior in fatigue. *J Neurol Psychiat,* 9:23, 1946a.
18. DAVIS, D.R.: Neurotic predisposition and the disorganisation observed in experiments with the Cambridge cockpit. *J Neurol Psychiat,* 9:119, 1946b.
19. DAVIS, D.R.: *Pilot Error.* London, H.M.S.O., 1948.
20. DAVIS, D.R.: Increase in strength of a secondary drive as a cause of disorganisation. *Quart J Exp Psychol,* 1:22, 1948.
21. DAVIS, D.R.: In Cassie, A. (Ed.) : *Psychological Mechanisms in Pilot Error in Aviation Psychology.* The Hague, Morton, 1964.
22. DAVIS, D.R.: *Flight Safety,* 1:1, 1967.
23. DiMASCIO, A., HAVENS, L., AND KLERMAN, G.L.: Psychopharmacology of phenothiazine compounds. *J Nerv Ment Dis,* 136:15, 168, 1963.
24. DREW, G.C.: *An Experimental Study of Mental Fatigue.* London, Air Ministry, 1940.
25. DREYFUS, J.J., JR.: The Beneficial Effects of Diphenylhydantoin on the Nervous Systems of Non-Epileptics. Read at the American College of Neuropsychopharmacology Symposium of DPH, San Juan, Puerto Rico, 1966.
26. DUREMAN, E.I.: Differential patterning of behavioral effects of three types of stimulant drugs. *Clin Pharmacol Therap,* 3:29–33, 1962.
27. FRANCIS-WILLIAMS, J.: Can normal poor development be distinguished from disorders due to brain pathology in nature and consequences of brain lesions? London, British Psychology Society, 1966.
28. GUTHRIE, E.R.: In Koch, S.: *Psychology: A Study of a Science.* London, McGraw-Hill, 1959, vol. II.
29. GUY, W., GROSS, M., AND DENNIS, H.: An alternative to the double-blind procedure. *Amer J Psychiat,* 123:12, 1967.
30. HAUTY, G.T., AND PAYNE, R.B.: Mitigation of work decrement. *J Exp Psychol,* 49:60,–67, 1955.
31. HAWARD, L.R.C.: Differential interdrug analysis. *Brit J Psychiat,* 110:514–519, 1964.
32. HAWARD, L.R.C.: Drug induced fatigue decrement in a complex task. *Bull Brit Psychol Soc,* 18:4A, 1965a.
33. HAWARD, L.R.C.: Drug-induced fatigue decrement in ATC. *Percept Motor Skills,* 20: 952, 1965b.
34. HAWARD, L.R.C.: A new central stimulant. *Med Officer,* 113:5, 1965c.
35. HAWARD, L.R.C.: Drug induced fatigue decrement in air traffic control. In Teerint, F.J.B.: *Aviation Psychological Research.* Munich, WEAAP, 1965d.
36. HAWARD, L.R.C.: Stimulant for airmen. *Chem Drug,* 185:38, 1966.
37. HAWARD, L.R.C.: The effects of a stimulant drug on an ATC task. *Flight Safety* 1:3–7, 1967a.
38. HAWARD, L.R.C.: *The Effect of Phenytoin-Aided Autogenic Training on Stress Threshold.* International Congress for Psychosomatic medicine and Hypnosis. Kyoto, Japan, 1967b, p. 91.
39. HAWARD, L.R.C.: A study of physiological responses of neurotic patients to diphenylhydantoin. *Int J Neuropsychiat,* 3 (Supple. 2):49–56, 1967.
40. HAWARD, L.R.C.: Drugs and concentration: Cognitive effects of DPH. *Portsmouth J Psychol,* 1:3–5, 1968.
41. HAWARD, L.R.C.: Effects of sodium diphenylhydantoinate on concentration. *Bull Brit Psychol Soc,* 1969.
42. HAUTY, G.T., AND PAYNE, R.B.: Mitigation of work decrement. *J Exp Psychol,* 49:60–67, 1955.

43. HAUTY, G.T.: Psychophysiological problems of manned space vehicles. In *Lectures in Aerospace Medicine*. Texas, Brooks Air Force Base, 1960.
44. HAWKINS, D.R., PAGE, R. PASTERNACK, B., AND SANDIFER, M.G.: A multivariant psychopharmacologic study in normals. *Psychosom Med, 23*:1–17, 1961.
45. HELBING, J.C.: Results of selection of RNAF air traffic control officers. In Cassie et al. (Eds.) : *Aviation Psychology*. Hague, Morton, 1964.
46. HOLLIDAY, A.R., AND DILLE, J.M.: Effects of meprobamate, chlorpomazine pentobarbital and placebo on a behavioural task performed under stress conditions. *J Comp Physiol Psychol, 51*:811–815, 1958.
47. KOCH, S.: *Psychology: Study of a Science*. London, McGraw-Hill, 1959, vol. 1.
48. KORNETSKY C.O., HUMPHTEYS, O., AND EVARTS, V.: Comparison of centrally acting drugs in man. *Arch Neurol Psychiat, 77*:318–324, 1957.
49. KORNETSKY, C.: Effects of meprobamate, phenobarbital and d-amphetamine on reaction time and learning in man. *J Pharmacol Exp Ther, 123*:215–219, 1958.
50. LAIRD, D.A.: Experiments on the physiological cost of noise. *J Nat Ist Ind Psychol, 4*:251–258, 1928.
51. LIENERT, G.A., AND JANKE, W.: Pharmakoligische Untersuchung uber 5-phenyl-2-immino-4-oxo-oxazoldin. *Arzneimitte forschung, 7*:436–439, 1957.
52. LOOMIS, T.A., AND WEST, T.C.: Comparative sedative effects of a barbiturate and some tranquilizer drugs on normal subjects. *J Pharmacol, Exp Ther, 122*:525–531, 1958.
53. LUCAS, C.J., AND KNOWLES, J.B.: The trial of a new stimulant, Pemoline, in the treatment of fatigue in students. *College Health, 12*:187–194, 1963.
54. MCKENZIE, R.E., AND ELLIOT, L.L.: effects of seconal and d-amphetamine on performance during a simulated tactical air mission. *SAM TDR, 64–79*, 1964.
55. MACKWORTH N.H.: *Special Report Serial No. 268*. London, Medical Research Council, 1950.
56. MARCHBANKS, V.H., HALE, H.B., AND ELLIS, V.P.: Stress responses of pilots flying 6 hour overwater missions in F100 and F104 aircraft. *SAM TR 62-112*, 1962.
57. MORGAN, J.J.B.: Overcoming distraction. *Arch Psychol, 5*:35, 1916.
58. NASH, H.: The design and conduct of experiments on the psychological effects of drugs. *J Nerv Ment Dis, 128*:129–147, 1959.
59. NASH, H.: Psychologic effects of amphetamines and barbiturates. *J Nerv Ment Dis, 134*:203–217, 1962.
60. NORLAND, E.: Children and serial reading II. *Psychol Abs, 34*:2, 1960.
61. ORME, J.E.: Relationship of obsessional traits to general emotional instability. *Brit J Med Psychol, 38*:269–272, 1965.
62. OSWALD, I.: The experimental study of sleep. *Brit Med Bull, 20*:60–64, 1964.
63. PARRY, J.B., AND FOKKEMA, S.D.: *Aviation Psychology in Western Europe*. Amsterdam, Swets & Zeitlinger, 1958.
64. PAYNE, R.B., HAUTY, G.T., AND MOORE, E.W.: Restoration of tracking proficiency as a function of amount and delay of analeptic medication. *J Comp Physiol Psychol, 50*:146–149, 1957.
65. PAYNE, R.B., AND MOORE, E.W.: Effects of some analeptic and depressant drugs upon tracking behaviour. *J Pharmacol Exp Ther, 115*:480–484, 1955.
66. PAYNE, R.B., AND HAUTY, G.T.: Effects of experimentally induced attitudes upon task proficiency. *J Exp Psychol, 47*:267–273, 1954.
67. PAYNE, R.B., AND HAUTY, G.T.: Effects of motion sickness preventives upon perceptual-motor components of a pilots task. *SAM Project 21-1601-004 Report No. 3*, 1953.

68. PAYNE, R.B.: Some effects of motion sickness remedies upon psychologic performance. *Int Rec Med, 168*:32–40, 1955.
69. PEARSON, R.G.: Effects of Benadryl and Dramamine on perceptual motor skill. *SAM 57–50*, 1957.
70. PEARSON, R.G., HUNTER, G.S., AND NEAL, G.I.: Development of evaluation of radar air traffic control research task. *Fed Air Agency AM, 65*–31, 1965.
71. PETERSON, E.A., HAUN, K., AND UPTON, M.: The effects of meprobamate, d-amphetamine and placebo on disjunctive reaction time to taboo and non-taboo words. *Psychopharm, 3*:173–187, 1962.
72. RESNICK, O., AND DREYFUS, J.J., JR.: *Worcester County Jail Study*. New York, Private publication, 1966.
73. RICKELS, K., LIPMAN, R., AND RAAB, E.: Previous medication, duration of illness and placebo response. *J Nerv Ment Dis, 142*:548–554, 1966.
74. SCHMIDT, L.: 5-phenyl-2-imino-4-oxo-oxazolidin ein Zentral erregender-stoff. *Arzeimittelforschung, 6*:423–436, 1956.
75. SEIFERT, R.: Presentation of information and task load. *Flight Safety, 1*:22–25, 1967.
76. SKOOG, G.: *The Anancastic Syndrome*. Copenhagen, Munksgaard, 1959.
77. STALLWORTHY, K.R.: *Facts of Mental Health and Illness*. Christchurch, N.Z., Peryer, 1958.
78. STEVENS, S.S.: *Handbook of Experimental Psychology*. London, Chapman Hall, 1951.
79. SUMMERFIELD, A.: Drugs and behaviour. *Brit Med Bull, 20*:70–74, 1964.
80. TURNER, W.J.: The usefulness of DPH in treatment of non-epileptic emotional disorders. *Int J Neurophychiat, 3* (Supple. 2) : 8–20, 1967.
81. TUTEUR, W.: The double-blind method: Its pitfalls and fallacies. *Amer J Psychiat, 114*:921–922, 1958.
82. VENABLES, R.H.: Changes in motor response with increase and decrease in task difficulty in normal industrial and psychiatric patient subjects. *Brit J Psychol, 16*:101, 1955.
83. WECHSLER, D.: *Manual for the W.A.I.S.*, New York, Psychological Corp., 1955.
84. WEISS, B., AND CATIES, V.G.: Enhancement of human performance by caffeine and the amphetamines. *Pharmacol Rev, 14*:1–36, 1962.
85. YATES, A.J.: Abnormalities in psychomotor function. In Eysenck, H.J. (Ed.) : *Handbook of Abnormal Psychology*. London, Pitman, 1960.

Chapter 11

Facilitating Verbal-Symbolic Functions in Children With Learning Problems and 14-6 Positive Spike EEG Patterns With Ethosuximide (Zarontin®)

W. LYNN SMITH

This paper follows as third in a sequence of studies on drugs which can be regarded as learning facilitators. Dr. Conners' excellent review has brought us current on various stimulant drugs and their effects on vigilence and learning enhancement. Dr. Haward's studies took on a different tack both in terms of drugs involved and study method. The *in situ* design of Dr. Haward's studies of vigilence and concentration, the effects of diphenylhydantoin and Pemoline in error reduction is very clever as well as productive. The present paper continues the study of specific drug effects except on a specific minimal cerebral dysfunction population.

Drug trials in children with learning deficits to improve learning have been reported by some researchers as encouraging while others have reported discouraging, even negative results (1, 2). In the observation process little recognition has been given to objective comparison, other than rating devices and mazes, or specific drugs for specific learning deficits, but where objective measurements have been employed, the results for the most part, have been inconsistent (3 to 6). Only a few drugs have been subjected to any but the most basic tests.

Pharmacological approaches to facilitate learning in children with learning problems have included a variety of psychoactive agents, stimulant drugs as methylphenidate and a host of other drugs as deanol, orphenadrine, various phenothiazines, and diphenylhydantoin. Recent studies on the latter drug's offering encouraging findings are reported in a earlier presentation in this part by Dr. Turner.

Open drug trials conducted at the Cortical Function Laboratory at Porter Hospital on most of the above drugs on children with learning problems have resulted in the same inconclusive results as far as changes within multiple intellectual functions in a pre/post psychological intelligence test measurements are concerned.

About two years ago it was noted that the children with learning prob-

Grateful acknowledgement for data collection and statistical evaluation is extended to Dr. M. J. Philipps, Dr. H. L. Guard, Mr. T. C. Weyl, Mr. N. H. Tracy and Dr. S. K. Campbell.

lems seen in the Cortical Function Laboratory not only manifested the usual specific learning deficies as poor attention span and reading and spelling deficiencies, but especially a high incidence of audioverbal receptivity impairment and a poor school performance in subjects as arithmetic or English, or both. Almost invariably they had atypical neuropsychological protocals as well as abnormal electrograms. The abnormal electrograms were preponderantly, in order of frequency, 14-6 positive spike pattern (hereafter referred to as 14-6), 6 cps positive spikes, mixed nomenclatures, borderline records, spike-wave phantoms and paroxysmal activity.

The electroencephalogram record denoting a 14-6 cps positive pattern is seen in EEG readings just before a patient drops off to sleep and again upon awakening (8). The montages used for the tracing on which the 14-6 pattern appears is a monopolar one, connecting the occipital, temporal both posterior and mid, and central leads alternately to the same side ear and to the opposite ear. Although not all neurologists agree on the significance of this pattern, it is seen by many as abnormal and as indicative of a cerebral dysfunction resulting from subcortical discharge of the diencephalic or limbic structures, or both (9, 14). Additionally, many patients with this pattern were observed to have had a history of stomachache, headache, and other autonomic symptoms of irritability, and with some episodes of rage (9). The great majority were regarded as management problems to their parents and teachers. A recent analysis of one hundred consecutive 14-6 cases of children and adolescents seen in the Cortical Function Laboratory, incidentally, reveal some curious facts. Autonomic symptoms reported by the children were 15 per cent for headache, 20 per cent abdominal pain, 60 per cent a combination of headache and stomachache, with unexplained backache 5 per cent. Learning problem was the referral reason in 12 per cent, 5 per cent for basically rageful behavior, while 83 per cent were a combination of learning problem and behavior where it was difficult to make a clear differentiation. The population was 2 to 1, male to female, with age range 5 through 18 with a majority between 10 and 14 years of age. Because of the high incidence of 14-6 cps EEGs, various medications were given to that group. Since there were occasional grand-mal convulsions occurring in the 14-6 positive spike group, and where auditory verbal dysgnosia and faulty attention span resembled petit-mal absence were strikingly major symptoms, a petit-mal enticonvulsant drug was selected and tried. Further, this drug selection is in keeping with some of Dr. Oettinger's work (1).

The first few patients on ethosuximide responded well to the drug, both behaviorally and in losing autonomic complaints, so a test/retest trial system was set up to assess medication effects. In terms of length, the three-week medication trial period seemed adequate. The first ten patients on this standard trial period comprised the first study.

FIRST STUDY (OPEN)

It was found in this preliminary open pre/post study that the Wechsler IQ Scales reflected changes while the subjects were being treated with ethosuximide. The mean verbal IQ change was 10.9 increase, which yields a t of 6.903 ($p<0.005$). The change in performance IQ scales was nonsignificant $t=0.731$ ($p<0.50$). The change in the full-scale IQ was 7.100, $t=9.2328$ ($p<0.0005$). It was found that psychomotor and personality tests did not change from premedication to postmedication testing. Thus the performance IQ scores of the Wechsler tests did not significantly change nor did quantitative Rorscharch test scores or Raven progressive matrices test scores. From these results the next step was to design a study to compare psychometric tests on patients being treated with ethosuximide but who would be receiving both the drug and a placebo within a double-blind series. The following is the report of the second investigation.

SECOND STUDY (DRUG/PLACEBO)

Method and Material

Ten patients (ranging in age from 8 to 14), eight male and two female, were subjects in this second investigation. All were being treated with ethosuximide up to the time of the study, and six of them were involved in the initial study. (11). In this study, all subjects were patients of the three referring pediatricians who administered the medication in an investigational sequence. Each subject received a supply of preparation which would last for three weeks. The subjects received either ethosuximide (250-mg capsule once a day) or placebo, depending upon the random packaging of the preparations. The administration of the drug was on a double-blind basis, where neither the physicians nor the investigators who tested these patients knew whether they were receiving placebo or ethosuximide. At the end of the three weeks, the subject received a battery of psychological tests; the subject was then crossed over to either the active medication or placebo, depending on the first preparation administered. At the completion of the investigation the code was broken and test scores obtained while the subject was taking placebo were compared with scores while he was receiving ethosuximide.

Tests Employed

Measures were selected to determine changes in functioning in the following areas: (1) intellectual functioning: Wechsler-Bellevue Forms I and II, Wechsler Intelligence Scale for Children; (2) perception: Raven's Progressive Matrices (revised order, 1956); and (3) personality: Rorschach Inkblot Test.

All the above measures have been used in studies of cerebral dysfunction as well as in the areas for which they were originally standardized (15, 16). Consequently, these devices give a cross-check upon certain cerebral dysfunctions in addition to their specific uses. Both sets of tests were administered by the same investigator. The subjects were randomly assigned to one of the two investigators. As the subject was accompanied by a parent (usually the mother) to the test session, the investigator would question the parent as to any observed behavioral changes in the weeks preceding the examination. In all cases, the parents had been in contact with the subjects' teachers and reported the teachers' impressions as well. The subjects in this study came from a middle-class and upper-middle class socioeconomic background. None of them received any other type of medical or psychological treatment during the course of this study. However, all subjects had been receiving ethosuximide before the start of this investigation and were taking the medication up to the beginning of the project. They were then given the investigation medicine sequence (or placebo) without interruption. As mentioned previously, whether the subject received a placebo or the drug in the initial part of the study depended on the randomization of the packaged preparations. For the second three weeks, the subjects were crossed over to the alternate preparation.

Results

Raven matrices test scores did not change significantly. The Rorschach technique was scored quantitatively (18) and X^2 analysis did not reveal significant changes. Scanning the Rorschach test responses qualitatively did not indicate obvious differences between the two testings. However, significant variations between placebo and drug treatment testings did occur on the intelligence measures.

In Table 11-1 it can be seen that highly significant changes of verbal IQ scores occurred when comparing the score attained on the placebo with that reached on ethosuximide. It should be noted that the means for the Wechsler IQ scales were quite different in the preliminary and the present study. It was necessary to replace four subjects in the preliminary study with different subjects, all previously on ethosuximide, to complete the present study due to errors in prescribing dosage. As indicated in Table 11-1 all but case 3 had an increase in verbal IQ scores while on ethosuximide. It might be clarified at this point subject 3 was the only one in the study who had a borderline EEG which was not of the 14-6 cps category. He was included as his test profile and behavioral symptoms appeared so consistant with others within the study. Since these subjects were being treated with the drug up to the initiation of the study, one could interpret this table as demonstrating a decrease in verbal IQ scores while on the placebo, since the subjects received the latter in accordance with a randomized drug administration.

TABLE 11-1
VERBAL IQ SCORE COMPARISONS OF TEN PATIENTS ON ETHOSUXIMIDE AND PLACEBO TREATMENT

Case No.	Placebo	Ethosuximide	Difference
1	97	113	16
2	106	113	7
3	106	101	-5
4	95	119	24
5	102	111	9
6	111	122	11
7	115	121	6
8	104	106	2
9	90	110	20
10	96	126	30
Means	102.2	114.2	

Difference between means, 12.00.
$t = 3.5853$; $p = 0.005$.

TABLE 11-2
PERFORMANCE IQ SCORE COMPARISONS OF TEN PATIENTS
ON ETHOSUXIMIDE AND PLACEBO TREATMENT

Case No.	Placebo	Ethosuximide	Difference
1	107	128	21
2	126	126	0
3	127	137	10
4	108	108	0
5	132	131	−1
6	135	138	3
7	114	125	11
8	122	119	−3
9	116	116	0
10	110	113	3
Means	119.7	124.1	

Difference between means, 4.4.
$t = 1.8739$; p −N.S.

TABLE 11-3
FULL-SCALE IQ SCORE COMPARISONS OF TEN PATIENTS
ON ETHOSUXIMIDE AND PLACEBO TREATMENT

Case No.	Placebo	Ethosuximide	Difference
1	103	124	21
2	121	121	0
3	116	121	5
4	101	115	14
5	119	124	5
6	126	136	10
7	109	125	16
8	114	113	−1
9	103	115	12
10	103	122	19
Means	111.5	121.6	

Difference between means, 10.1.
$t = 4.1666$; $p = 0.005$.

The next Table 11-2 depicts significant increases in full-scale IQ scores in all but case 8; the increase in verbal IQ scores in responsible for this, of course, since no increase in performance IQ scores occurred, as seen in the next Table 11-3. Although two of the subjects (cases 1 and 7) did show large increases in performance IQ scores, this was not sufficient to influence the group statistics. Case 1 showed increases of 21 points in both performance and full-scale scores.

In this second study, these data have demonstrated the efficacy of ethosuximide in its ability to increase verbal cognitive functions in this particular patient population. To attribute these changes to extraneous factors appears highly questionable, since the subjects randomly received the drug and placebo, and a statistically significant decrease in verbal IQ scores took place while on the placebo. These data are even more impressive when one considers the fact that six of these subjects had received the same tests employed in the first open study, and yet the only changes that occurred were decreases of verbal functions while on placebo and increases on ethosuximide. There is a general assumption in intelligence testing from studies of practice effect that learning gains do take place with performance items though not noticeably in verbal items (12). Even this did not occur in our study population, with tests being administered three weeks apart and, as mentioned above, six subjects had received these tests in our earlier investigation. Consequently, any distortion of results on the basis of learning factors was not evident in this investigation.

It should be noted that the mean difference for the second study on the Wechsler is higher than that for the preliminary open study. There are two possible explanations for this finding. One of these is due to the mild composing or integrating effect of ethosuximide. Since all subjects had been taking the drug regularly before the study began, one might expect a slight disintegration when placed on a placebo. This would tend to make the mean difference somewhat larger than in the first study where no placebo was used. This incidentally, indicates a difficulty with the double-blind crossover method where all subjects are already on medication. A second explanation for the larger difference between the means is a possible cumulative effect of ethosuximide which is characteristic of the drug in the author's experience. This does not remain through the three-week placebo period but could make the difference between test results greater in the double-blind study than when comparing test results in the preliminary study.

THIRD STUDY (OPEN)

Since the results of this second study were almost identical to the first study, more patients were studied on an open premedication and postmedication basis, children with learning deficits and various other abnormal EEG categories besides 14-6 as well as normal EEGs were included. This third study, an extension of the previous two ethosuximide studies, differs in that the EEG nomenclatures are various (4).

The subjects were forty-one additional patients, twenty-seven children with 14-6 cps positive spike EEG records and fourteen children with borderline, normal, and mixed abnormal (6 cps positive spikes, spike-wave phantoms, and psychomotor varients) EEG records. Ages ranged from six years of age to seventeen. The same tests were employed as previously mentioned. This open study procedure was the same as the initial study but dosage was 250 mg daily for about two-thirds and 500 mg daily for the remainder.

Results and Discussion

As in the second study, only the changes in the Wechsler scales were analyzed, as the other measures had previously shown no change with medication (7, 13). An analysis of variance showed no difference among the various EEG nomenclatures (see Table 11-4). It should be clarified that only twenty-two of the forty-one subjects were used in this analysis because they were the only subjects with complete batteries. The F between pre/post medication test scores was significantly different at greater that the .005 level ($F=28.15$) and the F between the subtests on the Wechsler scales was significantly different at greater than the .005 level ($F=6.07$). No first-order or second order interactions were found to be significant. Comparisons of the subtest changes from premedication to postmedication testing, using t test, showed significant changes in all but three of the eleven subtests; i. e., Vocabulary, Block Design, and Object Assembly. The failure to find differences between the 14-6 cps group and the non–14-6 group is not surprising when the electroencephalogram records are examined more closely. The 14-6 cps group comprised eleven cases. The second group of eleven was composed of six records interpreted as normal although all had some occipital slowing; one record was regarded as borderline although it too had some occipital slowing; of the remaining four abnormal nomenclature groups, one was spike-wave phantom, one positive spike, one 6 cps spikes, and one paroxysmal activity with positive spike. Obviously the numbers in the various EEG nomenclatures are too few to make accurate comparisons and these findings are viewed as merely suggestive. To bring the ethosuximide series current, further studies have been conducted which involve the same tests and open study procedure, and the above patterns continue to hold up remarkably well. It might be mentioned that the open study procedure involves various test/retest variations of four different testers where some subjects are tested by the same psychologist, two different psychologists for test and retest, and where the testing psychologist was aware and unaware of drug trial or kind of drug trial being involved. The results of these studies have demonstrated the efficacy of ethosuximide

TABLE 11-4
VARIANCE TABLE
(2 X 2 X 11 FACTORIAL DESIGN, 22 SUBJECTS, 11 14/6 AND 11 MIXED)

Source of Variation	Sum of Squares	Degree of Freedom	Mean Square	F	F:95	F:99	F:995
1. Between conditions (14/6 vs non-14/6)	2.250	1	2.25	.23	3.86	6.70	8.18
2. Between administrations (Before Z vs after Z)	272.250	1	272.25	28.15*	3.86	6.70	8.18
3. Between tests	587.232	10	58.72	6.07*	1.85	2.37	2.71
4. Conditions X administrations (1 and 2)	.002	1	.00	.00	3.86	6.70	8.18
5. Conditions X tests (1 and 3)	41.661	10	4.17	.43	1.85	2.37	2.71
6. Administrations X tests (2 and 3)	50.545	10	5.05	.52	1.85	2.37	2.71
7. Conditions X administrations X tests (1, 2, and 3)	29.405	10	2.94	.30	1.85	2.37	2.71
8. Within cells (error)	4254.182	440	9.67	—	—	—	—
Total	5237.527	483	10.84	—	—	—	—

* Significant at the .005 level.

in its ability to increase verbal cognitive functions in a patient population with largely learning problems and 14-6 positive spike patterns.

It is too early to assess the long-term effects of ethosuximide as most patients have been on the drug between twelve and eighteen months. Although teachers and parents have reports to support the contention that these particular children have improved in school and in their social behavior, the scope of the studies did not include premedication and postmedication school marks and teacher ratings. The obvious need exists for further studies to include these additional school assessments as well as conducting a much larger study involving similar EEG nomenclature groups with an without primary learning problems as well as children with normal EEG records with and without learning problems as well as the subnormal intelligence group.

In terms of changes in verbal functions, it appears that ethosuximide may have some influence on specific brain functions. If we consider the work of some other investigators in the light of our findings, we have some interesting speculations. Halstead, McFie, among others used the Wechsler intelligence tests on a large number of subjects with various types and location of discreet brain lesions and concluded that verbal cognitive functions were localized in the left hemisphere of the brain; further, left temporal brain trauma experienced the greatest loss of verbal functions regardless of dominance of handedness (15, 16). As our 14-6 group manifested initial reductions in verbal skills before treatment, it would appear that ethosuximide has some effect on left

TABLE 11-5

ETHOSUXIMIDE

SCORES OF ALL EEG NOMENCLATURES
(Matched Samples on the 14 Tests)

Type of Test	$\bar{d}$	Degrees of Freedom	t	t .05	t .01	t .005
1. Verbal	11.22	36	8.10*	1.69	2.44	2.72
2. Performance	6.66	34	4.05*	1.69	2.44	2.72
3. Full Scale	10.68	33	9.55*	1.69	2.44	2.72
4. Information	1.72	38	4.64*	1.68	2.42	2.70
5. Comprehension	2.85	38	6.26*	1.68	2.42	2.70
6. Digit Span	1.46	36	3.81*	1.69	2.44	2.72
7. Arithmetic	1.43	36	2.93*	1.69	2.44	2.72
8. Similarities	1.92	35	5.28*	1.69	2.44	2.72
9. Vocabulary	1.75	31	5.13*	1.70	2.46	2.75
10. Picture arrangement	.39	30	.86	1.70	2.46	2.75
11. Picture Completion	1.27	36	3.07*	1.69	2.44	2.72
12. Block Design	.74	33	1.68	1.69	2.44	2.72
13. Object Assembly	.93	26	1.69	1.71	2.48	2.78
14. Digit Symbol	1.00	32	2.80*	1.69	2.44	2.72

* Significant at the .005 level.

hemisphere functions and that the effect is more specific rather than secondary to some overall general effect. If it were a more general influence of the drug, changes would be seen at other levels, such as in performance items or in the personality tests and psychomotor skills. Another interpretation of these findings could regard verbal-symbolic functions merely as the highest cortical functions and specific hemispheric anatomical correlates may have nothing to do with the action of the drug. One can only speculate on the underlying biochemical process at this time. After observation of hemispherectomy patients Dr. C.W. Burkland concludes that elements of language may be in part diencephalic rather than completely telencephalic (17). There is this aspect of this study that poses a question for future investigation. It was our belief that the 14-6 positive spike pattern had something to do with verbal deficiency in these subjects before they received therapy. With the disagreement over the meaning of this particular EEG pattern, one could reason differently that these subjects were experiencing verbal difficulties and/or other problems, and the presence of the 14-6 pattern only served to exacerbate their already difficult situation. Undoubtedly, many of our subjects had had some problems, especially relating to schoolwork, for some time, months or possibly years. If this were the case, however, it would be difficult to explain how an anticonvulsant medication increased verbal functions in the drug/placebo study and decreased it when it was stopped.

Based on the results of the drug/placebo study and additional open research studies in our laboratory, it is our impression that the 14-6 positive spike pattern is associated with the minimal brain dysfunction that interferes with highest cortical functions i. e. the verbal skills are present but are "short-circuited" by this type of diencephalic dysfunction which in turn responds to ethosuximide.

REFERENCES

1. OETTINGER, L.: The use of drugs in children with learning disorders. *Int. Copenhagen Congr*, 1964.
2. COLE, J.O., AND CARR, C.J.: A synoptic review of psychoactive drugs. In Fisher, Seymour (Ed.): *Child Research in Psychopharmacology*. Springfield, Charles C Thomas. 1959.
3. BOUTHILET, L., AND FISHER, S.: Reference list on the use of psychopharmacological agents with children. In Fisher, Seymour (Ed.): *Child Research in Psychopharmacology*. Springfield, Charles C Thomas, 1959.
4. BRADLEY, C.: Problem children: Electroencephalographic diagnosis in pharmacologic treatment. *Conn State Med J, 6*:773, 1942.
5. UHR, L.: Objectively measured drug effects. In Uhr, L., and Miller, J. (Eds.): *Drugs and Behavior*. New York, John Wiley & Sons, 1960.
6. BARBER, B.: *Drugs and Society*. New York, Russell Sage Foundation, 1968, pp. 6–39.
7. SMITH, W. LYNN, AND PHILIPPUS, M.J.: A psychometric study before and after receiving Zarontin (ethosuximide) of children with 14–6 cycles per second positive spike patterns on the EEG. Mimeograph publication, 1968.

8. KELLAWAY, P., CRAWLEY, J., AND KOGARA, N.: A specific correlate of conclusive equivalent disorder in children. *J Pediat,* 55:582–592, 1959.
9. CHAO, D. H-C, DRUCHMAN, R., AND KELLAWAY, P.: *Convulsive Disorders of Children.* Philadelphia, W.B. Saunders, 1958.
10. HUGHES, J., MEANS, E., AND STILL, B.: A controlled study on the behavior disorders associated with the positive spike phenomenon. *Electroenceph Clin Neurophysiol,* 18:393–394, 1965.
11. SMITH, W. LYNN, PHILIPPUS, M.J., AND GUARD, H.L.: Psychometric study of children with learning problems and 14–6 positive spike EEG patterns, treated with ethosuximide (Zarontin) and placebo. *Arch Dis Child,* 43:616–619, Oct. 1968.
12. GUERTIN, W., RABIN, A., FRANK, G., AND LADD, C.: Research with the WAIS. *Psychol Bull,* 59:1–26, 1962.
13. LITTEL, W.: The WISC: Review of a decade of research. *Psychol Bull,* 57:132–156, 1960
14. SMITH, W. LYNN, AND WEYL, T.C.: The effects of ethosuximide (Zarontin) in intellectual functions of children with learning deficits and cortical brain dysfunction. *Curr Ther Res,* 10:265–269, 1968.
15. HALSTEAD, W.C.: *Brain and Intelligence.* Chicago University of Chicago Press, 1947.
16. McFIE, J.: Psychological testing in clinical neurology. *J Nerv Ment Dis,* 131, Nov. 1960.
17. BURKLAND, C.W.: Personal communication with Dr. Aaron Smith. August, 1968.
18. KLOPFER, B. et al, Developments in The Rorschach Technique, New York, Harcourt, Brace and World Inc., Vol. 1 & 2, 1956.

Chapter 12

Some Clinical and Laboratory Studies of Psychotropic Drugs in Children: An Overview

JOHN S. WERRY*

A review of the pharmacology of psychotropic drugs and of their clinical use in children has appeared elsewhere in this book (Ch. 8), so that this chapter will concern itself only with a series of studies carried out by the senior author and his colleagues during the past seven years. The purpose of this review is twofold: first, to present in summary these studies (sixteen in number), several of which are unpublished or in the form of theses, and second, to look at them as a whole and to attempt to draw some general conclusions about the effects of two classes of psychotropic drugs in children (the stimulants and the phenothiazines or major tranquilizers).

The studies fall into two broad groups as defined by their locus of prosecution: (1) Montreal Children's Hospital, by the senior author with Drs. Weiss, Minde, and Douglas and (2) the Children's Research Center, University of Illinois by the senior author with Dr. Sprague and students. Though defined by locus, the two groups also have important differences in experimental design and methodology which are set out in Table 12-1.

In summarizing these differences it may be said that while the Montreal studies are characterized by less meticulous experimental control (such as dosage, testing at the time of maximum drug effect, ensuring drug ingestion, and so forth) and by the use of more error-prone and functionally impure measures, they have the advantage of larger numbers and subjects, of longer sampling of behavior and cognitive function, of chronic rather than acute drug administration, and of a greater range of measures. In short, each group of studies has strengths and weaknesses and, thus, pooling of the results of both should add greater validity to the findings.

RESULTS AND DISCUSSION

There were sixteen studies in all, four of which were carried out in Montreal. Several of the twelve Illinois studies took the form of student theses

---

* Assisted by Robert L. Sprague, Gabrielle Weiss, Klans Minde.

Note: The studies described here were supported by USPH Grants MH 07346 and HD 03598; National Health and Welfare (Ottawa) grant to Dr. Weiss; the Canadian Mental Health Association; Smith, Kline and French, Ltd., Montreal; CIBA, Montreal and Summit, New Jersey; the Quebec Society for Emotionally Disturbed Children; the Canadian Medical Research Council and the Montreal Children's Hospital Research Fund.

TABLE 12-1
MAIN FEATURES OF MONTREAL AND ILLINOIS STUDIES

	Montreal, Quebec	Champaign, Illinois
1. *Subjects* (Ss)		
a. Source, IQ, Age, Diagnosis	Psychiatric outpatients of normal IQ at a pediatric hospital, hyperactivity a cardinal symptom. Most had associated symptoms of hyperkinetic syndrome. Age 6 to 12 years.	Children of normal IQ in special classes for emotionally disturbed children mostly antisocial behavior disorders. Age 6 to 11 years.
b. N	Large (>40)	Mostly small (<20)
2. *Drug*		
a. Design	Between Ss	Within Ss (crossover) with drug order counterbalanced or controlled
b. Type	Double-blind—simple (Drug/Placebo)	Double-blind—complex (Drug A/Drug B/Placebo/No-Drug)
c. Administration	Chronic (4 to 12 weeks)	Acute, 1 dose only
d. Dosage	Individual, titrated by effect	Fixed usually mg/kg, often several levels
e. Administered By	Parents (oral)	Usually research staff (oral)
f. Time of Testing	2 to 6 hours after administering	1½ to 2½ hours after administering
3. *Dependent Variables* (Measure of Drug Effect)		
a. Design	Repeated measures—simple (pre-drug and on-drug)	Repeated measures—complex
b. Statistic	ANCOVA	ANOVA
c. Behavior (Clinical)	Mostly mother's ratings	Mostly direct observation (time sampling) or automated measurements.
d. Cognitive Function	Mostly standard psychological tests yielding >30 scores	Special laboratory measures, automated, testing fewer functions, yielding <5 scores
e. Sampling of Behavior or Function	Several days or hours	<1 hour
4. *Other (Predictor) Variables*	Many clinical, demographic, neurological, family, etc.	Usually none

done under the direction of two of us (RLS and JSW). While all the Montreal studies combined clinical and "laboratory" type of observations, six of the Illinois studies were purely clinical and four purely laboratory. No attempt will be made to describe each study but the main features and findings of each are summarized in Table 12-2. For further details, readers are referred to the original papers or theses (unpublished papers are available from their senior authors) or a recent review of the Illinois studies by Sprague, and Werry (8). The emphasis will rather be on presenting an overview of the findings, drawing attention to similarities and differences, and on making some generalizations. The authors have in certain instances looked a little beyond the data such as accepting as valid certain consistent trends across studies even though no individual finding may have achieved statistical significance. This has been done with the hope of inducing some hypotheses which might prove heuristic for progress in pediatric psychopharmacological research.

The overall conclusions deriving from these studies are as follows.

Stimulants (Dextroamphetamine, Methylphenidate and Deanol)

While a majority of subjects used in these studies were hyperkinetic or so-called minimal brain dysfunction children, the response of the few children in other diagnostic groups such as those of schizoid personality suggests that the effects of these drugs is probably not confined to the former type of child and that it would be premature to study only those children.

In the *clinical* or naturalistic situation, when the drugs are effective they have the following effects.

> 1. They improve *attention in the home* (11, 12) and especially in the classroom (1, 9, 13, 14, 17). Even where the results do not achieve statistical significance the score for attention is consistently higher across studies for the stimulant drugs than for placebo. Thus, in the five Illinois studies (1, 9, 13, 14, 17) where classroom attention data was obtained, the mean score for methylphenidate was in all cases higher than for placebo.
>
> 2. Children taking these drugs are perceived as *generally improved* by adults responsible for their care such as mothers (11, 12), teachers (1, 9, 13, 14, 17), and recreation workers (17).
>
> 3. Stimulants *reduce inappropriate behavior* such as "hyperactivity" (globally defined) and *increase appropriate behavior* in the home (11, 12) and in the classroom. This beneficial effect in the classroom though it was never significant was present in four of five Illinois studies (1, 9, 13, 17) (the exception was a study [14] involving only one subject) and in the only study using deanol (6) and having as locus a residential treatment center.
>
> While the above generalization appears to be accurate at the moment, several of the Illinois studies also suggest (though rather weakly) that when objectively described and observed not all kinds of deviant behavior are necessarily reduced and the action of these drugs may well be differential especially where motor activity

TABLE 12.2
SUMMARY OF INDIVIDUAL STUDIES

Author(s)	Subjects	N (Total)	Drug(s)	a. Dose b. Time on Drug at Retest	Check on Ingestion	Experimental Design a. Drug b. Dependent Variables c. Statistics	Time of Testing After Ingestion	Dependent Variables a. Clinical b. Laboratory	Drug Results a. Clinical b. Laboratory	Other Results Side Effects
A. MONTREAL 1. Werry et al. (16)	Hyperactive (m.b.d.) children 6 to 12 years, psychiatric outpatient clinic	39	Chlorpromazine Placebo	a. Individual t.i.d. b. 4 to 12 weeks	Urine test for CPZ	a. Between Ss b. Repeated measures (pre-drug on-drug) c. ANCOVA	Variable	a. Mother's ratings* Teacher's ratings Classroom observations* b. Vigilance, psychometric, & motor tests	a. Hyperactivity↓ Global Improvement (mothers) Teacher ratings ?No change b. Improved classroom behavior No effect on cognitive or motor function	1. Diagnostic background, neurological variables did not influence drug effect. 2. CPZ or placebo guessed correctly in all but three cases. 3. Side effects: sleepiness, photosensitivity.
2. Werry et al. (15)	Same as #1 plus 10 normals	57	Chlorpromazine No drug: Dextroamphetamine Placebo	a. b. Same as #1	Mother's affirmation	a. Between Ss b. Single c. ANOVA ANCOVA	Variable	a. Behavior observations in playroom* b. None	a. Activity↓ Chlorpromazine v No-drug Dextroamphetamine-Placebo	—
3. Weiss et al. (12)	Same as #1	38	Dextroamphetamine Placebo	a. Indiv b.i.d. b. 3 to 5 weeks	Same	a. Between Ss b. Repeated (pre-drug & on-drug) c. ANCOVA, T²	1 to 4 hours	a. Mother's ratings* b. Vigilance, psychometric, & motor tests	a. Hyperactivity↓ Distractibility↓ Global improvement b. Overall improvement in cognitive function	1, 2. Same as #1 3. Side effects: insomnia weight loss (21%)
4. Weiss et al. (11)	Same as #1	51	Dextroamphetamine Placebo	a. Indiv b.i.d. b. 4 to 6 weeks	Same	a. Between Ss b. Repeated pre-drug & on-drug c. ANCOVA	1 to 4 hours	Same as #3	Same as #3 but more marked; also included vigilance & motor function	1. Same as #1 3. Side effects: insomnia, anorexia, weight loss, stomachache, toxic psychosis (1)
B. ILLINOIS 5. Sprague et al. (10)	Institutionalized male retardates (mild-moderate) mean age 12 years	8	Dextroamphetamine Placebo No drug	a. Fixed 10 mg b. one dose	Given by research staff	a. Within Ss (crossover) b. Repeated each condition c. ANOVA	2 hours	a. None b. Automated, discrimination learning task Direct measure seat activity during task	a. — b. No effect on accuracy, latency, activity↓ Practice & drug effect confounded	Side effects Toxic Psychosis (1)

TABLE 12-2—Continued
SUMMARY OF INDIVIDUAL STUDIES—Continued

	Author(s)	Subjects	N (Total)	Drug(s)	a. Dose b. Time on Drug at Retest	Check on Ingestion	Experimental Design a. Drug b. Dependent Variables c. Statistics	Time of Testing After Ingestion	Dependent Variables a. Clinical b. Laboratory	Drug Results a. Clinical b. Laboratory	Other Results Side Effects
6.	Sprague et al. (10)	Same as #5	24	Methylphenidate Thioridazine Placebo	a. Fixed .5/1.3 mg/kg	Same as #5	Same as #5 except drug order counterbalanced	2 hours	a. None b. Same as #3	a. — b. Thioridazine latency↓; Methylphenidate-Placebo	Side effects: methylphenidate, toxic psychosis (1), stomachache, nausea (1), thioridazine, sleepiness (1)
7.	Gonsky (5)	Boys with behavior disorders in special class Normal IQ	7	Methylphenidate No drug	a. Fixed 15 mg b. One dose	Same as #5	Same as #6	2 hours	a. None b. Same as #3	a. — b. ↑Drug reduces distractibility	
8.	Werry (13)	Same	10	Methylphenidate Phenobarbital Placebo	a. Fixed 10 mg 45 mg b. 4 days	Mother's affirmation Remaining pills counted	Same as #6	2 hours	a. Classroom behavior observations* Teachers' ratings b. None	a. Methylphenidate noise↓?; attention↑; Teachers' ratings↑; Phenobarbital-Placebo	Paranoid reaction on methylphenidate (1)
9.	Schickedanze (7)	Institutionalized male retardates (mild-moderate) mean age 12 years	24	Thioridazine Methylphenidate Placebo	a. 1.1/.45 mg/kg b. One dose	Given by research staff	Same as #6	2 hours	a. None b. Marble-dropping task Seat activity	a. — b. Performance Thioridazine↓ Methylphenidate↑ Activity no effect	Mental age no effect
10.	Breitmeyer (2)	Same (6 to 20 years)	54	Same as #9	Same as #9	Same as #9	Same as #6	2 hours	a. None b. Discrimination learning task, Telemetric motion transducer, seat activity	a. — b. ? Long term (48 hrs) storage impaired by both drugs Methylphenidate activity↓	Degree of hyperactivity did not affect drug action
11.	Davis et al. (3)	Same but profoundly retarded and all with Stereotypies	9	Same as #9	Same as #9	Same as #9	Same as #6	2 hours & 4 hours	a. Dayroom behavior observations* b. Telemetric motion transducer	Thioridazine stereotypis↓ but not other motor activity	

#	Author	Subjects	N	Drug/Condition	Dose	Design	Duration	Measures	Results	Comments
12.	Barnes (1)	Boys with behavior disorders in special class (normal IQ) 6 to 11 years	12	Same as #9	a. Meth. .25 & .35, Thio. et al. .75 & 1.1 mg/kg	Same as #9	Same as #6	2 hours	a. Classroom behavior observations* Teachers' ratings b. Automated recall task, seat activity	a. Methylphenidate: attention teacher-pupil interaction, teachers' ratings↑, Thioridazine-Placebo b. Methylphenidate-accuracy↑, latency↓, activity↓; Thioridazine accuracy↓, latency↑, activity↑, placebo	No dosage effect
13.	Werry (14)	Same as #12	1	Same as #9	Meth. .45, Thio. 1.1 mg/kg 6 doses/drug	Same as #9	Same as #6 but single subject	2 hours	a. Classroom behavior observations* Teachers' ratings	a. N too small for significant Trends same as #12	
14.	Werry et al. (17)	Same as #12	12	Same as #9	Same as #12	Same as #9	Same as #6	2 hours	a. Classroom behavior* Teachers' ratings Recreation ratings b. Discrimination learning	a. Trends same as #12 b. Accuracy increased with methylphenidate	
15.	Sprague et al. (9)	Same as #12	16	Methylphenidate Placebo No drug	.1, .2, .3, .4 mg/kg	Same as #9	Same as #6	2 hours	Same as #12	a. Trends same as #12 b. Dosage x difficulty interaction	.3 mg/kg ? optimal dosage for clinical & laboratory effects
16.	Myers (6)	Institutionalized emotionally disturbed boys age (i) 13 (ii) 8	2	a. Thioridazine Placebo b. Deanol/Placebo	Given by R.N. a. (i) 25 mg b.i.d. (ii) 100 mg b.i.d. b. 4 day/cycle 2 cycles		Same as #6 but 2 discrete single subject designs	1 to 4 hours	a. Cottage behavior observations* Child care staff ratings	a. (i) Thioridazine? depresses all behavior except interaction↑ (ii) Deanol? increases all behavior	

* Reliability demonstrated.

is concerned. In three of the five Illinois studies (1, 13, 14) hyperactive behaviors in the classroom actually increased, though not significantly, on methylphenidate, while in one (17) it was unchanged despite overall behavioral improvement. This is of particular interest since the stimulants would be predicted to be capable of increasing not only vigilance but also activity level. Thus, whether a child is perceived as "improved" or less "hyperactive" will depend on the algebraic summation of the increases in appropriate and deviant behavior. However, this is rather speculative and requires much more study using behavioral measures which include a number of "good" and "bad" behaviors.

4. The drugs increase positive and decrease negative teacher-pupil *interaction* in the classroom. Though only once statistically significant (1) this was the pattern in four of the five Illinois studies in which this was measured (1, 9, 14, 17).

In the *laboratory* or one-to-one test situation the following effects appear.

1. The *latency* of responding or reaction time is sometimes decreased (1) but never significantly increased (10,17).

2. Task *performance* is improved under certain conditions: (a) where the task is a simple repetitive motor one (7); (b) where the level of task difficulty is optimal, so that the subject is performing neither at floor or ceiling and where the intervals of potential increment in performance are small and do not require a higher level of cognitive organization, nor are subject to some threshold effect (1,11,17); and (c) where the task consists of a battery of standard psychological tests of intelligence and perceptuomotor function. While few of the individual tests are significantly changed, the overall pattern across tests is significantly in the direction of improvement (11,12).

From these studies it is hypothesized that task performance would be most likely to improve when one or several of the following functions are involved: vigilance, speed of responding, short-term memory, resistance to fatigue or boredom, ability to ignore distracting stimuli (5, 11, 17), and simple motor skills. Some preliminary data suggests in short-term but impairment in long-term storage (2).

3. *Seat activity* during performance of a task is reduced on some occasions (2,10), probably when task performance is improved, and thus reduction in seat activity may be a secondary effect or diminution in motor overflow.

In summary it may be noted that there is in most instances a good correlation between clinical and laboratory measures with improvement of behavior or function being apparent in both.

The most parsimonious hypothesis of the neuropsychological action of the stimulant drugs deriving from these findings and one consistent with pharmacological theory is that the stimulants *increase the level of arousal*, thus leading to improvement in behavior or function when this increment is within the optimal range (4). It follows from this hypothesis that the total amount of behavior (if it could be measured) may increase (6) and that performance may be deteriorated at certain high arousal levels. It thus becomes necessary to posit that hyperactive children are, from a neuropsychological point of view, underaroused, for which there is some evidence (see Ch. 8). Possibly these drugs also: *improve motivation,* which is the qualitiative counterpart of arousal.

Phenothiazines (Chlorpromazine and Thioridazine)

In the *clinical* or naturalistic situation these drugs have the following effects.

   1. Have no consistent effect on *attention* in the home (16) or in the classroom (1, 14, 17).
   2. Cause hyperactive, aggressive children to be perceived as "improved" by mothers (16) and by recreation workers (17) but less clearly so by teachers (all three appropriate Illinois studies [1, 14, 17] did show an improvement in teachers' global ratings of classroom behavior, but these changes were very small and not significant).
   3. *Reduce inappropriate motor behavior*—"hyperactivity"—as perceived by mothers (16) and stereotypies in retardates as observed directly (3). The effects in the home (16), classroom (1, 14, 17), playroom (15), or residential treatment center (6) are inconsistent both for motor behavior and for deviant behavior of all kinds, so it would seem best to assume for the moment that they are without beneficial effect on deviant behavior with the possible exception of motor behavior.
   4. Significantly *reduce positive teacher-pupil interaction* (two of three Illinois studies (1, 17), the exception being a single subject study [14]). At the same time, the amount of negative pupil-teacher interaction appears slightly though not significantly increased in all three Illinois studies (1, 14, 17). However these findings were the opposite of those for the single subject study in a residential treatment setting where the subject was a twelve-year-old schizophrenic boy (6).

In the *laboratory or one-to-one situation* these drugs

   1. increase the *latency* of responding (1, 10);
   2. deteriorate task *performance* under certain conditions (a) where the task is a simple, repetitive motor one (7), (b) where the level of task difficulty is optimal (1), and (c) where memory processes are involved (sketchy evidence only [2]).
   3. Have no consistent effect on *motor activity* (1, 2, 3, 7, 9, 10, 11) when measured directly (i.e. by mechanical or electronic means).

Unlike the stimulants, the correlation between laboratory and clinical studies of phenothiazines is not particularly good. The former (laboratory) tend to show, if anything, a slight deterioration of performance and the latter (clinical) a more mixed effect with improvement probably exceeding impairment. However, the laboratory studies are concerned chiefly with cognitive function and the clinical with behavior and, as has often been suggested, the improvement in behavior with phenothiazines may well be achieved by a simple depression of central nervous system function involving not only behavior but also cognitive functions. If a child is hyperactive, reduction of motor activity may appear as improvement even if there is slight impairment of cognitive function. This lack of conformity of findings may be attributable to acute as opposed to chronic effects of these drugs since the depression of task performance was characteristic of Illinois rather than the Montreal studies. However, when the complexity of the multivariate process involved in performance is considered (see below), effects on task performance in the home or classroom may be quite different from those observed in the laboratory, and there is little information in these studies on cognitive performance in the naturalistic situation except the measures of attention where the effects are inconsistent (1, 14, 16, 17). Many of these studies (1, 2, 7, 10, 11, 12) show the phenothiazines to be inferior to the stimulants in effects on behavior and cognitive function. The relationship to placebo is less clear and in the majority of instances the differences do not achieve statistical significance, rather it is more the overall pattern which is suggestive of impairment of cognitive function and/or certain kinds of behavior (other than hyperactivity). Furthermore, these findings are valid only for the type of children studied here (hyperkinetic, unsocialized aggressive and/or retarded children). In particular psychotic children may well react differently as one Illinois study suggests (16), though it should be noted that the commonest use of these drugs is in children of the former types.

Subject to these limitations then, it is hypothesized that the phenothiazines act as *weak depressants of arousal level* and thus that hyperactive children, already underaroused, would be expected to show reduction in both behavior and cognitive function. The former may or may not appear as an improvement.

GENERAL COMMENTS

1. Drug effects upon behavior and cognitive function in children appear to be difficult to detect in normal clinical dosage. While this may be due to inadequate dosage in the Illinois group, the use of the individually titrated method (pushing medication to the point of maximum therapeutic effect or the appearance of side effects) in the Montreal group as well as the occurrence of side effects in several of the Illinois studies (10, 13) make this unlikely as an explanation. Rather it must be assumed that drugs act in a multivariate situation where most of the variance is due to sources other than drugs notably individual differences, environmental effects, and above all error of measurement. This means that though clear trends may be apparent, statistically significant results are difficult to obtain. In this latter respect, it is of interest to note that the less reliable and less atomistic the measure, the greater chances of observing drug effects. Thus, the Montreal measure of "Mother's impression of overall improvement" has consistently shown drug effects (11, 12, 16). This probably relates to the fact that the mother (or teacher) acts as an online averaging computer in which the input data has the advantage of being based on long runs and of being multisituational. This helps to reduce the large error of measurement.

2. A large number of fundamental methodological problems make drug studies very often a hit or miss affair further reducing the chances of observing drug effects and even more of obtaining generality of findings across investigators or studies. Some of these problems are lack of knowledge about such basic pharmacological data as optimal dosage, duration of drug effect, factors influencing drug absorption, the lack of a standard set of valid and reliable measures of behavior and cognitive

function, and the primitive state of measurement of variables predictive of drug effect such as diagnosis, neurological status, etcetera which might enable the selection of subsamples containing only drug responsive children.

3. The theoretical issues surrounding drug action need clarification so that dependent variable measures may be developed to test the functions suggested by theory as being influenced by drugs. These theories may be physicochemical, neuropsychological, or psychological-behavioral. Typical clinical measures are generally too global to permit testing hypothesis about fundamental drug action, and functionally pure laboratory tests on behavioral measures would appear to be potentially more heuristic from the point of view of theory.

4. While no doubt consistent at a pharmacological level, the more molar effects of psychotropic drugs on task performance in children are often inconsistent because of the multivariate determinants of children's behavior. The observed effects are due to a complex interaction between (a) social environmental variables (value system of observers, distracting stimuli, etc.); (b) the nature of the task or activity (motivational qualities, difficulty, specific psychological or motor processes involved—some are apparently not drug sensitive while others are, etc.); (c) drug variables (dosage, absorption, acute chronic action, duration of action, drug sequencing effects, etc.); and (d) subject variables (arousal level, diagnosis, CNS status, etc.). Thus, on some tasks and/or in some children a drug may impair function while in others it may improve function, though more often it seems to have no effect.

5. Because of the complexity of the multivariate interaction described above, clinical studies which regard drugs as a treatment in themselves rather than a way of altering the state of the organism within a social learning context are likely to underestimate the value of pharmacotherapy in children. At best, a drug can probably only make certain behaviors more or less probable, their firm establishment or extinction requires a deliberate structuring of crucial environmental variables within some adequate theory of social learning.

REFERENCES

1. BARNES, K.R., SPRAGUE, R.L., AND WERRY, J.S.: Effects of methylphenidate and thioridazine on learning, reaction time and activity level in hyperactive emotionally disturbed children. Unpublished bachelor's thesis, University of Illinois, 1968.
2. BREITMEYER, J.M.: Effects of thioridazine and methylphenidate on learning and retention in retardates. Unpublished master's thesis, University of Illinois, 1969.
3. DAVIS, K.V., SPRAGUE, R.L., AND WERRY, J.S.: Stereotyped behavior and activity level in severe retardates: The effect of drugs. *Amer J Ment Defic* 73:721–727, 1969.
4. DUFFY, E.: The psychological significance of the concept of "arousal" or "activation." *Psychol Rev,* 64:265–275, 1957.
5. GONSKY, M.: The effects of methylphenidate on hyperactivity and learning. Unpublished bachelor's thesis, University of Illinois, 1967.
6. MYERS, H.F.: The effect of thioridazine (Mellaril) and deanol (Deaner) in the treatment of behavior disorder children in a residential treatment program. Unpublished bachelor's thesis, Claremont Men's College, 1968.
7. SCHICKEDANZE, D.I.: Effects of thioridazine and methylphenidate on performance of a motor task and concurrent motor activity in retarded boys. Unpublished bachelor's thesis, University of Illinois, 1967.
8. SPRAGUE, R.L., AND WERRY, J.S.: Methodology of psychopharmacological studies with

the retarded. In N.R. Ellis (Ed.), *International Review of Research in Mental Retardation,* Vol. 5. New York: Acadamic Press, in press.

9. SPRAGUE, R.L., WERRY, J.S., GREENWOLD, W., AND JONES, H.: Effect of methylphenidate in different dosages on learning, activity level and behavior in emotionally disturbed children. Unpublished paper, University of Illinois.
10. SPRAGUE, R.L., WERRY, J.S., AND SCOTT, K.G.: Effects of dextroamphetamine on activity level and learning in retarded children. Paper presented at Midwestern Psychological Association, Chicago, 1967.
11. WEISS, G., MINDE, K., WERRY, J.S., DOUGLAS, V., AND SYKES, D.: A comparison of the effects of chlorpromazine, dextroamphetamine and methylphenidate on the behavior and intellectual function of hyperactive children. Paper presented at the annual meeting of the Canadian Psychiatric Associatin, Toronto, 1969.
12. WEISS, G., WERRY, J.S., MINDE, K., DOUGLAS, V., AND SYKES, D.: The effects of dextroamphetamine and chlorpromazine on behavior and intellectual functioning. *J. Child Psychol Psychiat,* in press.
13. WERRY, J.S.: Effect of methylphenidate and phenobarbital on the behavior of hyperactive agressive children. Paper presented at the annual meeting of the American Psychiatric Association, Detroit, 1967.
14. WERRY, J.S.: The effect of methylphenidate and thioridazine on classroom behavior in a single subject design. Unpublished paper, University of Illinois.
15. WERRY, J.S., MINDE, K., MARTIN, J., AND WEISS, G.: Studies on hyperactive child: Direct observation of motor behavior in social isolation. Unpublished paper, University of Illinois.
16. WERRY, J.S., WEISS, G., DOUGLAS, V., AND MARTIN, J.: Studies on the hyperactive child. III. The effect of chlorpromazine upon behavior and learning ability. *J Amer Acad Child Psychiat,* 5:292–312, 1966.
17. WERRY, J.S., SPRAGUE, R.L., AND EPSTEIN, M.: The effect of methylphenidate and thioridazine on classroom behavior, distractibility and learning. Unpublished paper, University of Illinois.

II

Concluding Discussion on Learning Facilitators

C. KEITH CONNERS

Dr. Haward's presentation is in several respects a model of good investigation of the psychological properties of drugs. In the first place, he has carefully selected a sample of subjects with a common symptomatic complaint and differentiated them from subjects with superficially similar complaints but fundamentally different underlying psychological processes. This first step of attempting to achieve diagnostic homogeneity involves a real understanding of the personality processes of the patients and not a simple categorization based upon a manifest behavior complex. Any meaningful investigation of psychotropic drugs requires that such a procedure be followed, otherwise lack of effects in some subjects, together with opposite effects in different subjects can erroneously lead to the acceptance of the null hypothesis. Interindividual variance in drug studies is undoubtedly the most significant factor in the detection of drug effects, especially if the action of the drug is expected to be a subtle one as in the case of diphenylhydantoin.

Secondly, he has provided an operational definition of the dependent variable—in this case concentration ability—which is both highly objective and relevant to "real-life" behavior. It is quite easy to devise very objective but trivial indices of psychological processes. The simulated control-tower method has a long history of practical application and testing of demonstrable relevance to activities requiring concentration. In this sense, the test has high face validity and high criterion validity.

Thirdly, he has based the measurement procedure and the interpretation of results on a general theory of information processing which allows for an understanding of the phenomena in the most general terms, as opposed to a limited, *ad hoc* theory. In my opinion, information theory can provide a powerful approach to the investigation of psychotropic drugs, especially their effects on cognitive functioning. However, Dr. Haward has made an important contribution by linking this approach to the kind of clinical observation with which most of us are familiar. The linking of a phenomenological concept such as "concentration" with a more general view of information processing immediately illuminates a process that is both familiar clinically and elusive to understand in objective terms.

Fourthly, a careful baseline of performance was first established before the drug was introduced into the man-machine system, and both the effects of drug activity and drug withdrawal are clearly observable in the changing performance levels of the subjects.

Finally, Dr. Haward has included a comparison of two active drugs and shown that they have differential effects on performance levels as a function of time—a finding with very important practical consequences in applied situations requiring concentrative ability.

Perhaps the one objection to his paper is the lack of appropriate statistical analyses to complement the graphical demonstration of the changes. Either information-transmission measures or appropriate inferential statistics would have added to the persuasiveness of the study. It is important to note that when one compares changes from baseline to drug with placebo to drug, the relevant statistic compares the net changes, or differences between the change scores. It is quite possible that a change from baseline to drug would reach the .05 level of significance and changes from baseline to placebo were nonsignificant, but the net difference between these two sets of changes was nonsignificant. It is this latter comparison that one is really concerned with.

Dr. Werry has provided cogent arguments for the experimental study of drugs in children in which variables of interest are systematically manipulated, while other variables are controlled by using the subject as his own control. Such intrasubject designs have great merit in a field in which diagnostic heterogeneity is so ever present. In many ways, however, one finds a conflict between the need for experimental control and the clinical obligation to the patient, and it is only under exceptional circumstances that more basic studies of the type described by Dr. Werry are feasible. This problem is illustrated by the issue of fixed dosage schedules as opposed to individual titration of dosage. It is quite true that the effects of dose level of a drug can be systematically investigated using a fixed dose of different levels for different groups, or at several points in time for the same subjects, provided that measures (such as activity level) are available that do not suffer from practice effects or that appropriate counterbalancing is arranged to control for sequence and practice effects. However, in the latter case one must assume lack of interaction effects between sequence and dosage. In the former case (separate groups with different dosages) one faces the possibility, especially with small N's, that many subjects will be assigned a dosage that does not give an effect, especially if the effects have a narrow margin of dose-related activity or are all-or-none responses. This is not unusual with children, many of whom will not respond to amphetamine, say, until a certain dose level is achieved and who may show undesirable side effects at a slightly higher level. In other words, without individual titration the probability of hitting the right child with the right dosage in a random assignment may be very small, and one may erroneously conclude that the drug is ineffective or effective only for a small number of patients, when in fact, a careful individual adjustment might achieve much better results. This latter mode of approach, so typical of clinical studies, necessarily sacrifices a certain degree of control and has other problems associated with it.

Dr. Werry has also pointed to a most significant issue by electing to study basic molecular learning processes, linked to basic studies within experimental child psychology, at the same time that more molar observation of behavior are made. This insures that the laboratory changes have some relevance to the child's general behavior in a broader environmental context.

Dr. Smith has called our attention to an interesting and neglected class of drugs in the anti–petit-mal drugs and their possible role in learning. The criticism regarding appropriate statistical analyses applies to these studies, but the results indicate that there are fruitful questions for further research to be explored with these drugs. While it first appeared that the studies were designed to test the effect on learning of ethosuximide as it relates to different EEG patterns, it is not possible to conclude that the fourteen and six patterns have any bearing on the results of drug treatment (as Dr. Smith made clear in his presentation).

PART IV

BIOCHEMICALS

Chapter 13

Central Nervous System Metabolism, Drug Action, and Higher Functions

WALTER B. ESSMAN

The interrelationship between psychoactive drugs, brain metabolism, and specific higher functions in animals and man has been explored extensively over the past twenty years, and one possible goal of such exploration has been the emergence of meaningful hypotheses which may serve as a basis for defining psychoactive drug action and utilizing such a definition as a basis for description of therapeutic efficiency and therapeutic mechanisms. Such an undertaking is indeed an ambitious one inasmuch as it involves a broad spectrum of metabolic alterations in the brain which attend both the primary and secondary effects of psychoactive drugs, as well as possibly resulting from the consequence of peripheral drug action. Behavioral functions, similarly, may be dealt with in terms of correlaries with either central biochemical events, altered by drug action, or their possible interaction which underlies some physiological process or processes mediating behavioral change. It will not be our purpose to speculate further on the broad implications of the interrelationships between drug effects, brain metabolism, and behavior but to focus upon one series of interrelationships which may have possible significance for clinical problems and therapeutic indications at one end of a spectrum which, at its other end, concerns some basic interrelationships between brain metabolism, brain electrolytes, and drug effects. The system which we have chosen to deal with in this discussion involves some basic experiments from our laboratory, which may serve to illustrate the possible relationship between two compounds utilized clinically in the treatment of different phases of manic-depressive disorders. These compounds are lithium carbonate, which has been indicated as effective in the treatment of manic behavior; the first report of the clinical use of lithium salts resulted following initial testing in guinea pigs, in which it was noted that the result of such treatment was lethargy and protection from urea-induced convulsions (8). In the manic phase of manic-depressive psychosis, lithium salts were observed to reduce restlessness, irritability, euphoria, and excitement, without producing drowsiness. The clini-

Note: The work reported in this paper was supported, in part, by grants HD 03493 and Biomedical Sciences Support Grant 5-SO5-FR-07064-03 from the National Institutes of Health and by a grant from the Council for Tobacco Research (U.S.A.).

The author wishes to acknowledge the technical assistance of M.I. Golod and the research assistance of S. G. Essman.

cal efficacy of such treatment has been confirmed in a number of studies (23), although the mechanism by which such compounds act is still open to considerable speculation. Another compound chosen within the context of the present discussion was imipramine (Tofranil®), an agent which has been utilized with considerable success in the treatment of the depressive phases of manic-depressive disorders. This compound is of interest in that it does not significantly modify the behavior of normal animals (11) and results only in the very weak behavioral sedation (4). The choice of these compounds for discussion and consideration in specific experimental procedures rests upon certain parallels that emerge both in their clinical use as well as in their behavioral and biochemical effects. On a behavioral level, the specific function considered was the process of memory consolidation, the interference with which, by specific agents and/or events, has been shown to be modifiable by certain psychoactive drugs and, particularly, in this regard, we have shown that a variety of different, clinically effective, antidepressant agents serve to attenuate the amnesic effect upon behavior produced by postexperiential treatment with electroconvulsive shock (14a). The use of electroconvulsive shock treatment clinically is well known and has been well documented in the literature with some considerable speculation as to the mechanism or mechanisms by which the sequelae of such treatment produce amnesia and/or alterations in cognitive function. A specific interrelationship between the compounds considered in the present discussion, lithium salts and imipramine, and electroconvulsive shock (ECS), has been proposed (56), and specific brain substrates, which possibly parallel such a proposed interrelationship, have been considered.

The purpose of the present discussion and the presentation of the results of specific experimental findings is to propose a model system within which central nervous system changes, resulting from drug action, may be related to at least one behavioral function affected by such drug treatment and possibly finding a source of explanation in these central changes. We do not intend to exclude the many other hypotheses and sources of data available by the presentation of solely our own findings and perhaps these findings will suggest many more questions than those few which they do answer. However, the complexity of the many metabolic events which parallel the function of the central nervous system and the increased complexity by which such events are altered by psychoactive drugs have largely been responsible for directing our efforts in the exploration of those specific problems along those lines presented.

The effect of ECS upon two biochemical events, which may be considered of importance in the regulation of specific cognitive behaviors, has been demonstrated in a number of previous studies. The effect of ECS on the level of brain ribonucleic acid (RNA) was shown in cats, wherein the concentration of this nucleic acid was generally decreased in several regions of the brain (40a). Subsequent studies in our laboratory, utilizing mice, have consistently shown that ECS results in regional, as well as whole-brain decreases in the conventration of RNA (12 to 14a). This decrease was apparent up to at least one hour following the administration of a single transcorneal ECS of 10 to 20 ma applied for 200 msec and resulting in a full clonic-tonic convulsion. ECS has also been shown to elevate whole-brain levels of serotonin (5-HT) (20a), and this finding has also consistently emerged in our studies, utilizing mice where, in addition, ECS effects upon 5-hydroxyindoleacetic acid, the major end metabolite of 5-HT in brain, and 5-HT turnover, have also been altered up to one hour following ECS (16, 17). A relationship between the changes, produced by ECS, in RNA level and 5-HT concentration has been shown such that a significant negative correlation between these ECS-induced alterations has emerged (13). The basis of this negative relationship has been further clarified on the basis of physical evidence for the binding of the amine to the nucleic acid under several conditions. (6), and the major endogenous source of this relationship appears to reside in the diencephalon and structures of the limbic system. In this regard we have shown that single cells of the diencephalon showed decreases of approximately $7.1\mu\mu g$ ($\sim 21\%$) as a result of ECS, with a corresponding increase of 5-HT turnover time in this region (17). The relationship between the administration of post-training ECS and the subsequent retention of a response or responses for which such pre-ECS training was given have suggested that this event serves as one of several possible conditions sufficient to interfere with the consolidation of the neural memory trace. The relationship between alterations in RNA and 5-HT may not necessarily be causal in terms of a memory consolidation model. However, a number of studies have suggested that changes in these CNS constituents may parallel the amnesic events caused by ECS and attenuation of these biochemical changes by pharmacological means also serves to antagonize the amnesia induced by ECS (13, 14, 14a, 16, 17).

An example of the changes in RNA and 5-HT resulting from ECS may be seen in Figure 13-1, wherein whole-brain levels of the former are reduced and for the latter are increased. These values were obtained from mice twenty minutes after the administration of a single 10 ma ECS.

Within the context of the present consideration given lithium salts and the role played by these in the possible alteration of cognitive behavior, several studies utilizing lithium salts were conducted in mice. In an initial study either physiological saline or lithium carbonate (2.35 mEq/kg) were administered by intraperitoneal (i.p.) injection, either sixty minutes or thirty minutes prior to a single training trial, in an apparatus designed to provide for the establishment of a conditioned passive avoidance response (15). The technique basically consisted of placing animals individually into a clear lucite

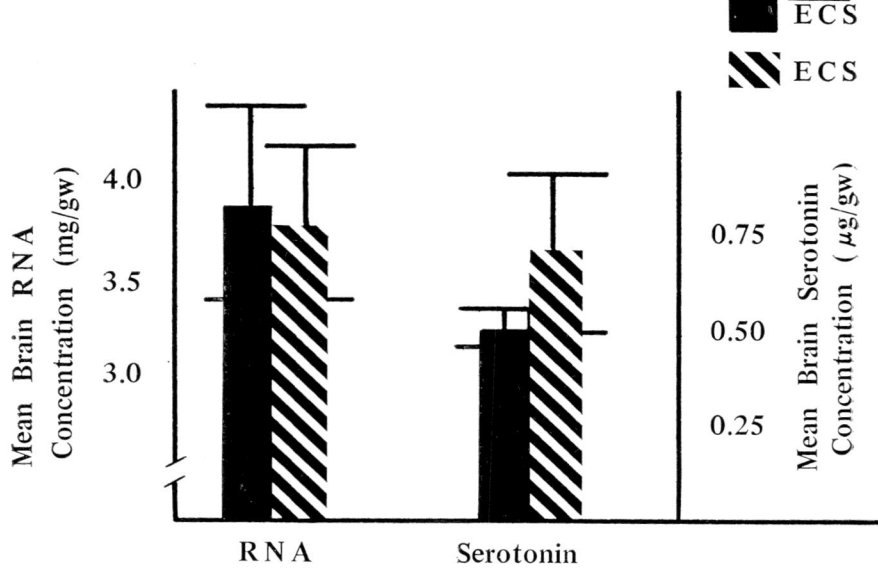

FIGURE 13–1. Mean ($\pm \sigma$) brain RNA and serotonin levels in mice given ECS or sham-ECS.

vestibule adjoining a larger darkened opaque chamber, entry into which was provided by a two-inch diameter hole between the two chambers; the floor of the larger chamber consisted of grids wired in series through a cam-operated grid scrambler to a 95 v power supply, which provided for a 3.0 ma foot shock to the paws of the mouse after entry with all four paws had been made. The animals were removed from the apparatus immediately following the foot shock, and at ten seconds following foot shock a single transcorneal ECS was given (10 ma, 200 msec). Control animals, under each of these conditions, were given sham-ECS ($\overline{ECS}$), consisting of application of the transcorneal electrodes without passage of current. On the training trial the response latency (interval between placement into the outer vestibule and entry into the larger chamber where foot shock was given) was measured. Testing trials were given to determine the extent to which animals showed retention of the conditioned avoidance behavior at 24, 48, and 72 hours following the training trial. The results of this study are summarized in Table 13-1, where the median response latency on the training trial and each of the testing trials and the percent incidence of conditioned response retention are shown. It may be noted that saline-treated control animals showed the characteristic predicted retrograde amnesia, as indicated by low testing trial response latencies comparable to that shown on the training trial, and a low incidence of conditioned response retention, as determined throughout by a criterion of a testing trial response latency of sixty seconds, or more. A ceiling latency of 120 seconds was utilized, wherein animals failing to enter the larger chamber, in which

TABLE 13-1

MEDIAN RESPONSE LATENCY AND PER CENT INCIDENCE OF CONDITIONED RESPONSE RETENTION FOR MICE TREATED WITH LITHIUM CARBONATE OR SALINE AND GIVEN POST-TRAINING ECS OR SHAM-ECS (ECS) TESTING TRIALS

Treatment Condition		Training Trial Median Response Latency	24 Hours		48 Hours		72 Hours	
			Median Response Latency	% CR Retention	Median Response Latency	% CR Retention	Median Response Latency	% CR Retention
Saline (0.9%)	ECS	6.0	9.5	5	9.0	5	9.5	5
	ECS	7.5	120.0	90	120.0	100	120.0	100
Li$_2$CO$_3$ (2.35mEq/kg) 60 min P.T.	ECS	7.0	13.0	5	13.0	5	12.0	5
	ECS	6.5	120.0	100	120.0	100	120.0	100
Li$_2$CO$_3$ (2.35mEq/kg) 30 min P.T.	ECS	6.0	12.0	5	15.0	30.5*	17.0	30.5*
	ECS	7.0	120.0	100	120.0	100	120.0	100

*$p < .001$

foot shock was previously given, by this time were removed by hand from the apparatus. The saline-treated control animals given sham-ECS showed a characteristically high incidence of conditioned response retention with a correspondingly high response latency characterizing the conditioned avoidance behavior which the technique was designed to provide for. Those animals treated with lithium carbonate sixty minutes prior to the conditioning trial differed only slightly from the saline-treated controls in that the response latencies of the ECS-treated animals under this condition were very slightly higher on the testing trials. However, criterion incidence of conditioned response retention did not differ from that of the controls. An interesting departure from this effect may be seen among animals treated with lithium carbonate thirty minutes prior to the training trial; at twenty-four hours post-training it appears as if the animals given ECS showed the characteristic retrograde amnesia shown by the saline-treated animals and the lithium carbonate-treated animals injected sixty minutes prior to training. By forty-eight hours, and again at seventy-two hours post-training, over 30 per cent of the animals given ECS showed a reinstatement of the conditioned avoidance behavior, suggesting that the amnesia produced by ECS in animals treated with lithium carbonate under these conditions was only a transient one and that for a significant percentage of the animals there was a reinstatement of retention for the conditioned avoidance response. Lithium carbonate-treated mice given sham-ECS, did not differ from saline-treated control mice given sham-ECS under any of the conditions, suggesting that drug treatment did not affect either the establishment or the retention of conditioned avoidance behavior. The result does, however, indicate that lithium carbonate treatment, at the dose given, within a critical time prior to ECS treatment, provides for only a temporary amnesic effect of post-training ECS. It should be noted that lithium carbonate treatment did not alter the characteristic clonic-tonic convulsion resulting from ECS, nor did it modify the recovery time or duration of postictal depression following ECS treatment; the effect of lithium carbonate treatment, therefore, cannot clearly be ascribed to any modifying properties that it possesses for the convulsive effect of ECS.

Since only trace amounts of lithium ion are found in tissue, it cannot be reasonably assumed that treatment with lithium carbonate appreciably modifies an endogenous lithium level necessary to the maintenance of any specific neural function. It was therefore our purpose, in another series of experiments, to determine the brain tissue lithium concentration following treatment with lithium carbonate. In this study, mice were treated with either 1.18, 2.35, or 4.70 mEq/kg of lithium carbonate, administered intraperitoneally, and were then killed under each dose conditioned at either 15, 30, or 45 minutes following injection. The whole brain was removed and with the exception of the olfactory bulbs and cerebellum, was frozen. An extraction, yielding ethanolic solution of a lithium-8-hydroxyquinoline complex was assayed spectrofluorometrically at 370 mμ excitation and 580 mμ fluorescence, according to modification of the principle for assay of fluroescent chelates from inorganic materials, outlined by White (68). Lithium carbonate and lithium chloride standards, added to tissue blanks, were run in parallel with this assay and the fluorescence of the oxine resulting was used as a basis for estimating the tissue lithium levels shown in Table 13-2. At doses of 1.18 and 2.35 mEq/kg the brain lithium levels, at fifteen minutes following injection, appeared to be maximum and, in fact, would suggest that the uptake into brain is preferential at this time in that the relative brain levels were in excess of the relative total dosage. The maximum tissue level was obtained fifteen minutes following the intraperitoneal injection of 2.35 mEq/kg, suggesting that dosage and postinjection time represent critical variables insofar as both the distribution of this lithium salt to brain tissue and its concentration decline from brain tissue.

Because of the previously suggested relationship between treatment with lithium salts and increased magnesium levels in serum and ethrocytes (3, 43, 44), it was our purpose to study the relationship between lithium treatment and brain magnesium levels. Some support for a role of brain magnesium may be derived from evidence indicating that magnesium deficiency in rats results in behavioral alterations, ranging from hyperexcitability to a hyperaccoustic response (36), and the further observation that the central effects of magnesium mediate changes which could have an important bearing upon cerebral function, e.g. activation of cerebral acetylcholinesterase (60).

Male CF-1 strain mice were treated with either 1.18, 2.35, or 4.70 mEq/kg of lithium carbonate, and matched groups of mice were treated with an equivalent volume of physiological saline, administered intraperitoneal. Mice in each group were killed at either fifteen, thirty, or sixty minutes following injection and the whole brain, with the exception of olfactory lobes and cere-

TABLE 13-2

MEAN ($\pm \sigma$) BRAIN TISSUE LITHIUM CONCENTRATION (μ/Eq/gw)
FOR MICE TREATED WITH LITHIUM CARBONATE

Time Post injection (min)	Dose (mEq/kg)		
	1.18	2.35	4.70
15	1.82 (0.99)	2.65 (0.23)	1.17 (0.11)
30	0.97 (0.16)	1.03 (0.29)	1.27 (0.12)
45	1.13 (0.35)	0.90 (0.25)	1.17 (0.20)

bellum, was removed, frozen, and an ethanolic extract, coupled with 8-hydroxyquinoline, was read spectrofluorometrically for the determination of the mg^{++}-8-hydroxyquinoline complex at pH 6.5 following a modification of a technique suggested by Schachter (52); excitation was at 420 mμ and fluorescence was read at 530 mμ. Estimates obtained from these determinations are summarized in Table 13-3, from which it may be seen that several doses of lithium carbonate at several postinjection times resulted in significant increases in the magnesium concentration of the brain tissue. It may be noted that, consistent with the previous data presented for brain lithium levels, fifteen minutes postinjection represents a peak increase in brain magnesium level, whereas at the higher lithium dose (4.70 mEq/kg) high brain magnesium levels resulted at all of the postinjection times tested. These findings tentatively suggested that brain magnesium levels were elevated as a result of lithium carbonate treatment and, in order to determine the relationship between the tissue levels of lithium resulting from systemic injection and the brain magnesium levels, the obtained concentrations were intercorrelated across both dose level and postinjection time. The result was a high, significant intercorrelation ($p = +0.892$, $p < .01$), which offers strong support for the suggestion that changes in brain magnesium level occur consistent with the uptake by brain tissue and lithium salts.

The results thus far obtained were considered in view of the previously obtained behavioral findings and the question of brain serotonin (5-HT) changes that may attend lithium treatment. Although it has been stated that lithium treatment does not alter brain monoamines (57), a recent report (42) has indicated that lithium carbonate treatment was accompanied by a significant increase in the uptake of serotonin by platelets; this observation was suggested to parallel previous findings obtained for brain synaptosomes. It was our purpose to determine the extent to which brain 5-HT and 5-HIAA levels were affected by lithium carbonate treatment. Mice, injected intraperitoneally, with either 1.18, 2.35, or 4.70 mEq/kg of lithium carbonate, or an equivalent volume of physiological saline, were killed at either fifteen, thirty, or sixty minutes following injection. Brain tissue, with the exception of olfactory lobes and cerebellum, were frozen and a solvent extractions for 5-HT (65) and 5-HIAA (66) were carried out. Estimates of the amine and its major metabolite were made from spectrofluorometric determinations, and these are summarized in Table 13-4. It may be noted from these data that the only significant increase in whole-brain 5-HT level was obtained for mice treated with 1.18 mEq/kg of lithium carbonate, from which tissue was obtained fifteen minutes following injection; the elevated brain serotonin level obtained at this time for this dosage significantly differed from both the saline treatment conditions and also from the highest doses for which tissue was obtained at this same time. There was no other significant departure in

TABLE 13-3

MEAN ($\pm \sigma$) BRAIN TISSUE MAGNESIUM CONCENTRATION (μ/Eq/gw)
FOR MICE TREATED WITH LITHIUM CARBONATE

TREATMENT

Time Postinjection (min)	Li_2CO_3 (1.18 mEq/kg)	Li_2CO_3 (2.35 mEq/kg)	Li_2CO_3 (4.70 mEq/kg)	Saline (0.9%)
15	9.02† (0.58)	8.89† (0.51)	8.84† (0.46)	7.89 (0.56)
30	8.51* (0.54)	7.65 (1.92)	9.02‡ (0.35)	7.74 (0.55)
60	8.60 (1.38)	7.76 (1.00)	8.86‡ (0.35)	7.82 (0.56)

* $p < .05$
† $p < .02$
‡ $p < .01$

either 5-HT or 5-HIAA level at other times resulting from lithium carbonate treatment.

In order to deal with this finding, another study was initiated in order to determine the turnover of brain serotonin under similar lithium carbonate dosage and postinjection time conditions. Turnover was estimated, utilizing a steady-state kinetics technique (64) that assumes synthesis rate equal to degradation rate, and with the administration of a monoamine oxidase inhibitor, tranglcypramine (20 mg/kg), the rate of 5-HIAA decrease and 5-HT increase was measured under comparable conditions of lithium carbonate treatment and appropriate postinjection tissue availability. The results, summarized in Table 13-5, indicate that fifteen minutes following intraperitoneal injection of 1.18 mEq/kg, 5-HT turnover rate has been significantly reduced and 5-HT turnover time significantly increased. This finding would suggest that 5-HT synthesis has been reduced as a result of lithium carbonate treatment, and the degradation of brain 5-HT has also been reduced.

The effects upon brain serotonin by low doses of lithium carbonate shortly after injection are similar in several respects to previous relationships explored between serotonin metabolism and the amnesic effects of electroconvulsive shock. This point may be of interest, inasmuch as Schou (56) has suggested that the therapeutic effects of lithium salts in manic-depressive illness are similar in several respects to the therapeutic effects of ECS and that these therapeutic effects of the former are, in fact, supplemental to the latter. In our work we have seen that ECS elevates whole-brain serotonin level and increases serotonin turnover time; this finding is partially consistent with the significant effect upon this amine and its metabolism, observed with a low dose of lithium carbonate by fifteen minutes after its systemic injection. The effect of pharmacological agents which attenuate the amnesic effect of ECS is to increase brain serotonin turnover time in the absence of ECS—an effect which would again be consistent with the observations made from the present data with regard to lithium carbonate. Our findings regarding the interrelationship between lithium carbonate treatment in mice and the metabolic and electrolyte changes which attend such treatment suggest that several relationships to the cognitive effects of such treatment may emerge. Other aspects of this interrelationship reside in the central effects of lithium salts, involving other amines. Schildkraut, et al. (53 to 59) have indicated that lithium salts administered to rats,

TABLE 13-4

MEAN ($\pm \sigma$) CONCENTRATION OF BRAIN 5-HYDROXYTRYPTAMINE (5-HT) AND 5-HYDROXYINDOLEACETIC ACID (5-HIAA) FOR MICE AT SEVERAL INTERVALS FOLLOWING LITHIUM CARBONATE TREATMENT

Dose	Time Postinjection (min)					
	15		30		60	
	5-HT	5-HIAA	5-HT	5-HIAA	5-HT	5-HIAA
Li_2CO_3 1.18 mEq/kg	0.98 (0.21)	0.41 (0.04)	0.46 (0.10)	0.42 (0.05)	0.45 (0.09)	0.44 (0.05)
Li_2CO_3 2.35 mEq/kg	0.56 (0.12)	0.55 (0.06)	0.58 (0.12)	0.51 (0.06)	0.46 (0.10)	0.42 (0.05)
Li_2CO_3 4.70 mEq/kg	0.56 (0.12)	0.45 (0.05)	0.53 (0.10)	0.44 (0.05)	0.56 (0.12)	0.47 (0.05)
Saline (0.9%)	0.51 (0.09)	0.43 (0.05)	0.52 (0.10)	0.44 (0.07)	0.54 (0.13)	0.45 (0.03)

TABLE 13-5

5-HT TURNOVER RATE AND TURNOVER TIME FOR MICE AT SEVERAL INTERVALS FOLLOWING LITHIUM CARBONATE TREATMENT

Dose	Time postinjection (min)					
	15		30		60	
	5-HT Turnover Rate ($\mu g/g/hr$)	5-HT Turnover Time (hr)	5-HT Turnover Rate ($\mu g/g/hr$)	5-HT Turnover Time (hr.)	5-HT Turnover Rate ($\mu g/g/hr$)	5-HT Turnover Time (hr)
Li_2CO_3 1.18 mEq/kg	0.24	4.08	0.47	0.97	0.48	0.94
Li_2CO_3 2.35 mEq/kg	0.56	1.00	0.72	0.81	0.46	1.00
Li_2CO_3 4.70 mEq/kg	0.61	0.91	0.56	0.95	0.64	0.87
Saline (0.9%)	0.53	0.96	0.55	0.95	0.59	0.92

while not altering brain norepinephrine level, increased the disappearance of labeled norpinephrine from the brain and suggested that the deanimation of norepinephrine may be increased following the administration of lithium salts. This may possibly be interpreted as an increase in the intraneuronal inactivation of norepinephrine by lithium salts, with the possible decrease in norepinephrine availability to adrenergic receptors. Decreased levels of normetanephrine may reflect decreases of the availability of norepinephrine at central synapses by presynaptic catabolism. This effect is strikingly similar to that seen with imipramine, and in this regard increased levels of normetanephrine excretion have been observed in depressed patients treated with imipramine (53, 54). The relationship between treatment with lithium salts and imipramine treatment has been discussed (34), and the increase in normetanephrine, resulting from imipramine treatment, may possibly be interpreted as interference with the re-uptake of norepinephrine into presynaptic terminals and an increase in norepinephrine availability at central synapses. A relationship that may be appropriate to consider at this point is the apparently critical role played by Mg^{++} in the o-methylation of epinephrine to normetanephrine (37). Facilitation of o-methylated products in catecholamine metabolism may be provided by elevated brain Mg^{++} levels which result from drug treatment; this hypothesis, however, remains to be tested. Thus, while there are certain parallels between the effects of these compounds, there appear to be, on the basis of some studies, differences in effect. Schou (56) has further suggested parallels between the therapeutic effects of imipramine and lithium salts, which he has classed as "normothymoleptics," in that both do not affect "normal behavior," produce no apathy or impairment of conscience or intellectual functions, have no euphoriant or mood-depressive properties, and their effects are similar to ECS in that they supplement the therapeutic efficacy of such treatment.

The central effects of imipramine, as compared to those of lithium salts, are difficult to appraise because of the relatively few studies concerned with the latter; in this regard, Gartside *et al.* (21) have shown that lithium carbonate treatment, over a five-day period, resulted in changes in both evoked cortical somatosensory responses in man, such that there was a reduction produced by lithium treatment in the second member of a response pair and a corresponding change in "cortical recovery function." Imipramine, correspondingly, has been studied more extensively insofar as its electrophysiological effects are concerned; in this regard, it has been shown to alter the EEG in the direction of a recruiting response in rabbits and cats, resulting in high amplitude slow waves, recorded from parietotemporal and occipital regions, and also results in the reduction or suppression of arousal, produced by electrical stimulation of the reticular formation or by auditory or pain stimuli (61). The increase in the arousal threshold to reticular stimulation has similarly been demonstrated in cats (7) for electrical stimulation; activation of electrocortical responses by sensory stimulation was also blocked at doses of 0.1 to 2.0 mg/kg of imipramine. The excitability of areas of motor cortex was reduced by imipramine treatment, and a tonic phase of the convulsions resulting from either ECS treatment or pentylenetetrazol injection was reduced (11). A decreased responsiveness in sensory thalamic nuclei has been shown, and a reduction in the cortical after-discharge produced by local stimulation also occurred (41). At doses of 2.0 and 4.0 mg/kg, given to cats, inhibition of REM periods of sleep, prolonged sleep, and decreased awakenings were observed (29). A difference in effect attendant upon dosage of imipramine was shown in studies of Rubio-Chevannier, et al. (51), in which low doses led to decreased arousal thresholds for sensory stimuli and for direct electrical stimulation of the reticular formation, whereas at higher doses (8 to 20 mg/kg) the excitability of the arousal system was depressed. It is of interest to note, in this regard, that these authors indicated that the electrogram of the olfactory bulbs represented a far more reliable index of the excitability state of the animal under their experimental conditions than could be observed in the electrocorticogram. The dose factor, again, leading to dual effects, was shown in alterations in threshold for the rage response (46). At low doses of imipramine (2 to 5 mg/kg) a decreased threshold for rage responsiveness occurred, whereas at higher doses (8 to 10 mg/kg) the threshold was increased, rage disappeared, and autonomic responsivity was decreased. These authors expressed the view that direct or indirect enhancement of hypothalamic excitability by imipramine may account for its clinically antidepressant action.

Imipramine, unlike a large variety of psychoactive and antidepressant compounds, does not lead to any significant modification of the behavior of normal animals (11) and, behaviorally, does not lead to any inhibition of conditioned escape behavior in the rat (22). It has been shown to exert a stimulant-like effect upon lever pressing avoidance behavior and to increase the rate of self-stimulation with electrodes implanted in the lateral hypothalamus (31, 32). A very slight degree of behavioral sedation has been reported by a number of investigators (4, 25, 27, 40, 63, 67).

With regard to the metabolic effects of imipramine, it has been shown that there is no significant effect upon monoamine oxidase activity produced (18, 35, 48, 49). Brain monoamines have been reported as being unaffected by imipramine treatment in rats (62, 67). However, in contrast to these findings, there have been reports of elevated levels of brain serotonin, produced by imipramine treatment (9, 35).

Imipramine, following its injection into the rabbit, has been shown to be rapidly taken up by kidney, heart muscle, and brain tissue (28), and the activity of C14 labeled imipramine, injected into rats and dogs, has been shown to be very high in the cerebrum (5). Following the intraperitoneal injection of 40 mg/kg of imipramine, the brain level, at forty-five minutes postinjection, showed a peak of 14 µg/g (24). The injection of 10 mg/kg of imipramine has been reported to result in a 30 per cent inhibition of brain cholinesterase activity (50), and the compound has also been shown to produce inhibition of respiratory activity in rat brain cortex slices and reduce oxidative phosphorelation in rat brain mitochondria (1).

The varied effects of imipramine treatment upon the electrophysiological and biochemical status of the central nervous system, in a number of different animal species, suggest that even in the absence of any presumed model of endogenous depression, this compound exerts rather profound effects. A rather interesting parallel with the behavioral effect of imipramine to be considered in the present discussion may be found in the work of Hyden (33), in which the RNA content of single cells was altered by imipramine treatment (4 mg/kg). In single neurons there was an 18 per cent increase in RNA, whereas in single glia there was a 45 per cent decrease. Neuronal protein was increased by 26 per cent, and cytochrome oxidase activity was increased by 250 per cent. The effects of imipramine, in the light of these findings, were interpreted as nonspecific and stimulatory for the neuron, whereas for glia, a specific effect of glial RNA synthesis was proposed. These findings are of interest in view of data from our laboratory indicating that other compounds, which elevate neuronal RNA and deplete glial RNA, such as tricyanoaminopropene and tetracyanopropene, are effective in antagonizing the amnesic effect of electroconvulsive shock (12, 16, 17). In this regard, our data, with respect to the cellular effects of electroshock, has indicated that following this event neuronal RNA is decreased and glial RNA is either relatively unchanged or increased, the net effect of this cellular interaction being a regional decrease in RNA. Because of the suggested interaction between the central effects of imipramine and those of electroshock, these were investigated on both a behavioral and biochemical level in several experiments.

CF-1 strain mice were injected, intraperitoneally, with either imipramine hydrochloride (20 mg/kg) or physiological saline, one hour prior to being given a single training trial designed to establish a passive avoidance response. This technique has been described earlier in this paper. One group of imipramine-treated mice and one group of saline-treated mice were given a single transcorneal ECS (10 ma, 200 msec) ten seconds following the presentation of the conditioning foot shock on the acquisition trial of avoidance training. Another group each of imipramine-treated and saline-treated mice were given sham-ECS (ECS) at ten seconds following the training trial, wherein no current was passed. A single testing trial was given twenty-four hours following training, at which the response latency was again measured, and from these measures the incidence of conditioned response retention was determined. A ceiling latency of thirty seconds was used in this experiment, and any animal that failed to respond by showing conditioned avoidance by thirty seconds was removed from the apparatus. Figure 13-2 shows the mean response latency difference between the training and testing trials and the percent incidence of conditioned response retention. A chi-square analysis of the differences in incidence of conditioned response retention in drug-treated and saline-treated mice, given ECS or sham-ECS, is summarized in Table 13-6. It may be observed that the imipramine-treated animals showed a highly significant degree of antagonism toward the amnesic effect of ECS, when compared with saline-treated animals given ECS, and that the ECS was highly effective in leading to a retrograde amnesia for the conditioned avoidance response. The fact that imipramine-treated and saline-treated animals, given sham-ECS, did not differ, in that the incidence of conditioned response retention was high in both cases, suggests that imipramine had no effect upon the acquisition and retention of the conditioned avoidance behavior under non-ECS conditions. It may further be noted that imipramine-treated animals did not show any alteration in their susceptibility to the full clonic-tonic convulsion produced by ECS, nor in the recovery phase following ECS. These data, therefore, support the

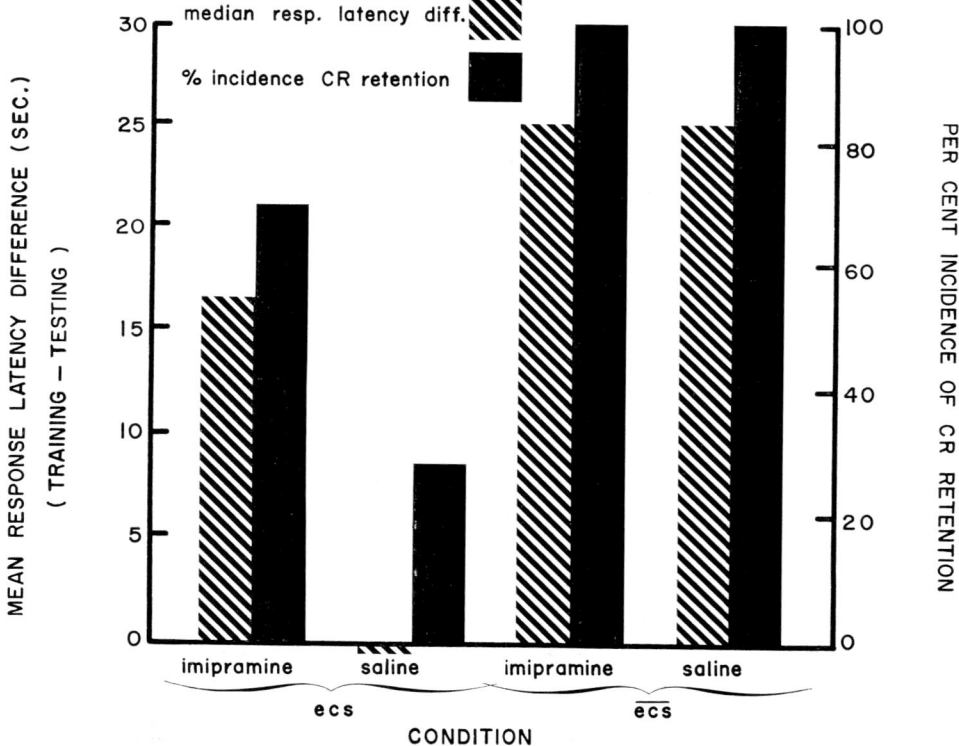

FIGURE 13-2. Mean response latency difference and per cent incidence of CR retention for saline-treated and imipramine-treated mice given ECS or sham-ECS.

hypothesis that the effects of imipramine interfere, in some way, with the amnesia-producing properties of electroconvulsive shock. This effect may reside in either imipramine-induced alterations in the central effects of ECS, which block the memory consolidation at some point within the interval in which the memory trace may be disrupted, or imipramine treatment may possibly potentiate those biochemical events which facilitate memory consolidation.

TABLE 13-6

CHI-SQUARE ANALYSIS OF DIFFERENCES IN INCIDENCE OF CONDITIONED RESPONSE RETENTION IN DRUG-TREATED AND SALINE-TREATED MICE GIVEN ECS OR SHAMECS ($\overline{ECS}$)

Comparison	df	X^2	p
Between All Conditions (Total)	3	51.16	<.001
Imipramine vs Saline-ECS	1	24.51	<.001
Imipramine vs Saline-$\overline{ECS}$	1	0.00	> .99
ECS vs $\overline{ECS}$	1	26.65	<.001

In order to explore the relationship between the central biochemical effects of imipramine and their interaction with alterations in the same biochemical parameters produced by electroconvulsive shock, mice were treated with either physiological saline or imipramine hydrochloride (20 mg/kg) one hour prior to being given either a single transcorneal ECS (10 ma, 200 msec) or sham-ECS. Mice were killed sixty minutes following ECS, at which time recovery from a full clonic-tonic convulsion and the brief period of postictal depression was complete. The whole brain, including the olfactory bulbs and cerebellum, was removed, frozen, and dissected, utilizing a stereomicroscope and stereotaxic coordinates for localization and isolation of the cerebral cortex, corpus callosum, thalamus, hypothalamus, and limbic system structures (including amygdala, hippocampus, fornix, and septum. Extraction and precipitation of RNA, with subsequent UV absorption determinations, were carried out according to the method of Scott, et al. (59). The concentrations of RNA obtained for those regions sampled are summarized in Table 13-7, and mean regional differences for each of the respective treatment conditions that emerged between saline-treated and imipramine-treated animals, are shown in Figure 13-3, where such differences are expressed in µg/ml. It may be noted that an appreciable decrease in the RNA content of the corpus callosum occurred as a result of ECS in saline-treated animals, whereas for cerebral cortex, ECS apparently led to an increased RNA concentration. The decrease in RNA, as a result of ECS, was apparent for all areas sampled, with the exception of the limbic system structures. These findings do not conclusively support any hypothesis regarding modification of the ECS-induced changes in

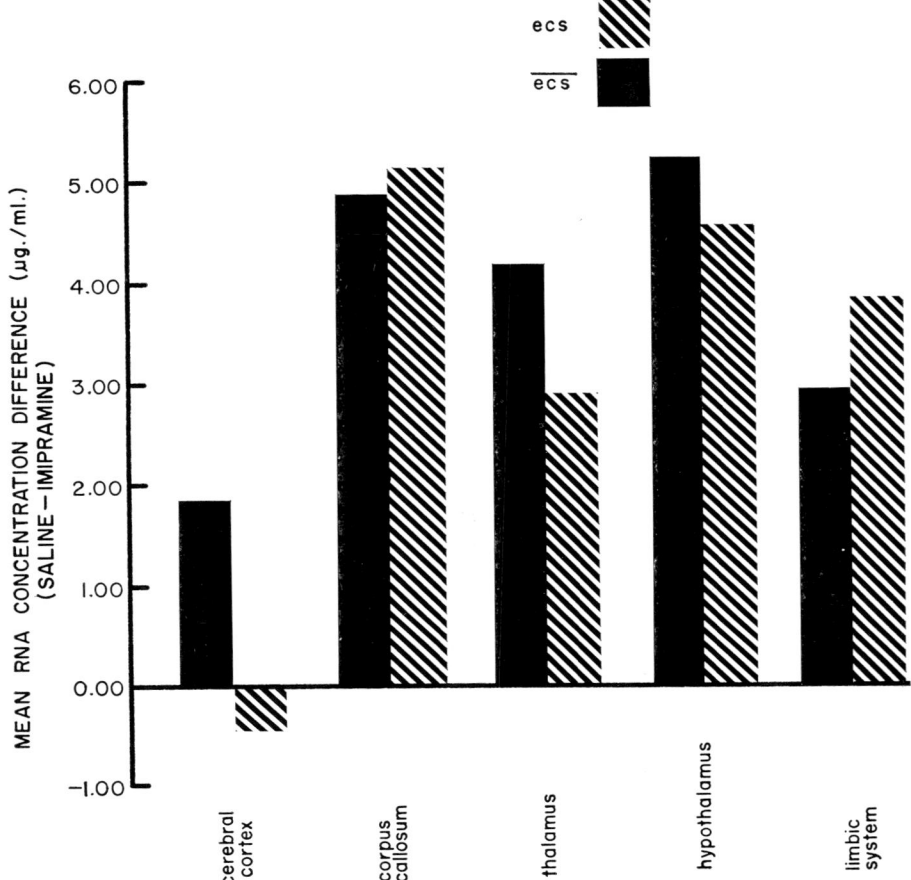

FIGURE 13-3. Mean regional brain RNA concentration difference between saline-treated and imipramine-treated mice.

brain RNA by imipramine and may suggest that the interval between electroshock administration and sampling of the tissue exceeded the point at which such critical changes may be apparent.

In another study, whole-brain serotonin level was determined for ECS and sham-ECS administration in imipramine-treated and saline-treated mice, wherein tissue samples were obtained twenty minutes following ECS or sham-ECS administration, given one hour postinjection. Serotonin levels were estimated following solvent extraction from spectrofluorometric determinations, and the results are summarized in Figure 13-4. It may be observed from these data that the effect of ECS in saline-treated animals was to increase whole-brain serotonin level by over 25 per cent, whereas treatment with imipramine alone, in the absence of ECS, was sufficient in elevating brain serotonin to ap-

TABLE 13-7

MEAN ($\pm \sigma$) REGIONAL BRAIN RNA CONCENTRATION (mg/g) FOR SALINE-TREATED AND IMIPRAMINE-TREATED MICE GIVEN ECS OR SHAM-ECS ($\overline{\text{ECS}}$)

Treatment	Cerebral Cortex	Corpus Callosum	Area Thalamus	Hypothalamus	Limbic System
Saline (0.9%)					
ECS	1.95 (0.20)	1.80 (0.27)	1.87 (0.18)	1.69 (0.15)	1.89 (0.21)
$\overline{\text{ECS}}$	1.77 (0.06)	2.35 (0.18)	1.93 (0.23)	1.65 (0.21)	1.98 (0.37)
Imipramine (20 mg/kg)					
ECS	1.77 (0.05)	1.32 (0.20)	1.45 (0.22)	1.75 (0.06)	1.60 (0.28)
$\overline{\text{ECS}}$	1.82 (0.24)	1.52 (0.26)	1.64 (0.23)	1.91 (0.05)	1.60 (0.25)

proximately the same degree as that produced by ECS. This finding of an imipramine-induced elevation in brain serotonin level, is consistent with earlier findings (9, 35). These findings further indicate that the increase in brain serotonin level, produced by ECS in imipramine-treated animals, is consistent with the increase produced under the same conditions in saline-treated animals. In order to investigate this relationship further, tissue was obtained under conditions identical with those described above and, following extraction, spectrofluorometric assay for 5-hydroxyindoleacetic acid and monoamine oxidase activity were carried out (these procedures have previously been described in reference 14a. In an additional series, mice, treated under comparable conditions, were carried through the procedure described earlier in this paper for estimation of brain serotonin turnover, utilizing steady-state kinetics. All of these findings are summarized in Table 13-8. It may be observed that whereas there was no significant difference produced in saline-treated animals for ECS, the latter treatment in imipramine injected animals resulted in a significant elevation in brain 5-HIAA concentration. Monoamine oxidase activity was unaffected by either imipramine treatment or ECS, or their interaction. This finding supports previous data from our laboratory (14a), as well as findings reported by others (18, 35, 48). ECS administration in imipramine-treated animals also resulted in a significant increase in brain serotonin turnover time, as compared with sham-ECS treated imipramine-injected mice, in which the turnover time was reduced from that observed in saline-treated controls. The reduced turnover time, under the latter treatment conditions, is suggestive of the fact that brain serotonin metabolism is accelerated by imipramine treatment, but that ECS, under such conditions, leads to a reduction in serotonin degradation.

The relationship between the behavioral effects of imipramine treatment and the biochemical alterations which such treatment mediate in the central nervous system is somewhat consistent with the hypothesis that retrograde

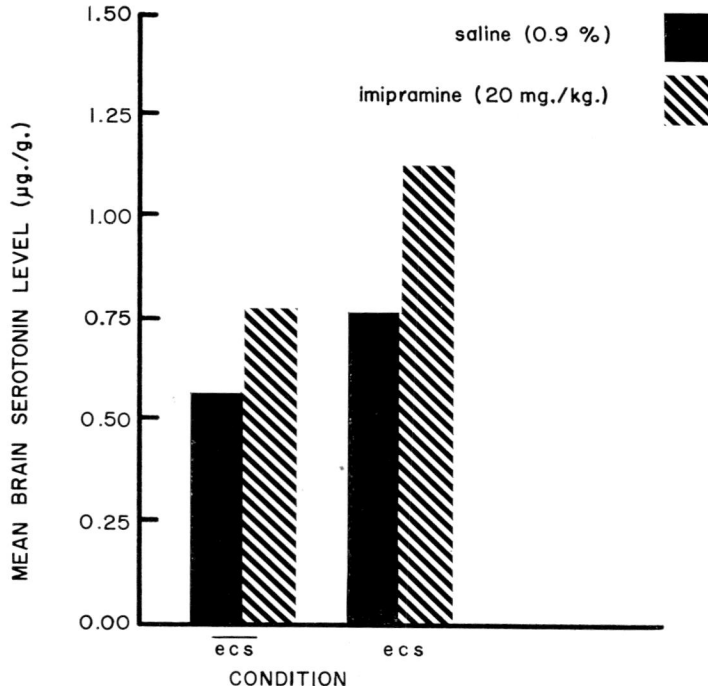

FIGURE 13-4. Mean brain serotonin level in saline-treated and imipramine-treated mice given ECS or sham-ECS.

amnesia, produced by ECS may, among other things, involve an alteration in brain serotonin metabolism. This alteration involves an increase in brain serotonin level and an increase in brain serotonin turnover time. Where drug treatment conditions have either led to an attenuation of the increase in 5-HT level, produced by ECS, or reduced the turnover time, as may be observed in the present data as well, the retrograde amnesia produced by ECS has been antagonized.

In order to relate the behavioral and biochemical effects of imipramine to those previously observed with lithium carbonate, a further experiment was conducted in order to assess the effect of imipramine upon endogenous brain magnesium levels. Mice were injected, intraperitoneally, with either 0.9% saline or imipramine hydrochloride) ; (20 mg/kg) sixty-minute postinjection the whole brain, excluding olfactory bulbs and cerebellum was excised, frozen lypholized and magnesium levels were estimated, as previously described. Mean brain magnesium levels in saline-treated controls were $9.154 \mu Eq/gd$ (± 2.81) and for imipramine-treated animals mean brain levels were $16.089 \mu Eq/gd$ (± 7.74) ; the significant ($p<.001$) elevation of brain magnesium level by one hour following imipramine treatment is, comparatively, a greater increment ($\sim 77\%$) than that resulting, on the average, from lithium carbonate treatment (~21%), however, because of the apparent difference in peak brain uptake (~45 min and ~ 15 min, respectively), the comparison may not be a fair one to appraise. The similarity, however, between lithium and imipramine in elevating brain magnesium level, suggests an important role which this cation may play in regulating those central events which are common to the central effects of both compounds. The possible implications which magnesium ion changes in the brain may have for present considerations are difficult, in several respects, to assess in a conclusive manner. The role of magnesium ions has been definitively established as a cofactor in cellular enzyme reactions, and has also been shown to mediate the release of acetylcholine at the neuromuscular junction (10). Magnesium salts have a strong effect in altering the distribution of acidic lipids in the brain and are capable of reversibly displacing other ions in brain lipids (20). Also, in brain, magnesium ions activity and ATPase activity of nuclei, mitochondria, and microsomes (45). The distribution of magnesium in brain tissue has been rather consistently reported, and most of these observations have been for human brain (26, 38, 47). Magnesium content in cortex has been estimated at approximately 11.3 mEq/g (30, 39, 58), and this probably consists of ions that are not free, but rather are bound to tissue elements. The brain magnesium levels that we have obtained and reported in this paper are only slightly lower, than average, (~35%) than those reported for human brain and are consistent with one another both under control, as well as conditions wherein they are altered. The potentiation of the narcotic action of several tranquilizers by magnesium has been reported (60), and the activation of cerebral acetylcholinesterase by magnesium may well be consistent with the narcotic action of higher doses of magnesium salts that has been reported and the reduced brain acetylcholine levels, which are attendant upon anesthesia. There is little else that can be

TABLE 13-8

MEAN ($\pm \sigma$) WHOLE BRAIN 5-HYDROXYINDOLEACETIC ACID (5-HIAA) LEVEL, MONOAMINE OXIDASE (MAO) ACTIVITY, AND 5-HYDROXTRYTAMINE (5-HT) TURNOVER IN MICE TREATED WITH SALINE OR IMIPRAMINE AND GIVEN ECS OR SHAM-ECS (ECS)

Treatment Condition	Mean Whole-Brain Level and Turnover			
	5-HIAA (μg/g)	MAO (μM4HOQ/g/hr)	5HT Turnover	
			Rate (μg/g/hr)	Time (hr)
Saline (0.9%)				
ECS	0.44 (0.20)	1.45 (0.36)	0.53	1.55
ECS	0.32 (0.17)	1.25 (0.34)	0.39	1.48
Imipramine (20 mg/kg)				
ECS	0.78 (0.23) *	1.37 (0.33)	0.95	1.22*
ECS	0.46 (0.19)	1.42 (0.28)	0.56	0.82

*$p < .05$

added concerning the specific role of magnesium as far as behavior or the effects of psychoactive agents are concerned. Admittedly, there are many metabolic events which are dependent upon magnesium or possible reciprocities between magnesium concentration and that of other cations in the brain with which it either competes or may replace; our present findings, however, suggest that magnesium may represent one of several possible sensitive indices for relating the action of psychotropic drugs to ongoing endogenous processes in the nervous system, which are important for a variety of cognitive behaviors.

In a final study, a series of psychoactive drugs were compared with one another utilizing a single trial active avoidance task. This task basically consisted of placing mice in a one-way hurdle box, with a ten-second delay, followed by a sixty-second, 3 mA foot shock. The foot shock was terminated whenever the animal crossed the hurdle. Twenty-four hours following the single trial, a second trial was given, and for both trials the latency to cross, following shock onset, was measured; and for the second trial, the incidence of crossings prior to shock onset, were recorded. The two drugs considered in the present discussion were specifically included, and all drug administration preceded the first training trial by one hour. It may be noted initially (Table 13-9) that saline-treated mice showed a statistically significant reduction in response latency to escape shock, with 35 per cent of the animals showing avoidance on trial 2. Imipramine-treated animals also showed a significant reduction in escape latency, with a high incidence of conditioned avoidance on the second trial. Lithium carbonate-treated animals showed no alteration in escape latency and no conditioned avoidance on the second trial. This finding may possibly reside in the rapid effects of acute lithium carbonate treatment, as

TABLE 13-9

MEAN ($\pm\sigma$) RESPONSE LATENCY FOR SHOCK ESCAPE
OR AVOIDANCE AND PER CENT INCIDENCE OF
CONDITIONED AVOIDANCE FOR DRUG-TREATED MICE

Drug Treatment	Trial Response Latency (sec)		% Cond. Avoidance
	1	2	
Saline (0.9%)	11.90 (2.90)	9.20 (3.80) *	35
Li_2CO_3 (100 mg/kg)	15.45 (11.41)	15.85 (16.85)	0
Reserpine (5 mg/kg)	15.90 (6.00)	9.90 (2.80) *	30
Nicotine Sulfate (1 mg/kg)	11.65 (4.30)	10.60 (3.00)	0
Chlorpromazine (6 mg/kg)	13.70 (2.00)	12.75 (1.50) *	0
Meprobamate (100 mg/kg)	13.50 (2.80)	10.25 (3.90) *	30
Amphetamine (5 mg/kg)	11.10 (3.10)	10.35 (3.30)	20
Chlordiazepoxide (30 mg/kg)	15.35 (4.80)	14.95 (11.50)	25
Imipramine (10 mg/kg)	11.10 (3.30)	7.15 (4.20) *	45
Tranylcypromine (20 mg/kg)	10.10 (3.70)	8.05 (5.40)	20
Amitriptyline (10 mg/kg)	10.20 (3.90)	9.90 (8.30)	5

* $p < .05$

observed in previous data; however, it does not explain why animals treated under such conditions should show such a marked departure in reduced active avoidance acquisition, as compared with saline-treated animals. It may be noted that, in general, antidepressant drugs did lead to some degree of conditioned avoidance acquisition, whereas chlorpromazine, although not leading to acquisition of conditioned avoidance, did allow for a reduction in escape latency. These data are intended to point toward a possible means of assessing behavioral differences between a variety of psychoactive drugs and suggest that the time course over which acute treatment with such compounds is effective behaviorally may well be dependent upon such considerations as the uptake of the drug into the central nervous system, the changes that it mediates there, and the time course over which other metabolic changes thus initiated take place. A case in point is perhaps best illustrated by a comparison in the present data between the lithium carbonate-treated and imipramine-treated animals. Our previous data would suggest that the optimal behaviorally facilitated effects of lithium carbonate occur within approximately thirty minutes following its systemic injection and, depending upon dosage, its uptake into brain and its effects therein appear critically time-dependent. Imipramine, on the other hand, reaches peak concentrations within approximately forty-five minutes following systemic injection, and in the present data its factitive effect upon conditioned avoidance acquisition may be noted. These data, perhaps, point to the difficulty in establishing interrelationships on a biochemical, pharmacological, and behavioral level because of such considerations as dosage, uptake, make, and site of action and, possibly, secondary effects which may involve other systems or pathways.

Our present findings suggest that the two compounds considered in this discussion, lithium carbonate and imipramine, hold certain effects in common with one another and, perhaps, some of the differences noted in the present investigation between these compounds may be resolved on a therapeutic level if considerations were given to such factors as dosage, uptake into brain, time course of central action, and the nature of the electrolyte and other metabolic changes which occur. These considerations may possibly bring the two extremes of the spectrum for therapeutic indication of the use of these compounds on a clinical level closer together and may possibly, thereby, serve as a basis for preventive chemotherapy, which has as its basis certain common features of brain function.

REFERENCES

1. Abadom, P.N., Ahmed, K., and Scholefield, P.G.: Biochemical studies on Tofranil. *Canad J Biochem Physiol,* 39:551, 1961.
2. Arnold, O.H., and Hoff, H.: The role of biological treatment in comprehensive psychiatric management. In Wortis, J. (Ed.): *Recent Advances in Biological Psychiatry.* New York, Grune and Stratton, 1961, vol. 3, p. 12.

3. ARONOFF, M.S., EVENS, R.G., AND DURELL, J.: Effect of lithium salts on electrolyte metabolism. *Proc 122nd Ann Mtg Amer Psychiat Assn, 20*: , 1969.
4. BÄTTIG, K.: Die Wirkunb pharmakologischer Stoffe auf verschiedene Funktionen des Verhaltens der Ratte. *Pflüger's Arch Ges Physiol, 274*:59, 1961.
5. BERNHARD, K., AND BEER, H.: Activity of expired carbon dioxide, CNS and other organs after the administration of C-14-labeled N- (Y-dimethylaminopropyl) imonodibenzyl (psychopharmacological drug Tofranil) in rats and dogs. *Helv Physiol Pharmacol Acta, 20*:114, 1962.
6. BITTMAN, R., ESSMAN, W.B., AND GOLOD, M.I.: Studies of RNA binding to 5-hydroxytryptamine. *Proc Amer Chem Soc,* 1969, in press.
7. BRADLEY, P.B., AND KEY, B.J.: A comparative study of the effects of drugs on the arousal system of the brain. *Brit J Pharmacol, 14*:340, 1959.
8. CADE, J.F.J.: Lithium salts in the treatment of psychotic excitement. *Med J Australia, 36*:349, 1949.
9. COSTA, E., GARRATINE, S., AND VALZELLI, L.: Interactions between reserpine, chlorpromazine, and imipramine. *Experientia, 16*:461, 1960.
10. DEL CASTILLO, J., AND ENGBAEK, L.: The nature of the neuromuscular block produced by magnesium. *J Physiol, 124*:370, 1954.
11. DOMENJOZ, R., AND THEOBALD, W.: Zur Pharmkolgie des Tofranil [N- (3-Dimethylaminopropyl) -imindibenzyl-hydrochlorid]. *Arch Int Pharmacodyn, 120*:450, 1959.
12. ESSMAN, W.B.: Effect of tricyanominopropene on the amnesic effect of electroconvulsive shock. *Psychopharmacologia (Berlin), 9*:426, 1966.
13. ESSMAN, W.B.: Changes in memory consolidation with alterations in neural RNA. *Proc Coll Int Neuropsychopharm,* :108, 1967.
14. ESSMAN, W.B.: Electroshock-induced retrograde amnesia and brain serotonin metabolism: Effect of several antidepressant compounds. *Psychopharmcologia (Berlin), 13*:258, 1968.
14a. ESSMAN, W.B.: Changes in ECS induced retrograde amnesia with DBMC: Behavioral and biological correlates of brain serotonin antagonism. *Physiol Behav, 3*:527, 1968.
15. ESSMAN, W.B.: Single trial learning: Methodology and results with mice. *Psychol Rep, 14*:731, 1964.
16. ESSMAN, W.B.; AND GOLOD, M.I.: Reduction of retrograde amnesia by TCAP: Drug dosage and electroshock intensity. *Comm Behav Biol, 1*:183, 1968.
17. ESSMAN, S.G., AND ESSMAN, W.B.: Enhanced memory consolidation with drug-induced regional changes in brain RNA and serotonin metabolism. *Pharmako-Psychiat Neuropsychopharm, 12*:28, 1969.
18. EXER, B., AND PULVER, R.: Some metabolic effects of Tofranil and metabolites. *Chimia, 14*:30, 1960.
20. FOLCH, J., LEES, M., AND SLOANE-STANLEY, G.H.: The role of acidic lysides in the electrolyte balance of the central nervous system of mammals. In Richter, D. (Ed.): *Metabolism of the Nervous System.* New York, Pergammon Press, 1957, p. 174.
20a. GARATTINI *et al.*:
21. GARTSIDE, I.B., LIPPOLD, O.C.J., AND MELDRUM, S.B.: The evoked cortical somatosensory response in normal man and its modification by oral lithium carbonate. *Electroenceph Clin Neurophysiol, 20*:382, 1966.
22. GATTI, G.L.: Some psychopharmacological characteristics recently introduced in the therapy of mental depression. *Riv Sper Freniat, 85*:1, 1961.
23. GERSHON, S., AND YUWILER, A.: Lithium ion: Specific pharmacological approach to the treatment of mania. *J Neuropsychiat, 1*:229, 1960.

24. GILETTE, J.R., DINGELL, J.V., SULSER, F., KUNTZMAN, R., AND BRODIE, B.B.: Isolation from rat brain of a metabolic product, desmethylimipramine, that mediates the antidepressant activity of imipramine (Tofranil). *Experientia, 17*:417, 1961.
25. HANSON, H.M.: The effects of amitriptyline, imipramine, chlorpromazine and nialamide on avoidance behavior. *Fed Proc, 20*:396, 1961.
26. HARRISON, W.W., NETSKY, M.G., AND BROWN, M.D.: Trace elements in human brain: Copper, zinc, iron, and magnesium. *Clin Chim Acta, 21*:55, 1968.
27. HERR, F., STEWART, AND CHAREST, M.P.: Tranquilizers and antidepressants: A pharmacological comparison. *Biochem Pharmacol, 8*:25, 1961.
28. HERRMANN, B., AND PULVER, R.: Der Stoffwechsel des Psychopharmakons Tofranil. *Arch Int Pharmacodyn, 126*:454, 1960.
29. HISHIKAWA, Y., NAKAI, K., IDA, H., AND KANEKO, Z.: The effect of imipramine, desmethylimipramine and chlorpromazine on the sleep-wakefulness cycle of the cat. *Electroenceph Clin Neurophysiol, 19*:518, 1965.
30. HOLMES, J.H., AND TOWER, D.B.: Intracranial fluids. In Elliott, K.A.C., Page, I.H., and Quastel, J.H. Eds.): *Neurochemistry.* Springfield, Charles C Thomas, 1955. p. 262.
31. HOROVITZ, A.P., CHOW, M.I., AND CARLTON, P.L.: Self-stimulation of the brain of cats: Technique and preliminary drug effects. *Psychopharmacologia (Berlin), 3*:449, 1962.
32. HOROVITZ, Z.P., CHOW, M.I., AND CARLTON, P.L.: Self-stimulation of the brain of cats: Effects of imipramine, amphetamine, and chlorpromazine. *Psychopharmacologia (Berlin), 3*:455, 1962.
33. HYDÉN, H.: Biochemical and functional interplay between neuron and glia. *Recent Advances Biol Psychiat, 6*:31, 1963.
34. KETY, S.: The central physiological and pharmacological effects of the biogenic amines and their correlations with behavior. In Quarton, G., Melnechuk, T., and Schmitt, F.O. (Eds.): *The Neurosciences.* New York, Rockefeller University Press, 1967, p. 444.
35. KIVALO, E., RINNE, U.K., AND KARINKANTA, H.: The effect of imipramine on the 5-hydroxytryptamine content and monoamine oxidase activity of the rat brain and on the excretion of 5-hydroxyindoleacetic acid. *J Neurochem, 8*:105, 1961.
36. KRUSE, H.D., ORENT, E., AND McCOLLUM, E.V.: Studies of magnesium deficiency in animals. I. Symptomatology resulting from magnesium deprivation. *J Biol Chem, 96*:519, 1932.
37. LA BROSSE, E.H., AXELROD, J., AND KETY, S.S.: O-methylation, the principle route of metabolism of epinephrine in man. *Science, 128*:593, 1958.
38. MAGNUS-LEVY, A.: Über den Gehalt normaler menschlicher Organe an Chlor, Calcium, Magnesium, und Eisen soure an Wasser, Eiweiss und Fett. *Biochem Z, 24*:364, 1910.
39. MANERY, J.F.: Inorganic metabolism of the brain. In *The Biology of Mental Health and Disease.* New York, Hoeber, 1952, p. 124.
40. MAXWELL, D.R., AND PALMER, H.T.: Demonstration of antidepressant or stimulant properties of imipramine in experimental animals. *Nature, 191*:84, 1961.
40a. MIHAILOVIC et al.:
41. MONNIER, M., AND KRUPP, P.: Electrophysiologische Analyse der Wirkung verschiedener Neuroleptika (chlorpromazin, reserpin, Tofranil, meprobamate). *Schweiz Med Wschr, 89*:53, 1959.
42. MURPHY, D.L., COLBURN, R.W., DAVIS, J.M., AND BUNNEY, W.E., JR.: Lithium and

imipramine effects of amine transport. *Proc 122nd Ann Mtg Amer Psychiat Assn,* 21:, 1969.
43. NIELSON, J.: Magnesium-lithium studies. Serum and erythrocyte magnesium in patients with manic states during lithium treatment. *Acta Psychiat Scand, 40*:190, 1964a.
44. NIELSEN, J.: Magnesium-lithium studies. The effect of lithium on serum magnesium in rabbits. *Acta Psychiat Scand, 40*:197, 1964b.
45. PALLADIN, A.V.: Distribution of enzymes among the various subcellular units of the brain. In Kety, S.S., and Elkes, J. (Eds.) : *Regional Neurochemistry.* New York, Pergammon Press, 1961, p. 8.
46. PEÑALOZA-ROJAS, J.H., BACH-Y-RITA, G., RUBIO-CHEVANNIER, H.F., AND HERNANDEZ-PEÓN, R.: Effects of imipramine upon hypothalamic and amygdaloid excitability. *Exp. Neurol, 4*:205, 1961.
47. PERRY, H.M., JR., TIPTON, I.H., SCHROEDER, H.A., ANE COOK, M.J.: Variability in the metal content of human organs. *J Lab Clin Med, 60*:245, 1962.
48. PLETSCHER, A., AND GEY, K.F.: Pharmacological influence of 5-hydroxytryptamine metabolism in the brain and monoamime oxidase inhibition *in vitro. Helv Physiol Pharmacol Acta, 17*:C35, 1959.
49. PLETSCHER, A., AND GEY, K.F.: Action of imipramine and amitriptyline on cerebral monoamines as compared with chlorpromazine. *Med Exp (Basel) 6*:165, 1962.
50. PULVER, R., EXER, B., AND HERRMANN, B.: Einige Wirkungen des (Y-Dimethylaminopropyl) iminodibenzyl-HCL und seiner Maetabolite auf den Stoffwechsel von Neurohormonen. *Arzneimittelforschung, 10*:530, 1960.
51. RUBIO-CHEVANNIER, H., BACH-Y-RITA, G., PEÑALOZA-ROJAS, J., AND HERNANDEZ--PEÓN, R.: Potentiating action of imipramine upon "reticular arousal." *Exp Neurol, 4*:214, 1961.
52. SCHACHTER, D.: The flourometric estimation of magnesium in serum and urine. *J Lab Clin Med, 54*:763, 1959.
53. SCHILDKRAUT, J.J., GREEN, R., GORDON, E.K., AND DURELL, J.: Normetanepherine excretion and affective state in depressed patients treated with imipramine. *Amer J Psychat, 123*:690, 1966.
54. SCHILDKRAUT, J.J., AND KOPIN, I.J.: The effects of lithium ion on H^3-norepinephrine metabolism in brain. *Life Sci, 5*:1479, 1966.
55. SCHILDKRAUT, J.J., LOGUE, M.A., AND DODRE, G.A.: The effects of lithium salts on the turnover and metabolism or norepinephrine in rat brain. *Psychopharmacologia (Berlin), 14*:135, 1969.
56. SCHOU, M.: Normothymoleptics "mood normalizers." Are lithium and imipramine drugs specific for affective disorders? *Brit J Psychiat, 109*:803, 1963.
57. SCHOU, M.: Lithium, sodium and manic depressive psychosis. In Walaas, O. (Ed.) : *Molecular Basis of Some Aspects of Mental Activity.* New York, Academic Press, 1967, vol. 2, p. 457.
58. SHANES, A.M.: Electrochemical aspects of physiological and pharmacological action in excitable cells. 1. The resting cell and its alteration by extrinsic factors. *Pharmacol Rev, 10*:59, 1958.
59. SCOTT, J.F., FRACOCASTRO, A.P., AND TAFT, E.B.: Studies in histchemistry. 1. Determination of nucleic acids in microgram amounts of tissue. *J Histochem Cytochem, 4*:1, 1956.
60. SHITOV, YE. YE.: Vliyaniye sul'fata magniya v kombinatii s trankvilizatorami na bioelektricheskuya i kholinesteraznuyu aktivnost' golovnogo nozza. *Farmakol Toksik, 28*:13, 1965.

61. SIGG, E.B.: Pharmacological studies with Tofranil. *Canad Psychiat Assoc J, 4*:75, 1959.
62. SULSER, F. WATT:, J., AND BRODIE, B.B.: On the mechanism of the antidepressant action of imipramine-like drugs. *Ann NY Acad Sci, 96*:279, 1962.
63. THEOBALD, W., BUCH, O., KUNZ, MORPUGO, C., WILHELMI, G., AND STENGAR, E.G.: Comparative pharmacological investigations with Tofranil, Pertofane, and Ensidon. *Arch Int Pharmacodyn, 148*:560, 1964.
64. TOZER, T.N., NEFF, N.H., AND BRODIE, B.B.: Application of steady state kinetics to the synthesis rate and turnover time of serotonin in brain of normal and reserpine-treated rats. *J Pharmacol Exp Ther, 153*:177, 1966.
65. UDENFRIEND, S., WEISSBACH, H., AND CLARK, C.T.: The estimation of 5-hydroxytryptamine (serotonin) in biological tissue. *J Biol Chem, 215*:337, 1955.
66. UDENFRIEND, S., WEISSBACH, H., AND BRODIE, B.B.: assay of serotonin and related metabolites, enzymes and drugs. In Glick, D. (Eds.) : *Methods of Biochemical Analysis*. New York, Interscience, 1958, p. 95.
67. VERNIER, V G.: The pharmacology of anti-depressant agents. *Dis Nerv Syst, 22*:7, 1961.
68. WHITE, C.E.: Fluorescence analysis. In Yoe, J.H. (Ed.) : *Trace Analysis*. New York, Wiley, 1957, 211.

Chapter 14

Drug Response Following Brain Damage

MARTIN W. ADLER

Before alterations in drug responses which occur following brain damage can be discussed effectively, a number of general considerations should be mentioned. If we can use the term "behavior" to indicate an organism's response or reaction to a given set of stimuli, there is a multiplicity of factors which can alter that response. For example, on a gross level, the environment itself may lead to a variety of responses: stress, circadian rhythms, enrichment, and so forth, all enter into the final behavioral pattern. On a chemical level, alterations in brain levels or turnover rates of postulated neurotransmitters can profoundly alter behavior.

If we now turn to the effects of brain damage on behavior, many studies have demonstrated that lesions in some areas of the brain result in marked alterations in behavioral patterns while lesions in other areas seem to have little effect. But in order to fully investigate this phenomenon, those factors referred to above, as well as others, must be taken into account. Thus, the effects of the lesions on neuroendocrine functions, postulated neurotransmitters, and other physiological mechanisms must be considered.

To all of these factors must be added what may be the most complicating element of all—the drug factor. Not only can drugs affect an organism in a variety of ways, but little is known about how most drugs exert their characteristic actions. The difficulties involved in studying the effects of drugs in brain-damaged subjects are thus readily apparent. However, since the title of this presentation is "Drug Response Following Brain Damage," I shall discuss and attempt to organize some of the work in this field into two parts: a general survey of the type of work being carried out in the field and a consideration of one specific area in detail in order to indicate some approaches to the overall problem.

SURVEY OF DRUG RESPONSE AND BRAIN DAMAGE

One group of studies in this field involves lesions in hypothalamic areas, especially the ventromedial nucleus of the hypothalamus, and their effects on patterns of eating behavior. These are exemplified by reports such as those by Stowe and Miller (27), Epstein (13), Reynolds (24) and Leonard *et al.*

Note: Studies in this laboratory have been supported by U.S. Public Health Service Grant MH05173 from The National Institute of Mental Health.

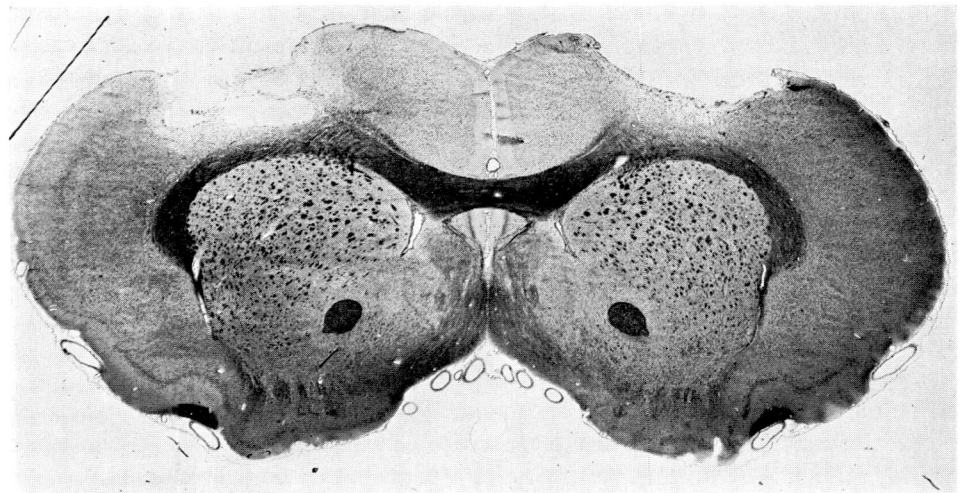

FIGURE 14-1. Bilateral ablation of frontal cortex. Luxol blue and cresyl violet. x12.

(21). In all of these investigations, lesions of the ventromedial nucleus of the hypothalamus of rats resulted in an increased food intake. Not only was amphetamine shown to be capable of supressing this increased feeding, but the drug had a greater effect in the hyperphagic rats than in control animals. This is illustrated in Table 14-1. The percentages shown for Epstein and Reynolds are based on estimates from graphs contained in their respective papers.

A second group of studies is concerned with the effects of drugs on locomotor activity of animals following brain damage. Because most of these studies have involved the use of amphetamine in primates with brain damage, quantitation and comparisons are almost meaningless since the doses of the drug employed produced no consistent effects on activity in either normal or brain-damaged animals. Some studies, however, have been reported in rats and allow certain conclusions to be drawn. Adler (1) reported that in rats with bilateral ablations of the frontal or posterior portions of the cerebral cortex there was a statistically significant increased response to the effects of amphetamine on locomotor activity, while rats with bilateral lesions of the caudate nucleus responded to amphetamine in a quantitatively similar way to control rats. Table 14-2 shows the results. The dose of amphetamine sulfate was 2.5 mg/kg i.p. and each rat was used as his own control in calculating the ratios. This change varied with the time of testing postoperatively and will be discussed in more detail below. It is interesting to note that although cocaine increases locomotor activity, lesions of the frontal or posterior cortex or caudate nucleus of rats do not result in any alterations in sensitivity to the drug (Adler, unpublished results). Furgiuelle *et al.* (14) showed that rats with lesions of the amygdala also manifested an increased sensitivity to the effects of amphetamine on locomotor activity. These results were confirmed by Allikmets and Lapin (7).

A third group of studies involves lesions which result in aggressive or hyperreactive behavior and drugs are used to quiet the animal or produce taming effects. The best examples are those in which lesions of the septal nuclei produce a sham-rage type of behavior which might be better characterized as an extreme hyperreactivity. Unlike the studies referred to above, these investigations do not lend themselves to a quantitative comparison of presurgical and postsurgical drug effects upon a specific form of behavior. This is due to the behavioral response being a consequence of the brain damage, the behavioral pattern being absent in the normal animal. However, the procedure can be used as a model to study and compare the ability of different pharmacological agents to suppress the hyperreactive behavior. Among the studies in this field are those of Horovitz et al. (19) and Stark and Henderson (26).

In any attempt to categorize, there is usually a miscellaneous group and the next group demonstrates that the area of interest in this report is no exception. The only common thread in the reports in this group is that all are concerned with the effects of drugs on some aspect of behavior following brain damage. Bilateral ablations of the frontal or posterior portions of the cortex or bilateral electrolytic lesions of the caudate nucleus were produced in adult male albino rats (Sprague-Dawley, Holtzman). Figure 14-1 shows a typical ablation of the frontal cortex. The area involved was primarily area 10 (20). Figure 14-2 is a typical ablation of the posterior cortex. Primary damage was to area 17 of the striate cortex, although adjacent areas were usually infringed upon. The drug used in these animals was harmaline, a short-acting monoamine oxidase inhibitor which is capable of producing tremors

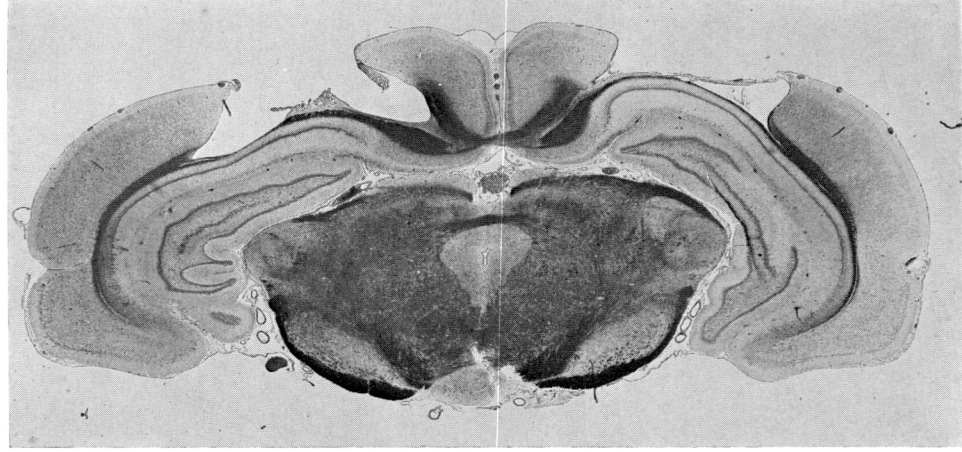

FIGURE 14–2. Bilateral ablation of posterior cortex. Luxol blue and cresyl violet. x12.

TABLE 14-1

EFFECT OF AMPHETAMINE ON EATING IN
HYPOTHALAMIC HYPERPHAGIC RATS

		Stowe and Miller	Epstein	Reynolds
Duration of Test		24 hours	6 hours	½ hour (rats food deprived)
Amphetamine Dose		5 mg/kg S.Q.	5 mg/kg i.p.	1 mg/kg S.Q.
% Depression of Eating	Normal	14	13	39
	Operated	53	61	58

Note: See the following references: Stowe and Miller 27; Epstein 13; and Reynolds 24.

in animals. A dose of 15 mg/kg of harmaline hydrochloride was administered intraperitoneally and the results are shown in Table 14-3. A pooling of the results in the brain-damaged rats shows that there is a statistically significant decrease in latency and an increase in duration of tremors in brain-damaged rats compared to control animals. Furthermore, the lesioned animals had a greater severity of tremors than did the controls. Although the lesions in our studies did not themselve produce tremor, the results are reminiscent of those of Poirier *et al.* (23) who reported that lesions interrupting nigrostriatal fibers cause tremors which are exaggerated by harmaline.

Harvey (17) demonstrated that bilateral lesions in the medial forebrain bundle of rats result in a 36 per cent decrease in total brain levels of serotonin and norepinephrine and a 2.8-fold increase in sensitivity to the behavioral depression produced by reserpine. The behavioral depression produced by chlorpromazine was unchanged.

Increased sensitivity to other drugs such as barbiturates have also been reported following brain damage. For example, Sequin and Stavraky (25) reported an increased sensitivity to barbiturates in cats after frontal ablations and semidecerebrations, while Heller *et al* (18) reported that septal damage in rats resulted in an increased barbiturate sleeping time.

TABLE 14-2

EFFECT OF AMPHETAMINE ON LOCOMOTOR ACTIVITY IN
RATS WITH BILATERAL BRAIN LESIONS
(15 weeks postoperatively)

	Number of Animals	Mean Ratio ± SE Amphetamine Counts Saline Counts
Controls	23	2.0 ± 0.32
Frontal Cortex	15	3.9 ± 0.45
Posterior Cortex	8	4.0 ± 0.77
Caudate	10	2.5 ± 0.28

TABLE 14-3

PRODUCTION OF TREMORS BY HARMALINE IN
RATS WITH BILATERAL BRAIN LESIONS
(17 weeks postoperatively)

	Number of Animals Showing Muscular Tremors	Number of Animals Not Showing Muscular Tremors	Median Latency for Onset of Tremors (min)	Median Duration of Tremors (min)
Controls	21	2	4	149
Frontal Cortex	15	0	3	176
Posterior Cortex	6	1	3.5	160
Caudate	10	0	3	179

ALTERED CONVULSANT THRESHOLDS FOLLOWING BRAIN DAMAGE

All of the studies mentioned thus far are indicative of the changes in sensitivity to pharmacological agents that may occur after brain damage. Few studies, however, have been concerned with the intimate mechanisms involved in such alterations in drug responsiveness. Although a number of approaches to the investigation of the phenomenon are possible, I would like to concentrate on those approaches utilized in our laboratory. In order to do this, I will focus on an area of particular interest to me—altered convulsant thresholds following brain damage.

It has been known for many years that damage to the central nervous system, whether produced by ablation, electrolytic lesioning, injection of irritant substances, or some other means, results in a change in convulsability. Cure et al. (11) demonstrated that epileptogenic foci in humans are activated by doses of pentylenetetrazol that induce no changes in most normal patients. Drake et al. (12) reported that an increased sensitivity to pentylenetetrazol resulted in cats after unilateral frontal ablations or semidecerebrations. Furthermore, they also noted that this phenomenon required several weeks to develop and then persisted indefinitely. The authors suggested that partially isolated neurons become supersensitive to the effects of the drug. Such a theory is based on the concepts of Cannon et al. (9) and Cannon and Rosenblueth (8) and is referred to as the Law of Denervation Supersensitivity.

Our own studies in this field began a number of years ago. We found that after bilateral ablations of either the frontal or posterior portions of the cerebral cortex of rats, an increased sensitivity developed to the convulsant effects of both flurothyl and pentylenetetrazol (2). Flurothyl chemically is bis-2,2,2 trifluroethyl ether. Single animals are placed in a one-gallon glass jar closed by a screw cap to which wire mesh containing a 3 by 3 inch surgical sponge is attached. A 10 per cent solution of flurothyl in 95 per cent ethanol (v/v) is continuously applied to the sponge at a rate of 0.103 ml/min by means of a Harvard Infusion Pump. Because of our earlier work with amphetamine in which we also suggested that denervation supersensitivity might play a role in the increased drug responsiveness (1), we felt that a study of the time course of the change was essential. If the increased convulsant sensitivity were due to diminishing or eliminating some inhibitory influences, one would expect that the sensitivity alterations would occur almost immediately. However, this change took several weeks to develop (3). Figure 14-3 shows the time course of the change in sensitivity. Frontal ablations again involved primarily area 10, while posterior ablations involved primarily area 17. The findings in this study lend support to the concept of denervation supersensitivity in the central nervous system. Thus, the time course of the alterations

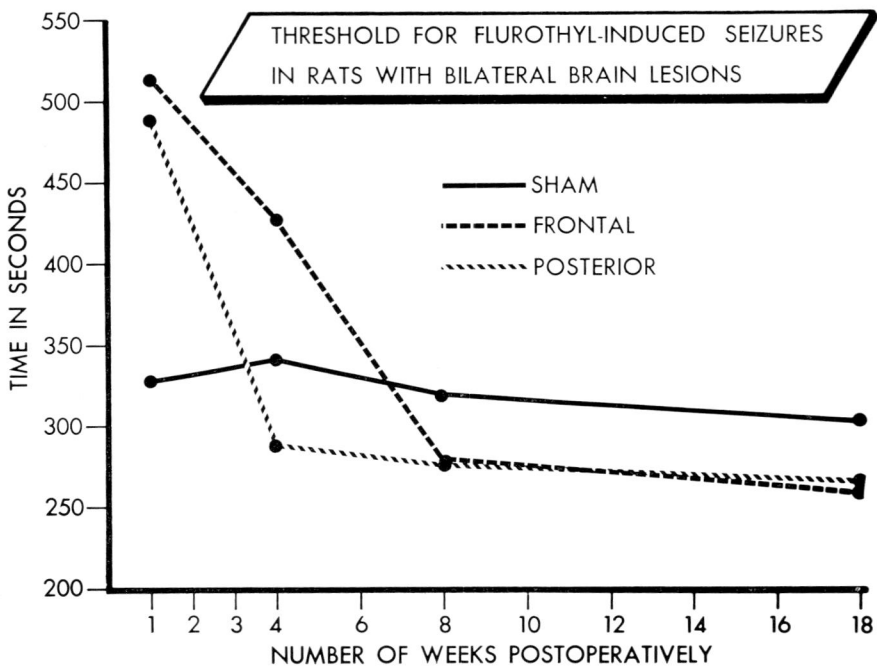

FIGURE 14–3. Time course of changes in sensitivity to flurothyl-induced seizures.

in sensitivity is one essential method in the study of altered drug response as a consequence of brain damage.

A second approach is to utilize known or postulated anatomical pathways in the study of the phenomenon. The increased convulsant sensitivity resulting from cortical ablations invited a series of studies in which lesions were placed in areas having intimate afferent and/or efferent connections with these two cortical areas. Without going into details as to the findings, I can summarize by saying that lesions of most areas had no effect on thresholds to chemically-induced seizures. A fascinating exception to these negative findings occurred in the case of the lateral geniculate nucleus. Here, the consequence of the bilateral destruction of the nucleus, especially the dorsal portions which relay visual impulses to the cortex, was a statistically significant increased sensitivity to flurothyl. Lesions of another sensory nucleus, the medial geniculate nucleus, did not result in any change in threshold to flurothyl. However, when the lesions were combined, there was a potentiation of the effects noted with lateral geniculate lesions alone. The results are shown in Table 14-4. The changes noted above occurred both with the myoclonic (preclonic) jerk endpoint and the endpoint of the frank seizure with loss of posture. We are currently investigating other combinations of sensory nuclei damage to see if these also potentiate changes in convulsability.

Recent studies in several laboratories have shown the convergence of a variety of sensory stimuli on single neurons. This may well be related to our results. Our studies of combined sensory nuclei damage and altered sensory input should provide important clues as to the pathways and mechanisms involved.

A third approach is to look for biochemical correlates of the altered thresholds. Numerous investigators have implicated the biogenic amines (serotonin, norepinephrine, dopamine) in convulsability and it thus seemed appropriate to investigate possible correlations between brain levels of the amines and thresholds to convulsants following brain damage. It was mentioned earlier that bilateral ablations of the frontal or posterior portions of the rat cerebral cortex result in an increased sensitivity to chemical convulsants. Yet, we have found that these lesions do not alter brain levels of the amines either acutely (6) or chronically (Adler and Maynert, unpublished results). It is possible that levels in localized areas of the brain or turnover rates are affected by the lesions, but that remains to be demonstrated. Miller *et al.* (22) have reported that ablation of the visual cortex in rats causes a 27.9 per cent fall in acetylcholine content in the dorsal lateral geniculate nucleus while enucleation causes a 22.6 per cent drop in acetylcholine concentration. While it is tempting to speculate that these findings are directly relevant to our work, it is unlikely that such changes could explain our results, since enuceation does not alter convulsant threshold to flurothyl (4). At the present time, in collaboration with Dr. Leon Salganicoff, we are investigating the interrelationships between amino acids and convulsability.

Finally, I would like to mention the approach of drug interactions in brain-damaged animals. Although centrally acting drugs are used to treat patients with various brain disorders including brain damage per se, most studies of drug action are carried out in normal animals, a circumstance that may explain to some extent the poor predictability of many of these tests. The use of brain-damaged animals might well provide us with useful models. As a specific example, a number of investigators (10, 15, 16) are studying the effects of anticonvulsants in animals with implanted irritant substances such as alumina cream and cobalt to see whether the anticonvulsant drugs are effective in preventing the seizures which occur as a consequence of the implantation. In our own laboratory, we have been studying the effects of anticonvulsants in rats with brain damage to see if animals with lowered convulsant thresholds have quantitatively different responses to anticonvulsants than do control animals (5). This seems to be a reasonable expectation in light of the known changes in drug sensitivity which follow brain damages. The uniqueness of the study lies in superimposing sensitivity testing to a second drug upon a background of increased sensitivity to a first drug. This could be a model in studying the reasons why certain drugs are effective in treating some

TABLE 14-4
THRESHOLD FOR FLUROTHYL-INDUCED SEIZURES IN RATS WITH
BILATERAL BRAIN LESIONS (sec ± SE)

Time After Surgery	Endpoint	Sham-Operated (n=22)	Lateral Geniculate (n=13)	Medial Geniculate (n=6)	Medial + Lateral Geniculate (n=7)
1 week	Preclonic	305 ± 6	294 ± 10	307 ± 19	338 ± 14
	Convulsion	348 ± 6	374 ± 18	351 ± 17	481 ± 26
16 weeks	Preclonic	310 ± 6	256 ± 9	305 ± 9	217 ± 19
	Convulsion	333 ± 5	272 ± 11	329 ± 8	244 ± 16

TABLE 14-5

EFFECT OF ETHOSUXIMIDE ON THRESHOLD TO FLUROTHYL-INDUCED
SEIZURES IN RATS WITH BILATERAL BRAIN LESIONS (sec+SE)
(12 weeks postoperatively)

	N	Saline	Drug	% Change
Sham-Operated	11	335 ± 6	536 ± 14	60%
Frontal Cortex	5	297 ± 5	500 ± 27	68%
Posterior Cortex	5	286 ± 10	469 ± 22	64%
Lateral Geniculate	7	294 ± 12	567 ± 24	93%

cases of brain damage but ineffective in other cases with similar symptomatology. Our data thus far indicate that such differences may, indeed, exist (Table 14-5). Ethosuximide* was administered intraperitoneally in a dose of 135 mg/kg and animals were tested one hour after injection. A greater effect is seen after lesions of the lateral geniculate nucleus than in controls or rats with cortial ablations. Preliminary studies with lesions of the limbic system also indicate specificity of response.

CONCLUSIONS

It should be quite obvious, even from this brief presentation, that brain damage can cause profound alterations in responses to pharmacological agents. From the viewpoint of knowledge about the functioning of the central nervous system, additional information about the intimate mechanisms involved in such alterations in drug response would provide valuable clues as to both the mechanisms of drug action and recovery mechanisms following brain injury. From the viewpoint of more effective treatment of patients with brain injury, such knowledge would be an invaluable aid to therapy.

* Ethosuximide was generously supplied by Drs. Graham Chen and Duncan McCarthy, Parke, Davis & Co., Ann Arbor, Michigan.

REFERENCES

1. ADLER, M.W.: Changes in sensitivity to amphetamine in rats with chronic brain damage. *J Pharmacol Exp Ther, 134*:214, 1961.
2. ADLER, M.W.: Increased sensitivity to pentylenetetrazol and flurothyl following cortical ablations in rats. *J Pharmacol Exp Ther, 148*:131, 1965.
3. ADLER, M.W.: Time course of altered sensitivity to flurothyl following cortical ablations in rats. *J Pharmacol Exp Ther, 153*:396, 1966.
4. ADLER, M.W.: Lowered thresholds to flurothyl seizures after lateral geniculate lesions in rats. *Int J Neuropharmacol, 8*:393, 1969a.
5. ADLER, M.W.: Laboratory evaluation of antiepileptic drugs: Use of chronic lesions. *Epilepsia, 10*:263, 1969b.
6. ADLER, M.W., KURIYAMA, K., AND MAYNERT, E.W.: Norepinephrine and 5-hydroxytryptamine in rat brain stem following cortical lesions. *Life Sci, 4*:141, 1965.
7. ALLIKMETS, L.H., AND LAPIN, I.P.: Influence of lesions of the amygdaloid complex on behaviour and on effects of antidepressants in rats. *Int J Neuropharmacol, 6*:99, 1967.

8. CANNON, W.B., AND ROSENBLUETH, A.: *The Supersensitivity of Denervated Structures.* New York, MacMillan, 1949.
9. CANNON, W.B., ROSENBLUETH, A., AND RAMOS, J.G.: Sensibilizacion de las neuronas espinales por denervacion parcial. *Arch Inst Cardiol Mex, 15*:327, 1945.
10. CHUSID, J.G.: Laboratory evaluation of antiepileptic drugs: Use of chronic irritative foci. *Epilepsia, 10*:239, 1969.
11. CURE, C., RASMUSSEN, T., AND JASPER, H.: Activation of seizures and electroencephalographic disturbances in epileptic and control subjects with "Metrazol". *AMA Arch Neuro Psychiat, 59*:691, 1948.
12. DRAKE, C.G., SEGUIN, J.J., AND STAVRAKY, G.W.: The effects of convulsant agents on partially isolated regions of the central nervous system. *Canad J Biochem, 34*:689, 1956.
13. EPSTEIN, A.N.: Suppression of eating and drinking by amphetamine and other drugs in normal and hyperphagic rats. *J Comp Physiol Psychol, 52*:37, 1959.
14. FURGIUELLE, A.R., AUMENTE, M.H., AND HOROVITZ, Z.P.: Acute and chronic effects of imipramine and desipramine in normal rats and in rats with lesioned amygdalae. *Arch Int Pharmacodyn, 151*:170, 1964.
15. GUERRERO-FIGUEROA, R., RYE, M.M., AND HEATH, R.G.: Effects of two benzodiazepine derivates on cortical and subcortical epileptogenic tissues in the cat and monkey. I. Limbic system structures. *Curr Ther Res, 11*:27, 1969a.
16. GUERRERO-FIGUEROA, R., RYE, M.M., AND HEATH, R.G.: Effects of two benzodiazepine derivates on cortical and subcortical epileptogenic tissues in the cat and monkey. II. Cortical and centrencephalic structures. *Curr Ther Res, 11*:40, 1969b.
17. HARVEY, J.A.: Comparison between the effects of hypothalamic lesions on brain amine levels and drug action. *J Pharmacol Exp Ther, 147*:244, 1965.
18. HELLER, A., HARVEY, J.A., HUNT, H.F., AND ROTH, L.J.: Effect of lesions in the septal forebrain of the rat on sleeping time under barbiturate. *Science, 131*:662, 1960.
19. HOROVITZ, Z.P., FURGIUELLE, A.R., BRANNICK, L.J. BURKE, J.C., AND CRAVER, B.N.: A new chemical structure with specific depressant effects on the amygdala and on the hyper-irritability of the "septal rat." *Nature, 200*:369, 1963.
20. KRIEG, W.J.S.: Accurate placement of minute lesions in the brain of the albino rat. *Quart Bull Northwestern Univ Med Sch, 20*:199, 1946.
21. LEONARD, C.A., FUJITA, T., TEDESCHI, D.H., AND FELLOWS, E.J.: Effect of d-amphetamine in hypothalamic hyperphagic rats. *The Pharmacologist, 7*:155, 1965.
22. MILLER, E., HELLER, A., AND MOORE, R.Y.: Acetylcholine in rabbit visual system nuclei after enucleation and visual cortex ablation. *J Pharmacol Exp Ther, 165*:117, 1969.
23. POIRIER, L.J., SOURKES, T.L., BOUVIER, G., BOUCHER, R., AND CARABIN, S.: Striatal amines, experimental tremor and the effect of harmaline in the monkey, *Brain, 89*:37, 1966.
24. REYNOLDS, R.W.: The effect of amphetamine on food intake in normal and hypothalamic hyperphagic rats. *J Comp Physiol Psychol, 52*:682, 1959.
25. SEGUIN, J.J., AND STAVRAKY, G.W.: The effects of barbiturates on partially isolated regions of the central nervous system. *Canad J Biochem, 35*:667, 1957.
26. STARK, P., AND HENDERSON, J.K.: Differentiation of classes of neurosedative drugs using rats with septal lesions. *Int J Neuropharmacol, 5*:385, 1966.
27. STOWE, F.R., JR., AND MILLER, A.T., JR.: The effect of amphetamine on food intake in rats with hypothalamic hyperphagia. *Experientia, 13*:114, 1957.

Chapter 15

Effects of Flurothyl on Memory Processing

ARTHUR CHERKIN

The landscape architects of Greek mythology watered the Nether World with five rivers. A drink from Lethe, the River of Forgetfulness, had a unique effect upon brain function—it completely blocked memory recall. This convenient amnesia enabled the spirits of the dead to revisit the Upper World without pining for the bliss of the Elysian Fields. The Greek mythopsychopharmacologists endowed Lethe with properties not available in modern amnesic agents. Lethean amnesia was instantaneous, complete, and purely retrograde. It wiped out the memories of a lifetime but apparently left intact the processes of information input, short-term storage, consolidation, long-term storage, and retrieval (Fig. 15-1). I should like to tell you what we are learning about these processes in the chick with the aid of flurothyl, a non-mythical amnesic agent applied by Jarvik and others (1, 4) to the study of memory consolidation in the mouse.

The action of drugs upon cortical functions interests us because it gives information about the mechanism of those functions and because we seek pharmacologic correction of cortical dysfunctions. I therefore feel obliged at the outset to justify talking about the chick, an animal with *little* neocortex, and about flurothyl, a drug that *induces* dysfunction.

The neonate chick is an advantageous subject for quantitative memory research for several reasons. Like man, and unlike rodents, its major sensory modality is vision and its active period is the daytime. It has a weak blood-brain barrier, so that experimental drugs can penetrate the brain. It can learn quickly—in a single peck—and remember well, for at least nine days. It can reliably discriminate between a target it has been trained to avoid and a novel target. Chicks are inexpensive and require little space and care, so one can afford the large numbers of subjects required for quantitative studies; we have used over twenty-five thousand chicks in my laboratory alone. Finally, the chick is remarkably resistant to the toxic effects of flurothyl. For example, we regularly expose chicks to 1.7 per cent flurothyl vapor for eight minutes, with a mortality rate of only 1.3 per cent. In contrast, such exposure

---

The author wishes to thank Professor Linus Pauling for critical comments on portions of this work. Mayme Y. Bailey and Mary A. Garman skillfully carried out the arduous chick experiments and Daniel C. Cherkin assisted with the calculations.

would kill about 95 per cent of mice, imposing a constraint on the range over which dose-dependence can be studied.

The rationale of flurothyl as an amnesic agent is as follows. It is a volatile compound (boiling point 63.9° C) of the type that passes readily through the blood-brain barrier and diffuses into the brain with relatively rapid uptake and elimination. Vapor phase administration obviates the need for injections and permits each chick to remain in its individual container throughout an experiment, thus avoiding the complications of handling and of environmental shifts. As compared to electroconvulsive shock, flurothyl has a longer induction time for convulsions but it eliminates the complications of attached electrodes (31) and the uncertainties of current flow at the brain sites relevant to memory consolidation (10, 17).

Flurothyl ($CF_3CH_2OCH_2CF_3$) is diethyl ether with the six terminal hydrogen atoms replaced by six fluorine atoms, a molecular change that confers high convulsant potency in this case. Flurothyl was introduced by Krantz *et al.* (20) as a clinical chemoconvulsant, now available as Indoklon®, for the treatment of mental disturbances. The conflicting clinical observations of its amnesic effects in man (8, 9, 16, 20, 21, 37) are not surprising in view of the chick experiments I shall describe, the gist of which is that the amnesic effect of flurothyl is dose-dependent rather than all-or-none. I shall then propose the argument that this dose-dependence provides a parsimonious interpretation of the embarrassing richness of conflicting experimental answers to the question, How much time does the brain take to consolidate information input into a long-term memory trace? Finally, I shall mention what our experiments seem to tell us about other memory processes.

Consolidation (Fig. 15-1) is a process of particular interest because it is vulnerable not only to clinical impairment, as by aging, cranial injury, Korsakoff psychosis, and viral encephalitis, but also to experimental interruption, as by ECS, chemoconvulsants and anesthetics. My laboratory and others are interested to add to the facts known about consolidation. One such fact is its time course—how long does consolidation progress? The experimental question is, How does memory retention vary as a function of the time elapsing between

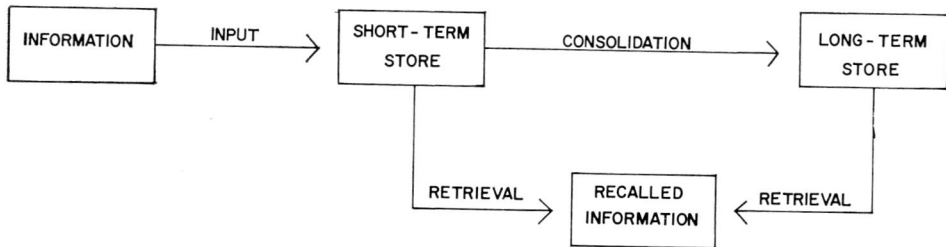

FIGURE 15-1. An oversimplified sketch of an oversimplified two-store model of memory.

Effects of Flurothyl on Memory Processing 189

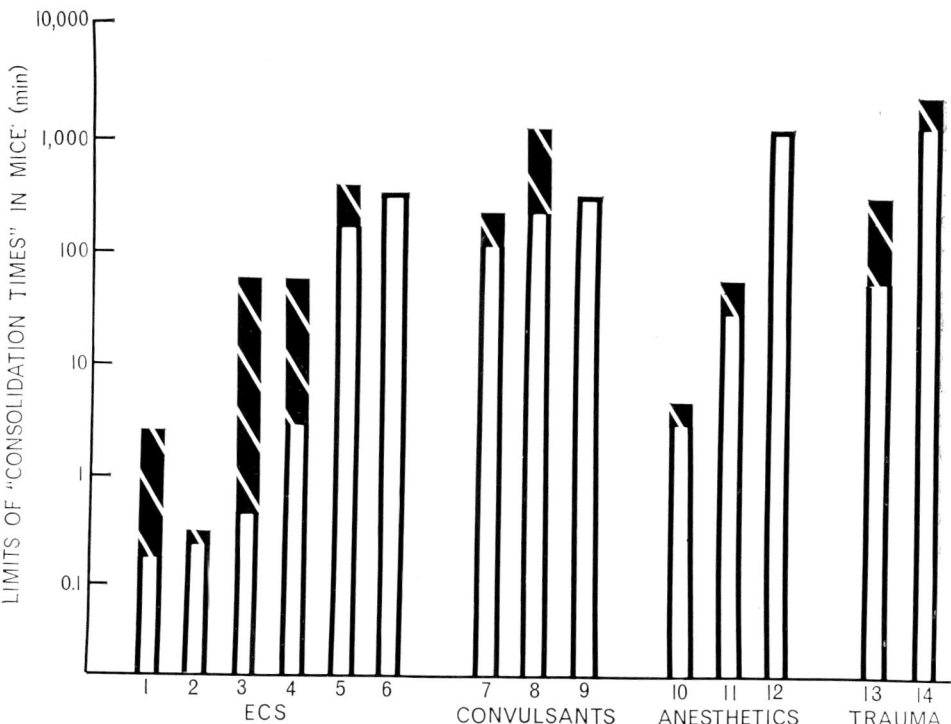

FIGURE 15-2. Divergence of "consolidation times" reported with mice; similar divergence has been reported with rats and chicks. The open bars indicate the longest post-training interval at which "consolidation" was disrupted by the specified amnesic treatment. The striped bars indicate the shortest interval at which no disruption was observed. The references are (1) Ray and Bivens, 1968; (2) Sprott, 1966; (3) McGaugh and Alpern, 1966; (4) Stephens and McGaugh, 1968; (5) McGaugh, 1966; (6) Kopp, Bohdanecky, and Jarvik, 1966; (7) Nieschulz, 1967; (8) Alpern and Kimble, 1967; (9) Bohdanecky, Kopp, and Jarvik, 1968; (10) Paolino, Quartermain, and Miller, 1966; (11) Taber and Banuazizi, 1966; (12) Alpern and Kimble, 1967; (13) Bohdanecka, Bohdanecky, and Jarvik, 1967; (14) Nieschulz, 1967.

a learning experience and an amnesic treatment? Work of the past decade has provided half the answer, namely, approximately twenty. The other half of the answer—the unit—is controversial; the leading candidates are seconds, minutes, and hours. The divergence, displayed in Figure 15-2, has been ascribed (5, 12) to differences in species, age, training situation, testing situation, and amnesic treatment.

Our chick experiment asks the question, How does "consolidation time" vary as a function of the intensity of the amnesic treatment, when all the other variables are held constant? When we apply conventional data analysis to our results, we too obtain divergent values of "consolidation time," ranging from four minutes to twenty-four hours, depending solely upon the flurothyl dose—with a single species, strain, sex, age, and experimental situation. The fact that such wide divergence results from manipulating the RA (retrograde amnesia) treatment parameters alone does not prove that these parameters are the sole determinant of the divergence shown in Figure 15-2. But it does point up the futility of interlaboratory comparisons of consolidation gradients when the intensity of amnesic treatment is an uncontrolled variable.

METHODS AND MATERIALS

Our retrograde amnesia experiment (Fig. 15-3) utilizes a simple one-trial avoidance procedure in the two-day old White Leghorn cockerel. Naive chicks peck repeatedly at a small bright target but they are readily trained to avoid it after a single trial in which the target is coated with an aversive liquid. Our standard target is a microminiature lamp bulb (5 mm by 3 mm) and the aversive liquid is methyl anthranilate. Each chick is housed in an individual carton under controlled environmental conditions (32.5 to 34.5° C; 40 to 46 % relative humidity; 23 foot-candles of illumination; and 76 db of masking white noise). The typical group size is forty chicks. They are not fed, watered, or touched during an experiment and the testing is "blind."

For the training trial, the microminiature lamp is dipped into methyl anthranilate and presented to the chick for ten seconds, during which 94 per cent of the chicks peck, with a median latency of two seconds. At graded intervals after the training trial, we dispense a measured volume of liquid flurothyl into each carton and apply a cover. The flurothyl vaporizes rapidly and tonic convulsions set in within sixty seconds. After one, two, four, eight, or sixteen minutes we replace the vapor by room air. The memory retention test trial is applied twenty to twenty-four hours later and is identical with the training trial except that the lamp is dry. The criterion of memory retention is avoidance of the lamp for ten seconds. Coversely, a peck within ten seconds is interpreted as retrograde amnesia for the prior training peck at the anthranilate-coated lamp.

RESULTS

The effects of flurothyl upon memory processes, i.e. information input, consolidation, storage, or retrieval (Fig. 15-1) are studied by selecting the time in the processing sequence at which the flurothyl treatment is interpolated. Let us first consider the dose-dependence of consolidation, for the study of which we administer the flurothyl *after* the information input. The "dose" of flurothyl has two components: (1) the *concentration* (v/v) of flurothyl in the inspired vapor and (2) the *exposure time,* by which I mean the duration of inhaling the vapor after the onset of tonic extension (opis-

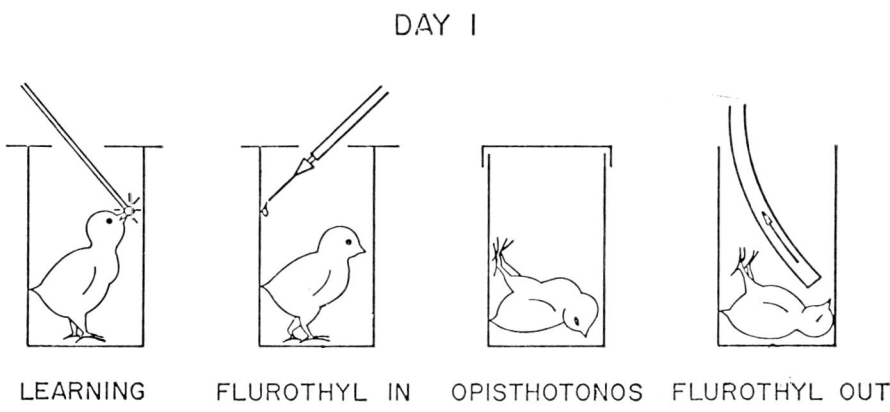
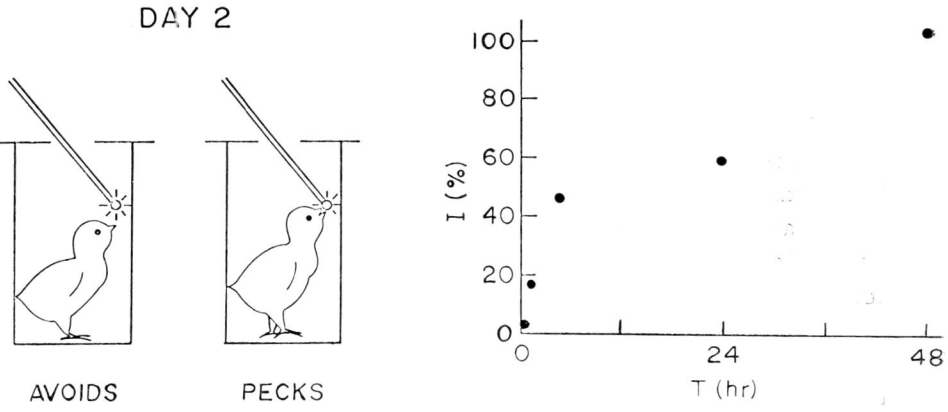

FIGURE 15–3. One-trial avoidance learning experiment in the chick. The gradient shown was obtained by exposing chicks to 1.7% flurothyl for 4, 8, and 16 minutes after onset of tonic extension (opisthotonos). The ordinate is a measure of memory retention, expressed as the "induced avoidance score"; $I = 100 \times \dfrac{\text{experimental avoidance (\%)}}{\text{control avoidance (\%)}}$. Each point represents 110 to 119 experimental chicks and 38 to 40 control chicks.

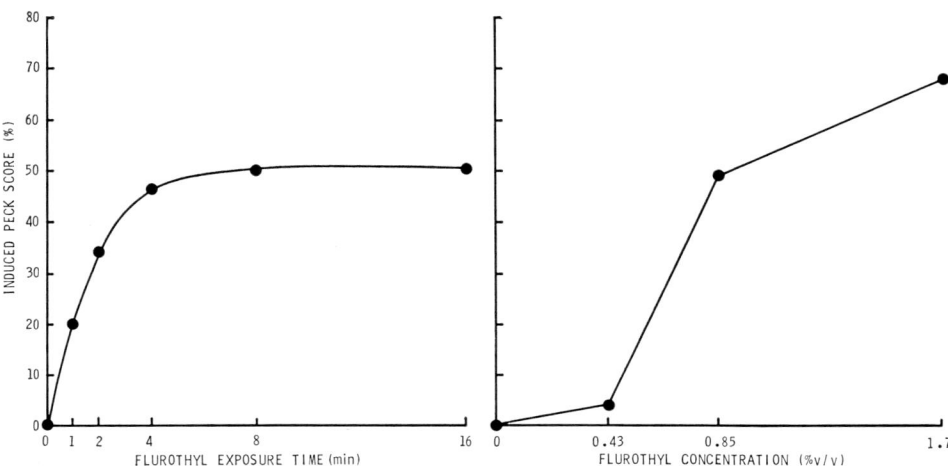

FIGURE 15-4. Dependence of retrograde amnesia upon flurothyl exposure time (*left*) and concentration (*right*). Retrograde amnesia is measured by the induced peck score, equal to $100 \frac{\text{experimental score} - \text{control score}}{100 - \text{control score}}$; the experimental and control scores are the percentage of chicks that peck during the test trial. Each point ($N = 381$ to 400) represents the pooled results of ten experiments conducted at training-treatment intervals of 4, 64, 256, and 1440 minutes, with 0.43, 0.85, and 1.7% flurothyl. (The induced peck scores for 0.43% flurothyl at training-treatment intervals of 256 and 1440 minutes were taken as zero, by extrapolation.)

thotonos). The graded effect of these two parameters (Fig. 15-4) makes it clear that the retrograde amnesia effect is dependent upon each of them, approaching a maximum in our experiment at a flurothyl concentration of 1.7 per cent and an exposure time of eight minutes. A more detailed view of the data is provided in Figure 15-5. These results confirm the preponderance of evidence for the dose-dependence of retrograde amnesia as reported with ECS using rodents,[*] convulsant drugs (42 [1967]), anesthetics (1, 6 [1968], 34, 35) and with ECS using chicks (22).

Our results confirm also the growing evidence that the standard experimental criterion of retrograde amnesia, tonic convulsion, is unreliable.[†] The rationale for this criterion was presumably the following: (1) short-term memory is sustained by a pattern of reverberatory electrical activity in the brain, (2) the pattern is disorganized by the electrical brainstorm indicated by tonic convulsions, and (3) this disorganization prevents consolidation of short-term memory into long-term memory. Our results are not consistent with this rationale. For example, we observed only negligible retrograde amnesia in two groups that experienced full tonic convulsions (Fig. 15-5,

---

[*] See the following references: 2, 10 (1968b), 15, 30, 33, 42 (1964 & 1965).

[†] See the following references: 10 (1968b), 15, 17, 23, 29, 30, 42 (1965).

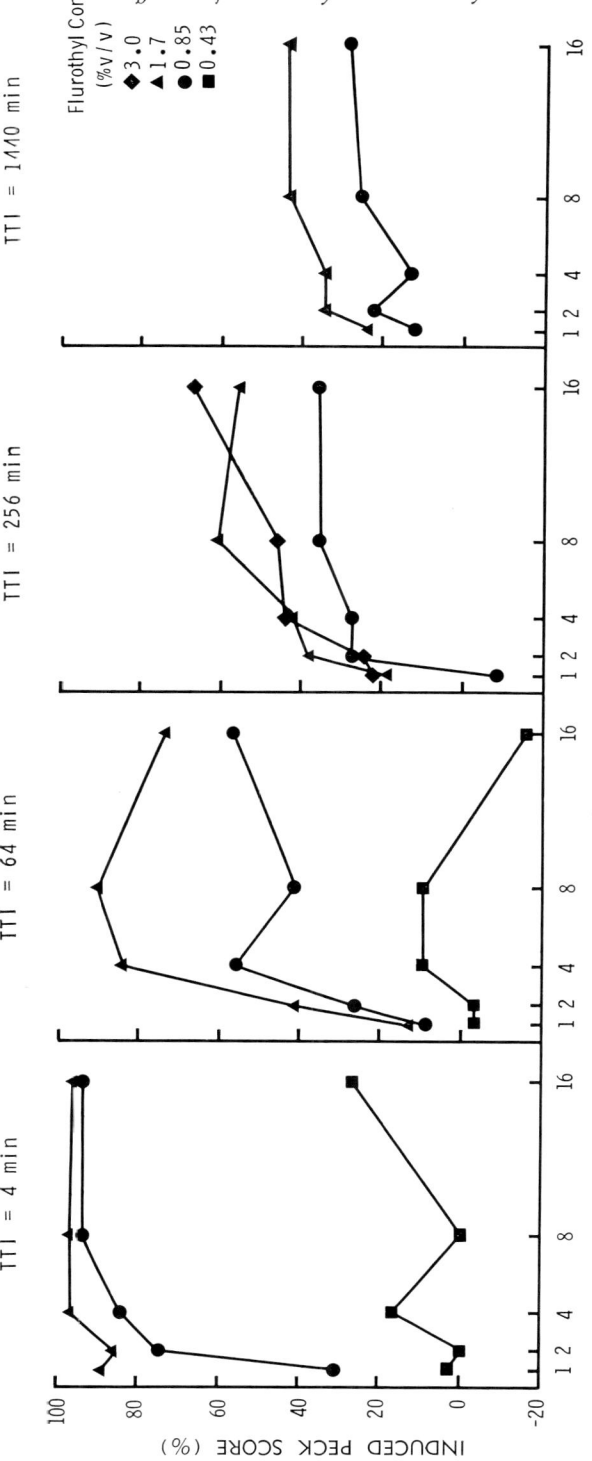

FIGURE 15-5. Dependence of induced peck score upon flurothyl exposure time and concentration. TTI = training-treatment interval. Each point represents 33 to 40 experimental chicks, except that for 3.0% flurothyl, 16-minute exposure (N = 28) which is uncertain because of excessive mortality (32%).

TTI = 64 min, 0.85% and 1.7% flurothyl, one-min exposure). Conversely, retrograde amnesia has been demonstrated in chicks (29) and mice (10 [1968b], 15) with subconvulsive electroshock and in mice (29) and rats (42 [1965]) with the overt convulsant effect of ECS suppressed by anesthetic agents. These observations of tonic convulsions without amnesia (6 [1969]) and of amnesia without overt convulsions[‡] call for a reassessment of tonic extension as a criterion for retrograde amnesia. A more appropriate criterion may develop from studies of the electrophysiological correlates of retrograde amnesia treatment with ECS (28 [1966], 23) and with flurothyl (14).

DISCUSSION

Memory Consolidation

The role of treatment intensity in retrograde amnesia studies has been recognized for years (12) but a generally acceptable interpretation is lacking. I have proposed (6 [1969]) the following synthesis within the framework of consolidation theory. A maximal retrograde amnesia treatment blocks consolidation completely, freezing the engram at the level existing at the moment of treatment. A submaximal retrograde amnesia treatment slows but fails to block consolidation, therefore it can progress at a reduced rate until the test trial, that is customarily delayed for twenty-four hours in order to avoid the confounding effects of residual short-term memory, pro-active performance deficits, and circadian variations. The assumption that retention measured after twenty-four hours is a true measure of the engram present at the moment immediately after retrograde amnesia treatment, is valid only when post-treatment consolidation is *completely* blocked. Otherwise, the twenty-four-hour retention score reflects two periods of engram consolidation: (1) between training and retrograde amnesia treatment and (2) between retrograde amnesia treatment and testing. The inflated retention score reaches the control level more rapidly than the true retention score and is interpreted as more rapid consolidation. The weaker the retrograde amnesia treatment, the shorter is the observed vulnerable period of consolidation.[§]

In our chick experiment, the extent of retrograde amnesia after treatment with 1.7% flurothyl was similar for exposure times of four, eight, and sixteen minutes (Fig. 15-4). The pooled data permit us to calculate a CT_{50} (consolidation half-time) of 9.8 hours, i.e. if chicks were flurothyl-treated 9.8 hours after the training trial and tested 24 hours later, the proportion avoiding would be 50 per cent of the proportion of untreated control chicks avoiding. The data have been subjected to the empirical log-probit trans-

---
[‡] See the following references: 10 (1968b), 15, 22, 29, 42 (1965).
[§] See the following references: 1, 2, 6 (1969), 10 (1968b), 30, 34.

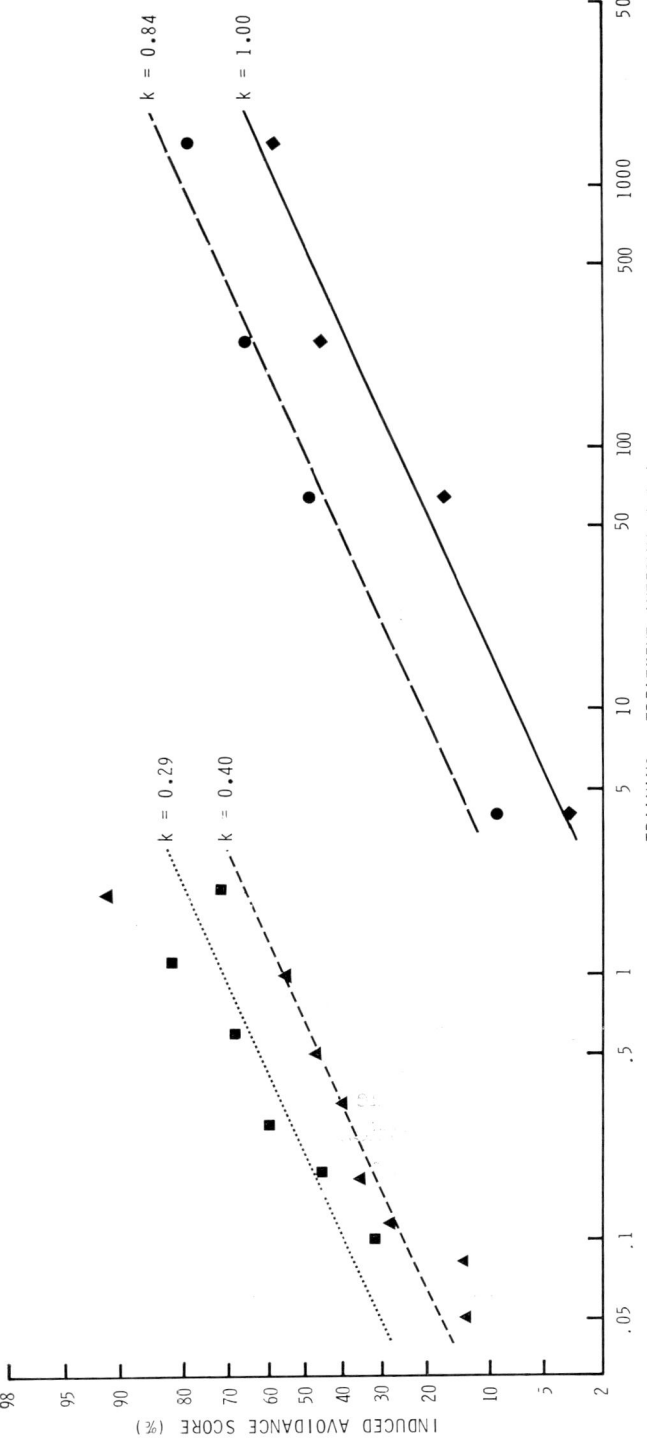

FIGURE 15–6. "Consolidation" gradients with various amnesic treatments in chicks. The ordinate is on probit scale, the abcissa on the logarithmic scale. The values of k represent the relative amnesic effectiveness compared with that of 1.7% flurothyl. The regression lines represents $y = 1.27 + 0.82 \log t + 0.82 (1 − k) \log t'$, as explained in the text. The points represent experimental data. *Diamond* = 1.7% flurothyl (a value of 102.3% at 2880 minutes is not shown); *circle* = 0.85% flurothyl; *triangle*- from ECS data of Magnus, Kanner and Hochman; *square* = z from ECS data of Lee-Teng and Sherman, 1966 (5 plateau values after 2.1 minutes, of 67% to 83%, are not shown). (N.B. Permission to re-publish this figure must be obtained from the Proceedings of the National Academy of Sciences.) (6, 1959).

formation, which permits a not unreasonable fit to a straight line (Fig. 15-6). The equation for the transformed regression line is $y = 1.27 + 0.82 \log t + (1 - k) \, 0.82 \log t'$, where t is the training-treatment interval (in seconds), t' is the treatment-test interval (in seconds), and k is a measure of the effectiveness of the retrograde amnesia treatment. The results with 0.85% flurothyl (Fig. 15-6) correspond to a CT_{50} of 1.6 hours. I have calculated that 0.85% flurothyl reduces the transformed rate of consolidation by 84%, compared to the 100% reduction assumed for 1.7% flurothyl. I have also calculated that a treatment 29% as effective as that with 1.7% flurothyl, i.e. $k=0.29$, will result in a CT_{50} of eleven seconds under our conditions. Thus, the proposed interpretation is potentially consistent with the entire range of reported gradients. Obviously, this correlation indicates that the interpretation is plausible but not that it is correct. An alternative interpretation is that different mechanisms are involved at different intervals after training. Thus, a vulnerable initial phase, lasting for less than sixty seconds after training, might be completely blocked by relatively mild amnesic treatments (34, 41).

Significant differences in avoidance were observed between control chicks and flurothyl-treated chicks (1.7%, 8-min exposure), when treatment occured twenty-four hours but not forty-eight hours post-training. The corresponding figures reported in mice (1.7% flurothyl, inspired until onset of tonic convulsions) were six but not twelve hours (4) and four but not twenty-four hours (1). The divergences by a factor of 2 to 6 are not unreasonable and are in the predicted direction.

When the consolidation process is slowed but not blocked it is potentially susceptible to additional slowing or acceleration by events during the treatment-test interval. A re-examination of post-ECS manipulations from this point of view might prove instructive, for example, the attenuating effect on retrograde amnesia of *post*-ECS injection of strychnine sulfate (28 [1968]) is plausibly interpreted as a strychnine-acceleration of an ECS-retarded consolidation.

Information Input

We are not able to test the effect of flurothyl upon information input alone. When flurothyl is administered prior to the training trial, it can affect not only input but also the ensuing consolidation. (Our finding that consolidation block requires such severe conditions of flurothyl treatment suggests, but does not prove, that the effects exerted one hour after flurothyl administration are likely to be on acquisition rather than on consolidation.) The results of our unpublished anterograde effect experiments lead to the conclusion that pretraining administration of 1.7% flurothyl impairs input, or consolidation, or both for four hours but that this effect largely disappears within twenty-four hours.

Short-term Memory

As pointed out by McGaugh (28), the gradient of long-term memory consolidation suggests a system of "short-term memory which develops within a few seconds or minutes and lasts for several hours." Consider a group of chicks flurothyl-treated four hours after the training trial. Our results indicate that their avoidance score is 37 per cent of the avoidance score determined for non-flurothyl-treated chicks, four hours post-training. The avoidance assignable to long-term memory is only 37 per cent of the total avoidance; the remaining 63 per cent presumably reflects avoidance based upon "short-term memory." Furthermore, for the entire interval during which a retrograde amnesia treatment reduces the rention score below the control level, the differential presumably reflects the contribution of "short-term" memory. In our experiments, that interval is more than twenty-four hours. This is far beyond the few seconds or minutes usually associated with short-term memory but it appears to be consistent with the McGaugh (28) interpretation. What an interesting question we have—how do decaying short-term memory and growing long-term memory interact after a learning experience?

Engram Storage

Our consolidation experiments suggest that flurothyl does not affect a consolidated engram while it is in the long-term store, because when flurothyl treatment is delayed for forty-eight hours, no impairment of retention is observed. This is consistent with the dogma that well-consolidated memory traces are highly resistant to disruption.

Memory Retrieval

Weiskrantz (41) has examined the question of why retrograde amnesia should vary with the intensity of the amnesic treatment and has suggested the following synthesis. Consolidation is affected for only about five seconds after a learning trial, an interval that suffices for "priming" the consolidation of the long-term trace, which is invulnerable thereafter to amnesic treatment. The latter, however, raises the threshold for memory retrieval in a dose-dependent manner.

Our dose-dependence results are consistent with this model but the results of two other experiments are not. First, Weiskrantz predicts a shrinkage of experimental retrograde amnesia, i.e. a recovery of memory analogous to that seen clinically after cranial injury. The experimental evidence is conflicting, with reports of recovery within two to four days (18, 25, 31, 43) and of nonrecovery after three to thirty days (7, 11, 13, 26). Our chicks showed no decrease in retrograde amnesia when tested four, twenty-four or forty-eight hours after flurothyl treatment (unpublished results). An apparent decrease after nine days, the maximum tested, was fully accounted for by a comparable fall in peck activity in control chicks "trained" on a neutral target (water-coated lamp).

Second, Weiskrantz imposes a temporal requirement upon the *order* of memory retrieval; older memories must become accessible before newer ones. Our retrograde amnesia experiment permitted us to fit a time scale to the Weiskrantz model. After a training trial, followed in four minutes by a strong flurothyl treatment, there was no recovery of memory for at least nine days. Therefore, our chicks should *not* remember to avoid the anthranilate-lamp, when the training trial occurs after flurothyl treatment, followed by a test trial within nine days. Our results, however, differed markedly from this prediction. Flurothyl-treated chicks trained two, four, twenty-four, or forty-eight hours after treatment and tested four hours or twenty-four hours later, clearly remembered to avoid the anthranilate-lamp, whereas similarly treated controls "trained" on a water-coated lamp showed normal peck performance.

CONCLUSIONS

The convergence of evidence concerning the effects of ECS or convulsant drug treatment upon the subsequent performance of a learned behavioral response makes it clear that the effect depends upon the intensity of the amnesic treatment as well as upon the time elapsing between the learning experience and the treatment. The evidence of the chick experiments reported here suggests that the amnesia reflects a major interference with consolidation of the engram rather than with retrieval of the engram. It is conceivable that both consolidation and retrieval are affected and that further research will permit partition of the total amnesic effect between the two processes. The dose-dependence of retrograde amnesia that now enables preselection of graded retrograde amnesia effects, may prove to be as clarifying in future research as it has proved to be confusing in past research. Then our modern agents, with their controllable amnesic effects, may turn out to be more useful than Lethean water, with its all-or-none effect.

REFERENCES

1. ALPERN, H.P., AND KIMBLE, D.P.: Retrograde amnesic effects of diethyl ether and bis(trifluoroethyl) ether. *J Comp Physiol Psychol, 63*:168, 1967.
2. ALPERN, H.P., AND MCGAUGH, J.L.: Retrograde amnesia as a function of duration of electroshock stimulation. *J Comp Physiol Psychol, 65*:265, 1968.
3. BOHDANECKA, M., BOHDANECKY, Z., AND JARVIK, M.E.: Amnesic effects of small bilateral brain puncture in the mouse. *Science, 157*:334, 1967.
4. BOHDANECKY, Z., KOPP, R., AND JARVIK, M.E.: Comparison of ECS and flurothyl-induced retrograde amnesia in mice. *Proc Vth Int Cong Collegium Int Neuropsychopharmacol,* 1966; *Psychopharmacologia (Berlin), 12*:91, 1968.
5. BOOTH, D.A.: Vertebrate brain ribonucleic acids and memory retention. *Psychol Bull, 68*:149, 1967.

6. CHERKIN, A.: Retrograde amnesia: Role of temperature, dose, and duration of amnesic agent. *Psychon Sci, 13*:255, 1968; Kinetics of memory consolidation: Role of amnesic treatment parameters. *Proc Nat Acad Sci USA, 63*:1094, 1969.
7. CHEVALIER, J.: Permanence of amnesia after a single post trial electroconvulsive seizure. *J Comp Physiol Psychol, 59*:125, 1965.
8. DELAY, J., DENIKER, P., GINESTET, D., BOUREAU, J., VERDEAUX, G., PERON-MAGNAN, P., AND VILLENEVUE, A.: Preliminary polygraph tests of flurothyl (by inhalation) in psychiatry. *Thérapie, 22*:793, 1967.
9. DOLENZ, B.J.: Indoklon: A clinical review. *Psychosomatics, 6*:200, 1965.
10. DORFMAN, L.J., AND JARVIK, M.E.: Comparative amnesic effects of transcorneal and transpinnate ECS in mice. *Physiol Behav, 3*:815, 1968a; A parametric study of electroshock-induced retrograde amnesia in mice. *Neuropsychologia, 6*:373, 1968b.
11. GELLER, A., AND JARVIK, M.E.: Electroconvulsive shock induced amnesia and recovery. *Psychon Sci, 10*:15, 1968.
12. GLICKMAN, S.E.: Perseverative neural processes and consolidation of the memory trace. *Psychol Bull, 58*:218, 1961.
13. HERZ, M.J., AND PEEKE, H.V.S.: Permanence of retrograde amnesia produced by electroconvulsive shock. *Science, 156*:1396, 1967; ECS-produced retrograde amnesia: Permanence vs. recovery over repeated testing. *Physiol Behav, 3*:517, 1968.
14. HERZ, M.J., SPOONER, C.E., AND CHERKIN, A.: EEG and multiple unit responses to the amnesic agent flurothyl in the chick. *Proc West Pharmacol Soc 12*:62, 1969.
15. JARVIK, M.E., AND KOPP, R.: Transcorneal electroconvulsive shock and retrograde amnesia in mice. *J Comp Physiol Psychol, 64*:431, 1967.
16. KAFI, A., TODD, R., AND DENNIS, M.S.: A comparative study of memory in patients receiving ECT and Indoklon inhalation treatment. *123d Ann Meeting Amer Psychiat Assoc*, 1967.
17. KESNER, R.P., AND DOTY, R.W.: Amnesia produced in cats by local seizure activity initiated from the amygdala. *Exp Neurol, 21*:58, 1968.
18. KOHLENBERG, R., AND TRABASSO, T.: Recovery of a conditioned emotional response after one or two electroconvulsive shocks. *J Comp Physiol Psychol, 65*:270, 1968.
19. KOPP, R., BOHDANECKY, Z., AND JARVIK, M.E.: Long temporal gradient of retrograde amnesia for a well-discriminated stimulus. *Science, 153*:1547, 1966.
20. KRANTZ, J.C., JR., TRUITT, E.B., JR., LING, A.S.C., AND SPEERS, L.: Anesthesia. LV. The pharmacologic response to hexafluorodiethyl ether. *J Pharmacol Exp Ther, 121*: 362, 1957.
21. KURLAND, A.A., HANLON, T.E., ESQUIBEL, A.J., KRANTZ, J.C., JR., AND SHEETS, C.S.: A comparative study of hexafluorodiethyl ether (Indoklon) and electroconvulsive therapy. *J Nerv Ment Dis, 129*:95, 1959.
22. LEE-TENG, E.: Retrograde amnesia in relation to subconvulsive and convulsive currents in chicks. *J Comp Physiol Psychol, 67*:135, 1969.
23. LEE-TENG, E., AND GIAQUINTO, S.: Electrocorticograms following threshold transcranial electroshocks for retrograde amnesia in chicks. *Exp Neurol, 23*:485, 1969.
24. LEE-TENG, E., AND SHERMAN, S.M.: Memory consolidation of one-trial learning in chicks. *Proc Nat Acad Sci USA, 56*:926, 1966.
25. LEWIS, D.J, MISANIN, J.R., AND MILLER, R.R.: Recovery of memory following amnesia. *Nature, 220*:704, 1968.
26. LUTTGES, M.W., AND MCGAUGH, J.L.: Permanence of retrograde amnesia produced by electroconvulsive shock. *Science, 156*:408, 1967.
27. MAGNUS, J.G., KANNER, M., AND HOCHMAN, H.: Unpublished results.
28. MCGAUGH, J.L.: Time-dependent processes in memory storage. *Science, 153*:1351, 1966;

A multi-trace view of memory storage processes. *Accad Nazionale Dei Lincei, 109*: 13, 1968.
29. McGaugh, J.L., and Alpern, H.P.: Effects of electroshock on memory: Amnesia without convulsions. *Science, 152*:665, 1966.
30. Miller, A.J.: Variations in retrograde amnesia with parameters of electroconvulsive shock and time of testing. *J Comp Physiol Psychol, 66*:40, 1968.
31. Nielson, H.C.: Evidence that electroconvulsive shock alters memory retrieval rather than memory consolidation. *Exp Neurol, 20*:3, 1968.
32. Nieschulz, V.O.: Experimentelle retrograde Amnesien bei Mausen. *Arzneimittelforschung, 17*:1151, 1967.
33. Pagano, R.R., Bush, D.F., Martin, G., and Hunt, E.B.: Duration of retrograde amnesia as a function of electroconvulsive shock intensity. *Physiol Behav, 4*:19, 1969.
34. Paolino, R.M., Quartermain, D., and Miller, N.E.: Different temporal gradients of retrograde amnesia produced by carbon dioxide anesthesia and electroconvulsive shock. *J Comp Physiol Psychol, 62*:270, 1966.
35. Quinton, E.E.: Retrograde amnesia induced by carbon dioxide inhalation. *Psychon Sci, 5*:417, 1966.
36. Ray, O.S., and Bivens, L.W.: Reinforcement magnitude as a determinant of performance decrement after electroconvulsive shock. *Science, 160*:330, 1968.
37. Spreche, D.: A quantitative comparison of electroconvulsive therapy with hexafluorodiethyl ether. *J Neuropsychiatry, 5*:132, 1963.
38. Sprott, R.L.: Retrograde amnesia in two strains of mice. *Psychol Rep, 19*:1247, 1966.
39. Stephens, G., and McGaugh, J.L.: Retrograde amnesia—effects of periodicity and degree of training. *Comm Behav Biol, 1*:267, 1968.
40. Taber, R.I., and Banuazizi, A.: CO_2-induced retrograde amnesia in a one-trial learning situation. *Psychopharmacologia (Berlin), 9*:382, 1966.
41. Weiskrantz, L.: Experimental studies of amnesia. In Whitty, C.W.M., and Zangwill, O.L. (Eds.): *Amnesia*. New York, Appleton-Century-Crofts, 1966.
42. Weissman, A.: Retrograde amnesic effect of supramaximal electroconvulsive shock on one-trial acquisition in rats: A replication. *J Comp Physiol Psychol, 57*:248, 1964; Effect of anticonvulsant drugs on ECS-induced retrograde amnesia. *Arch Int Pharmacodyn, 154*:122, 1965; Drugs and retrograde amnesia. *Int Rev Neurobiol, 10*:167, 1967.
43. Zinkin, S., and Miller, A.J.: Recovery of memory after amnesia induced by electroconvulsive shock. *Science, 155*:102, 1967.

Chapter 16

Pharmacology, Limbic Regulation, and Cortical Function

RUSSELL C. LEAF

An interesting modification of physiological relationships between the cerebral cortex and subcortical brain structures was first noted by Horovitz, Furgiuele, Brannick, Burke, and Craver (18). They discovered that a new drug, thiazesim, had a selective depressant action on convulsive seizures, elicited by electrical stimulation of the amygdala of cats. By *selective* depressant action, I mean that thiazesim did not affect cortically recorded seizures elicited by stimulation of the septum or hippocampus. In view of these latter results, it was clear that the action of thiazesim was not directly on cortical excitability and that it was not simply a general, nonspecific, depressant of subcortical excitability.

Thiazesim was tested clinically in man, and proved to have substantial efficacy as an antidepressant (12, 38). Because thiazesim had a selective action on amygdaloid regulation of cortical excitability, it seemed useful to consider whether this action might somehow explain the antidepressant effect of the drug in man. Horovitz (16, 17) has discussed evidence that thiazesim acts selectively on amygdaloid function in all mammalian species in which its effects have been studied, including primates (5), and he has argued that an inhibitory action on amygdaloid target sites may be characteristic of antidepressant drugs.

This suggestion about a possible mechanism of action of antidepressant drugs has been evaluated in a series of studies carried out by Horovitz and myself, together with a number of our associates (19, 20, 35). In general, these studies tend to support Horovitz's suggestion.

Note: This research was partly supported by United States Public Health Service Research Grants MH 13261-01, MH 13261-02, and MH 13261-03 from the National Institute of Mental Health; by Wesleyan University faculty research grants; and by gifts of equipment and supplies from the Squibb Institute for Medical Research, Wyeth Laboratories, Chas. Pfizer and Co., Inc., Hoffman-La Roche, Inc., Schering Corp., and Merck, Sharp and Dohme, Inc.

The author wishes to thank Anita S. Miller, Warren T. Johnson, Joanne L. Hager, Susan R. P. Leaf, John S. Andrews, Jr. and David Siegel for assistance in carrying out experiments described in this report; and Zola P. Horovitz, Peter L. Carlton, Larry Stein, David Margules, Stanley S. Tenen, Albert Weissman, Bernard Beer, and Solomon S. Steiner for critical discussion of its contents.

MOUSE KILLING BY RATS: A BEHAVIORAL INDEX OF AMYGDALOID FUNCTION

Our first step in testing Horovitz's hypothesis was to develop a technique for measuring the strength of a behavior that was selectively affected by amygdaloid manipulations. Then we used this technique to test the predicted effects of various drugs. The principal behavior we have studied has been mouse killing by rats. (Rats kill mice by breaking the spinal cord in the cervical region, biting through the cord in a highly stereotyped motor fashion.) Karli (26, 27) and Woods (63) had found that this response, which is characteristic of a small percentage of laboratory rats (41), was eliminated by small lesions of the central and medial amygdala. We confirmed their finding and, in addition, demonstrated that amygdaloid lesions that eliminate mouse killing usually do not depress several other behaviors that provide good measures of nonspecific, debilitating effects of psychotropic drugs (20).

For drug studies, we chose the ratio of the median effective dose (ED_{50}) of a drug required to inhibit mouse killing to the ED_{50} that was necessary to inhibit walking on a slowly rotating wooden rod suspended in the air (rotarod), as an index of selective action. Drugs for which the ED_{50} necessary to inhibit mouse killing was significantly lower than that necessary to inhibit walking on the rotarod were identified (20).

Selective inhibition of mouse killing was produced by a variety of antidepressants, including amphetamine-like stimulants, and by antihistamines. In rats antihistamines have amphetamine-like stimulant actions; in man these actions do not seem evident. Anti-anxiety agents, neuroleptics, barbiturates, and other psychotropic drugs without antidepressant or antihistaminic activity have been studied and have been consistently found to lack selective ability to inhibit mouse killing (4, 20, 23, 28, 29). If we put aside the antihistamines, these findings indicate that the ratio of the Ed_{50} necessary to inhibit mouse killing to the ED_{50} necessary to inhibit walking on the rotarod provides a convenient preclinical, animal essay for predicting potential clinical, antidepressant activity. As a rule compounds that selectively inhibit mouse killing in the rat have antidepressant activity in man. This indirectly supports Horovitz's hypothesis.

The effect of intra-amygdaloid injections of antidepressants provides a critical test of Horovitz's hypothesis (21, 35). In studies of such amygdaloid injections, we found that antidepressants, such as imipramine and thiazesim, immediately and selectively inhibited mouse killing for a duration of two to three hours. On the other hand, drugs lacking antidepressant action, such as chlorpromazine, did not inhibit mouse killing until more than an hour after injection, and this inhibitory action was not selective. When chlorpromazine inhibited killing, for example, this inhibition was accompanied by impairment of walking on the rotarod, partial ataxia, and sedation. These effects of direct amygdaloid injections support Horovitz's hypothesis that antidepressants inhibit mouse killing by selectively acting on amygdaloid function (21, 35).

Identification of the neurochemical mechanisms that control mouse killing has been the subject of several investigations. One neurochemical system that activates mouse killing appears to be cholinergic, as hypothesized by McCarthy (37). McCarthy had observed that some rats kill mice irregularly and that these rats became more reliable killers when administered low doses of cholinomimetric drugs. Subsequently, Leaf, Lerner, and Horovitz (35) were able to initiate mouse killing in rats that had never killed mice, by direct amygdaloid implantation of crystalline eserine, a cholinesterase inhibitor. In addition, they observed that intra-amygdaloid injections of methyl scopolamine inhibited mouse killing. (Siegel and Leaf, [48] found that such scopolamine-induced inhibition usually becomes irreversible after only one to three administrations.) Still more recently, Smith, King, and Hoebel (49) found that intrahypothalamic injections of cholinomimetic and anticholinesterase drugs caused initiation of mouse killing by rats that had not previously killed mice. This site appears to be identical to that at which Karli and Vergnes (30) were able to eliminate killing by lesioning, and at which King and Hoebel (32) were able to elicit killing by electrical stimulation. In addition, Smith, King, and Hoebel (49) were able to inhibit killing by administering methyl atropine to this lateral hypothalamic site. These various findings suggest that killing is activated by a cholinergic brain system that may include portions of several subcortical structures. The exact size and locus of the region from which killing can be initiated after electrical (32) or cholinergic chemical stimulation (35, 49) requires additional investigation, however. The medial amygdala and lateral hypothalamus lie close to each other in the rat brain, and it is possible that physiological manipulations have been effective in initiating killing at both sites because of spread of chemicals or of electrical current within the brain, rather than because of an extended neuroanatomical substrate for killing activation.

A neurochemical system for inhibition of mouse killing by rats seems related to metabolism of norepinephrine. Leaf, Lerner, and Horovitz (35) have observed that intra-amygdaloid norepinephrine implanation inhibits mouse killing, and Siegel (47, 48), working in my laboratory, has shown that laevo-forms of norepinephrine precursors, such as l-tyrosine, l-DOPA, and l-dopamine also inhibit mouse killing after brief postimplantation delays. Control injections of various sodium salts or of dextroisomers of catecholamines produce only infrequent and unstable inhibition of mouse killing. In addition, a number of drugs that inhibit mouse killing seem to do so by means of their effects on norepinephrine. Leaf, Lerner, and Horovitz (35) found that if rats had been adequately depleted of norepinephrine prior to amphetamine administration, no inhibitory effect on mouse killing was seen.

When compared to nonkillers, killer rats have elevated levels of norepinephrine in their forebrains, however. Reduced levels might be expected in view of the evidence that implanted norepinephrine inhibits mouse killing. Goldberg and Salama (15) have shown that mouse killers synthesize about 50 per cent more norepinephrine in forebrain, including the amygdala, than nonkillers. Killers maintain endogeneous levels of forebrain about 25 per cent higher that nonkillers although forebrain morepinephrine efflux rates are about the same as in nonkillers, and forebrain levels of tyrosine (a norepinephrine precursor) are also about equal to those of nonkillers. It is necessary to reconcile the fact that mouse killing rats have usually high synthesis rates, levels, and utilization of norepinephrine with the fact that norepinephrine implanted intra-amygdaloidally inhibits mouse killing. Unfortunately, reconcilation of these facts cannot presently be carried out. Perhaps the high rate of synthesis of norepinephrine in killer forebrains reflects some sort of reduced feedback control of norepinephrine synthesis, or some insensitivity of the target sites in the inhibitory physiological systems in which it is utilized. Acceptance of these, or of other possible hypotheses must await further experimentation.

Norepinephrine is unlikely to be the sole neurochemical inhibitor of mouse killing, because so many of the drugs that inhibit mouse killing do not appear to influence norepinephrine metabolism. In support of the apparent presence of other amygdaloid neurochemical inhibitors, Leaf, Lerner, and Horovitz (35) found that thiazesim and antihistamines retain their full inhibitory effectiveness against mouse killing in rats that have been depleted of norepinephrine, even though emphetamins were no longer effective inhibitors. In addition, Karli, Vergnes, and Didiergeorges (31) have reported evidence of an amygdaloid serotoninergic mouse killing inhibitory system, and Kulkarni (33) has observed effects of serotonin precursors that support their findings.

As might be expected from these indications of multiple inhibitory systems, attempts to deplete a single neurochemical inhibitor have not produced a highly effective method for killing activation in nonkilling rats. Leaf, Lerner, and Horovitz (35) were able to initiate killing in a few rats with highly toxic doses of 1-α-methyl-tyrosine, and Karli, Vergnes and Didiergeorges (31) were able to initiate killing in some rats with parachlorophenylalanine, but neither drug was able to activate killing in all subjects. All of these findings are consistent with the view that multiple neurochemical systems for inhibition of mouse killing exist.

Complex as its neurochemical basis may be, drug action that produces inhibition of mouse killing seems to be correlated with a selective action of drugs on cortical excitability. Wedeking and Bagington (61), using Goddard's (14) technique for inducing seizures by low intensity brain stimulation, found that impramine, amitryptyline, and thiazesim all have a selective anticonvulsant action on seizures induced by amygdaloid stimulation. They found that blocking of these seizures occurred at antidepressant drug doses significantly lower than those necessary to inhibit seizures elicited by stimulation of other sites, such as the septum or motor cortex. Chlordiazepoxide and meprobamate had a nonspecific anticonvulsant action on seizures elicited by stimulation of all brain sites tested. A number of other psychoactive drugs, such as chlorpromazine and haloperidol, were not effective anticonvulsants.

The apparent correlations between amygdaloid and cortical function, antidepressant action, and inhibition of mouse killing may indicate that the cortex plays a role in the mechanism of inhibition of mouse killing. Alternatively, a single amygdaloid mechanism may act simultaneously on cortical function and a wholly subcortical mechanism that control mouse killing.

If I might summarize at this point, we can assert three rather general hypotheses that have arisen from, or received some support from, the findings I have outlined. First, inhibition of mouse killing seems to provide an index of the physiological state of the amygdala. Second, antidepressant drugs seem to inhibit mouse killing by acting selectively on amygdaloid physiology. Third, the amygdaloid changes that cause inhibition of mouse killing seem to be associated with an encephalically ascending mechanism that produces selective changes in cortical excitability.

BRAIN SYSTEMS FOR BEHAVIORAL PLASTICITY

Why should mouse killing, antidepressant drug action, amygdaloid function, and cortical excitability be related? Our knowledge is presently so sketchy that any attempt to interpret their relationships must be highly speculative and is likely to prove wrong in many details. Systematic speculation has both critical and heuristic functions, however, which guide future experiments. With these aims in view, I would like to outline some ideas about why inhibition of mouse killing predicts antidepressant drug action, and how amygdaloid and cortical function might be involved in that relationship.

The evolution of brain systems for the inhibition of mouse killing should be associated with some change that increased the survival capacity of rats. Since forebrain structures play critical roles in inhibition of mouse killing, the behavioral functions of these structures may have participated in that change. Interpretations of the behavioral functions of the amygdala, cerebral cortex, and other forebrain structures have traditionally stressed the role of these areas in the plasticity of individual behavior (58). Within this tradition, Jackson (22) deserves special credit for his careful explication of the importance of inhibition of lower encephalic structures by higher ones. He discussed "release of lower centers," as a necessary consequence of damage to structures mediating "higher" levels of function (which he assumed were controlled by higher encephalic structures). Jackson's recognition that evolution of "higher" mechanisms for behavioral control usually required efficient mechanisms for inhibition of the "lower" mechanisms is an important, though often ignored, fundamental principle. The development of higher encephalic structures appears, in fact, to be largely due to evolution of inhibitory mechanisms. Today, of course, we recognize that mechanisms of "higher" functions may involve encephalically ascending, as well as decending, pathways. A modern extension of Jackson's thesis suggests, however, that new mechanisms that could successfully take over the function for which mouse killing had evolved might necessitate evolution of higher ecephalic inhibition of the older mechanisms.

There is some available support for such a Jacksonian view from data on inhibition of mouse killing. Karli (27) had demonstrated long ago that forebrain removal could lead to initiation of mouse killing in some rats that did not kill mice. More recently, Siegel and Leaf (48) found that complete lesions of the medial and lateral septal nuclei of rats at the level of the anterior commissure caused release of killing in all nonkiller rats. The mouse killing caused by septal lesions occurred immediately after presentation of a mouse, and it had the same stereotyped motor pattern that spontaneously initiated killers exhibit. Like spontaneously initiated killing, it was permanently blocked by amygdaloid lesions, and reversibly blocked by crystalline intraamygdaloid implantation of norepinephrine (2, 48). In view of the extensive anatomical interconnections of septum and amygdala, these latter findings suggests that release of amygdaloid inhibition may be the cause of fore-brain lesion-induced initiation of mouse killing.

The mouse killing released by septal lesions usually disappeared in a few days, at approximately the same rate as the biting attack directed toward gloves worn by experimenters, another aggressive component of the septal "hyperirritability" syndrome (6). The disappearance of these two components of the syndrome occurred at different times in different animals, however, and I should stress that each of the aggressive responses caused by septal lesions had a different motor pattern and different stimulus controls. The cortex may play a role in the disappearance of components of the septal syndrome, since Teitelbaum and Cytawa (59) have observed that the syndrome can be reinstituted after a single instance of depression of cortical function with topical KCl.

We might speculate, then, that active amygdaloid inhibition of mouse killing may have been developed as a consequence of the development of some "higher" brain functions, in which the cortex may play a role. What is the nature of these "higher" functions? They must have high adaptive value because they can completely replace mouse killing, for rats can live without ever exhibiting the killing response. It may be significant that the Norway rat seems to be a rapidly evolving species. Like man's, the Norway rat's environment has changed rapidly in the recent past. Like man, the Norway rat has been exceptionally successful in adapting to these changes. One of its "higher" functions may involve high individual ability to adapt to new environmental circumstances. Interestingly enough, the best understood mechanism that plays a role in such adaptation in the rat is the forebrain reinforcement system discovered by Olds and Milner (42). This system is hypothesized to have some selective, ascending effect on cortical function during behavioral adaptation (43) and, therefore, it should be considered as a mechanism which might play a role in inhibition of mouse killing.

Olds and Olds (43) have suggested that this system is anatomically associated with the medial forebrain bundle and that it is the physiological substrate of a final common path for all behavioral changes that occur as a function of consequences of the rat's past behavior. Olds and Olds' hypothesis may be incorrect (60) but its basic ideas provide a useful frame for some pharmacological, physiological, and neurochemical data that seem relevant to our present concerns. Stein (50 to 52) has discussed a variety of evidence that endogenous norepinephrine, released from ascending fibers of the medical forebrain bundle by reinforcing brain stimulation, may mediate the reinforcing effectiveness of that stimulation. Stein and Wise (53) found that both amphetamine and reinforcing brain stimulation caused release of norepinephrine in the amygdala. In addition, Wise and Stein demonstrated that the reinforcing effectiveness of stimulation of the medial forebrain bundle can be inhibited by pharmacological blockage of norepinephrine biosynthesis and restored by intracerebral administration of norepinephrine. If some single, noradrenergic final common path of physiological activity is involved in all operant reinforcement, then we might expect the same noradrenergic system to both facilitate new, "higher" behavior and inhibit old, "lower" behavior. When we consider the self-stimulation and mouse killing findings, amygdaloid norepinephrine does seem a possible candidate for roles in both processes.

The behavioral effects of amygdaloid norepinephrine are not limited to self-stimulation and mouse killing, of course. Margules (39) observed that the suppressant effects of punishment on a previously trained operant response were inhibited by implantation of intra-amygdaloid norepinephrine. In confirmation of this finding, Andrews and Leaf (3) found that the rate of highly suppressed, intermittently punished, operant avoidance responses were increased by the same treatment. These results suggest that changes in amygdaloid norepinephrine may tend to suppress any old, previously prepotent behavior and stimultaneously facilitate any relatively new behavior.

THE PROBLEM OF ACTIVE BEHAVIORAL INHIBITION

Facilitative effects of subcortical norepinephrine, and particularly amygdaloid norepinephrine, on the development of new behavior can be profitably attacked by self-stimulation studies. The inhibitory behavioral effects of subcortical norepinephrine are not so easily illuminated by such an approach, however. Behavioral tasks in which subjects are required to inhibit responding would seem, at first glance, to be appropriate for studying the inhibitory behavioral effects of norepinephrine. Unfortunately, no method of assuring a clear physiological manipulation of norepinephrine in such situations is available. The results of Stein and Wise (53) and Endroczi and Koranyi (10) suggest that norepinephrine must be released by reinforcement in brief spurts, rather than at a slow steady rate. The effect of single stimuli is too small to measure at present. The apparent phasic action of norepinephrine may be functionally critical, since Steiner, Beer, and Shaffer (55) found that the reward value of self-stimulation is not determined by the average rate of stimulation, but by moment-to-moment fluctuations in the reinforcing and aversive properties of the consequences of stimulation. Thus, techniques that modify tonically available norepinephrine probably do not provide a physiological manipulation in studies in which rapid, often conflicting, response sequences are required of subjects.

In a preliminary attempt to develop a method for studying the relationship between inhibitory behavioral effects of norepinephrine and cortical function we have turned, not to self-stimulation or punishment, but to some problems associated with rapid eye movement sleep (REM). The REM state provides a physiological condition in which extended periods of cortical desynchronization are associated with active inhibition of essentially all muscular output and in which norepinephrine appears to be functionally necessary for the inhibition to occur (24, 25).

Our initial studies of REM sleep, unfortunately, have proven of limited interpretive value. I shall try to describe two of them briefly, primarily to bring out some problems they raise.

We chose to study operant avoidance acquisition because Leaf and Muller (34) had shown that sympatholytic drugs like chlorpromazine easily impair operant avoidance acquisition. Drugs that only temporarily increase available norepinephrine, like amphetamine or imipramine, did not seem to facilitate it significantly. These findings suggest that endogenous norepinephrine may be necessary for the slow acquisition of new behavior that does occur, but the available norepinephrine seems to be utilized at a maximal rate during the first acquisition session, (one possible reason for maximal norepinephrine utilization is the very large number of electric shocks received during this period of acquisition.)

We deprived rats of REM for seventy-two hours by the method of Morden, Mitchell, and Dement (40), and allowed controls to obtain REM. We expected this treatment to cause an impairment in utilization of norepinephrine in the REM-deprived rats, which we hoped would lead to impaired avoidance acquisition. We also studied groups of REM-deprived and control rats that were given either imipramine or electroconvulsive shock (ECS) subsequent to the seventy-two hour period, but prior to avoidance acquisition. It was possible that these treatments might impair performance in avoidance acquisition significantly beyond the level produced by REM deprivation alone, even though both imipramine and ECS can alleviate the need for REM during the period of REM rebound following REM deprivation (8, 24). Such impairment might be expected, in spite of possible subsequent alleviation of need for REM, because imipramine and ECS might both reduce total norepinephrine available during the first two hours of avoidance acquisition (13). (In behavioral situations in which much less total norepinephrine utilization seems to occur than in operant avoidance acquisition, of course, imipramine or ECS might alleviate effects of REM deprivation on acquisition of new behavior. Stern (56, 57) has reported such findings with imipramine.).

TABLE 16-1

AVOIDANCE ACQUISITION PERFORMANCE

Treatment Group	N	Mean Avoidance Responses + SEM
Home Cage	10	492.8 ± 83.2
Large Pot Controls	20	497.2 ± 56.1
Small Pot Controls	20	399.4 ± 47.2
Home Cage Imipramine	10	505.0 ± 55.9
Large Pot Imipramine	10	463.7 ± 44.7
Small Pot Imipramine	10	352.8 ± 36.5
Large Pot ECS	10	394.2 ± 66.1
Small Pot ECS	10	229.8 ± 42.3

*Rats were given a single 2-hour operant avoidance acquisition session, beginning one hour after removal from their 72-hour treatment, under conditions similar to those described by Leaf and Muller (34). The response-shock interval was 45 sec, the shock-shock interval was 3 sec, and the scrambled shocks were 0.3 sec at 85 v ac, generated by a Scientific Prototype 4008J shocker. Home cage subjects were in individual colony cages for the 72 hours preceding the beginning of their experimental treatment; large pot subjects were maintained on large flower pots surrounded by water for 72 hours, as described by Morden, Mitchell, and Dement (40); and small pot subjects were maintained on small flower pots surrounded by water for 72 hours, as described by Morden, Mitchell, and Dement (40). Imipramine subjects received 7.5 mg/kg imipramine HCl i.p., one hour prior to the beginning of avoidance acquisition; ECS subjects received one, 0.2 sec, one 150 ma ac convulsive shock via ear electrodes one half hour prior to the beginning of the avoidance acquisition; and control subjects received either i.p. saline injections or sham-ECS administration.

Our results, which are shown in Table 16-1, were not wholly consistent with our expectations (36). Although it decreased responding somewhat, REM deprivation did not have a significant effect on avoidance acquisition. This may reflect the fact that absolute norepinephrine levels in the rat brain are not significantly affected by seventy-two hours of REM deprivation (44, 46). There are many experiments that demonstrate that REM deprivation produces substantial effects on norepinephrine synthesis and utilization, however, and these metabolic changes seem to last well into the time period we used to study avoidance acquisition. Unfortunately, two available studies of these metabolic changes report exactly opposite findings. Pujol, Jouvet, and Glowinski (44) report that norepinephrine utilization remains low during REM deprivation and increases during REM recovery, and Schildkraut and Hartman (46) report the opposite. Our behavioral findings are as difficult to interpret as these contradictory biochemical reports, because other investigators have sometimes reported learning deficits and sometimes not, during acquisition of a variety of responses, as a consequence of REM deprivation similar to ours (1, 7, 11, 56, 57).

Imipramine and ECS tended to impair operant avoidance acquisition performance and their effects seemed greater in REM-deprived rats. While these results are consistent with the argument about the role of norepinephrine in this task outlined above, the magnitude of the effects we observed was not impressive.

In spite of our difficulties in designing and interpreting studies on this issue, several recent reports suggest that norepinephrine, REM sleep atony, reinforcement systems, and cortical function may be mutually related. Steiner and Ellman (54) observed that REM deprivation reduces the threshold levels of reinforcing electrical current that are necessary for self-stimulation at medial forebrain bundle sites. In addition, Ellman and Steiner (9) found that rats were allowed to self-stimulate at such sites during REM deprivation did not show any REM rebound after the deprivation. Both results suggest new approaches for testing implications of our speculative argument.

CONCLUSIONS

Attempts to provide a rational explanation for why pharmacological inhibition of mouse killing by rats should be related to the antidepressant action of drugs in man are presently highly speculative, and highly incomplete. The viability of such attempts will depend, in large part, on the correctness of our views about how the brain is organized to carry out the control of behavioral functions.

Two ideas are central in the view of amygdaloid inhibition of mouse killing which I have tried to sketch here. First, of course, is the classical concept of encephalic levels of function, which views the newer, higher levels as functioning by modifying the actions of lower, phylogenetically older, control mechanisms. Second, and perhaps as important as the concept of encephalic levels, is the relatively new concept that diffuse, nonspecific, modulating systems are at least as important in controlling the behavior of higher organisms as are specific information-processing and motor systems.

The regulatory role of the amygdala in "higher adaptive functions" and the explication of how such posited functions became concerned with mouse killing by rats and depression in man is an effort which may never prove of much rational value, in spite of the empirical observations that led to such a quest. On the other hand, it is surprising that this effort is consistent with a variety of facts that have also not received penetrating interpretations, in spite of their ubiquity. The view that the amygdala may be a center for the action of diffuse, nonspecific, inhibitory systems on motor systems "explains" several well-known facts which did not initially concern me, in the course of the intellectual quest I have been reporting on here: for example, stimulation of the amygdala erratically facilitates, elicits, or inhibits a wide variety of behaviors, suggesting that its principal function is not specific to any one, easily defined, class of behaviors; destruction of the amygdala does not impair survival under typical laboratory conditions, suggesting that it is not essential for the performance of any behaviors of universal adaptive importance (feeding, copulation, etcetera); and destruction of the amygdala does cause changes in the timing and frequency of a wide variety of behaviors, even though it is not essential for their performance, suggesting that its function is one of modulation rather than control of the patterning of behavior. These "explanations" support and extend the preliminary interpretations of our own data which I have outlines here, and they lend some indirect encouragement to the effort to find a rational explanation of the relationship between mouse killing by rats and depression in man.

As we deepen our very imperfect understanding of mouse killing, we also have some reason to hope that our observations will have value for understanding issues about brain function that are broadly significant, in man as well as the rat.

REFERENCES

1. ALBERT, I., CICALA, G.A., AND SIEGEL, J.: Further studies on the behavioral effects of REM deprivation. Paper presented at the annual meeting of the Assoiciation for the Psychophysiological Study of Sleep, 1969.
2. ANDREWS, J.S., JR.: Unpublished observations, 1969.
3. ANDREWS, J.S.. JR., AND LEAF, R.C.: Effect of amygdaloid norepinephrine on active-passive avoidance-avoidance conflict. *Proceedings of the 77th Annual Convention of the American Psychological Association.* In press, 1969.
4. BARNES, H.W., CUNNINGHAM, N.L., PENBERTHY, C., AND GOGERTY, J.H.: Effects of various CNS-active substances and CNS-modifying influences on mouse-killing behavior of rats. *Pharmacologist,* 9:200, 1967.

5. BARRATT, E.S., AND PRAY, S.L.: The effect of a chemically depressed amygdala on the behavioral manifestations of LSD-25 in cats. *Exp Neurol, 12*:173, 1965.
6. BRADY, J.V., AND NAUTA, W.J.H.: Subcortical mechanisms in emotional behavior; affective changes following septal forebrain lesions in the albino rat. *J Comp Physiol Psychol, 46*:339, 1953.
7. BRILL, R.W., AND GOODMAN, I.J.: Effects of REM sleep deprivation on memory in cats. Paper presented at the annual meeting of the Association for Psychophysiological Study of Sleep, 1969.
8. COHEN, H.B., DUNCAN, R.F., AND DEMENT, W.C.: Sleep: the effect of electroconvulsive shock in cats deprived of REM sleep. *Science, 156*:1646, 1967.
9. ELLEMAN, S.J., AND STEINER, S.S.: The effect of electrical self-stimulation on REM rebound. Paper presented at the annual meeting of the Eastern Psychological Association, 1969.
10. ENDROCZI, E., AND KORANYI, L.: Integration of emotional reactions in the brain stem, diencephalic and limbic system. In Garattini, S., and Sigg, E.B. (Eds.: *Aggressive Behaviour*. Amsterdam, Excerpta Media Foundation, 1969, p. 132.
11. FISHBEIN, W.: The effects of paradoxical sleep deprivation during the retention interval on long-term memory. Paper presented at the annual meeting of the Association for the Psychophysiological Study of Sleep, 1969.
12. FREEMAN, H., OKTEM, M.R., KRISTOFFERSON, M.W., AND GORBY, C.K.: Theraputic efficacy of a new antidepressant, thiazenone (SQ 10,496). *Curr Ther Res, 7*:655, 1965.
13. GLOWINSKI, J., AND BALDESSARINI, R.J.: Metabolism of norepinephrine in the central nervous system. *Pharmacol Rev, 18*:1201, 1966.
14. GODDARD, G.V.: Development of epileptic seizures through brain stimulation at low intensity. *Nature, 214*:1020, 1967.
15. GOLDBERG, M.E., AND SALAMA, A.I.: Norepinephrine turnover and brain monoamine levels in aggressive mouse-killing rats. *Biochem Pharmacol, 18*:532, 1969.
16. HOROVITZ, Z.P.: Psychoactive drugs and limbic system of the brain. *Psychosomatics, 6*:281, 1965.
17. HOROVITZ, Z.P.: The relationship of the amygdala to the mechanism of action of two types of anti-depressants. In Wortis, J. (Ed.): *Recent Advances in Biological Psychiatry*. New York, Plenum Press, 1966, vol. III, p. 21.
18. HOROVITZ, Z.P., FURGIUELE, A.R., BRANNICK, L.J., BURKE, J.C., AND CRAVER, B.N.: A new chemical structure with specific depressant effects on the amygdala and on the hyperirritability of the "septal rat." *Nature, 200*:369, 1963.
19. HOROVITZ, Z.P., RAGOZZINO, P.W., AND LEAF, R.C.: Selective block of rat mouse-killing by antidepressants. *Life Sci, 4*:1909, 1965.
20. HOROVITZ, Z.P., PIALA, J.J., HIGH, J.P., BURKE, J.C., AND LEAF, R.C.: Effects of drugs on the mouse-killing (muricide) test and its relationship to amygdaloid function. *Int J Neuropharmacol, 5*:405, 1966.
21. HOROVITZ, Z.P., AND LEAF, R.: The effects of direct injections of psychotropic drugs into the amygdalae of rats, and its relationship to antidepressant site of action. In Brill, H., Cole, J.O., Deniker, P., Hippius, H., and Bradley, P.B. (Eds.): *Proceedings of the Vth International Congress of the Collegium Internationale Neuropsychopharmacologicum*. International Congress Series No. 129. Amsterdam, Excerpta Medica Foundation, 1967, p. 1042.
22. JACKSON, J.H.: *Selected Writings of John Hughlings Jackson*. London, Hodder and Stoughton, 1931.
23. JANSSEN, P.A.J., NIEMEGEERS, C.J.E., AND VERRUGGEN, F.S.: A propos d'une methode d'investigation de substances susceptibles de modifier le comportement agressif inne

du rat blanc vis-a-vis de la souris blanche. *Psychopharmacologica (Berlin), 3*:114, 1962.
24. JOUVET, M.: Neurophysiology of the states of sleep. *Physiol Rev, 47*:117, 1967.
25. JOUVET, M.: Biogenic amines and the states of sleep, *Science, 163*:32, 1969.
26. KARLI, P.: Effects de lesions experimentales des noyaux amygdaliens et du lobe frontal sur le comportement d'agression du rat vis-avis de la souris. *Compte Rendus des Scenes, Societe de Biologie et de ses filiales, 149*:2227, 1955.
27. KARLI, P.: The Norway rat's killing response to the white mouse: An experimental analysis. *Behaviour, 10*:61, 1956.
28. KARLI, P.: Action des substances dites "tranquillisa tes" sur l'agressivite interspecifique rat-souris. *Compte Rendus des Seances, Societe de Biologie et de ses Filiales, 153*: 467, 1959a.
29. KARLI, P.: Recherches pharmacologiques sur les comportement d'agression rat-souris. *J Physiol (Paris), 51*:497, 1959b.
30. KARLI, P., AND VERGNES, M.: Dissociation experimentale du comportement d'agression interspecifique rat-souris et du comportement alimentaire. *Compte Rendus des Sceanes, Societe de Biologie et des Filiales, 158*:650, 1964.
31. KARLI, P., VERGNES, M., AND DIDIERGEORGES, F.: Rat-mouse interspecific aggressive behaviour and its manipulation by brain ablation and by brain stimulation. In Garattini, S., and Sigg, E.B. (Eds.) *Aggressive Behavior*. Amsterdam, Excerpta Medica Foundation, 1969, p. 47.
32. KING, M., AND HOEBEL, B.: Killing elicited by brain stimulation in rats. *Communications in Behavioral Biology (Part A), 2*:173, 1968.
33. KULKARNI, A.S.: Muricidal block produced by 5-hydroxytryptophan and various drugs. *Life Sci, 7*:125, 1968.
34. LEAF, R.C., AND MULLER, S.A.: Central cholinergic response inhibition during massed free-operant and discrete-trial avoidance acquisition. In Brill, H., Cole, J.O., Deniker, P., Hippius, H., and Bradley, P.B. (Eds.) : *Proceedings of the Vth International Congress of the Collegium Internationale Neuropsychopharmacologicum*. International Congress Series No. 129. Amsterdam, Excerpta Medica Foundation, 1967, p. 1043.
35. LEAF, R.C., LERNER, L., AND HOROVITZ, Z.P.: The role of the amygdala in the pharmacological and endocrinological manipulation of agression. In Garattini, S., and Sigg, E.B. (Eds.) : *Aggressive Behaviour*. Amsterdam, Excerpta Medica Foundation, 1969, p. 120.
36. LEAF, R.C., MILLER, A.S., HAGER, J., AND JOHNSON, W.T.: Unpublished observations, 1969.
37. MCCARTHY, D.: Mouse-killing in rats treated with pilocarpine, *Fed Proc, 25*:385, 1966.
38. MAPP, Y.I.S., DYKYJ, R., GORBY, C.L., AND NODINE, J.H.: Initial human pharmacology of SQ 10, 496, an amygdaloid depressant compound. *Pharmacologist, 5*:234, 1963.
39. MARGULES, D.L.: Noradrenergic basis of inhibition between reward and punishment in amygdala. *J Comp Physiol Psychol, 66*:329, 1968.
40. MORDEN, M., MITCHELL, G., AND DEMENT, W.: Percent REM sleep deprivation and compensation phenomena in the rat. *Brain Res, 5*:339, 1967.
41. MYER, J.S.: Early experience and the development of mouse killing by rats. *J Comp Physiol Psychol, 67*:46, 1969.
42. OLDS, J., AND MILNER, P.: Positive reinforcement produced by electrical stimulation of septal area and other regions of rat brain. *J Comp Physiol Psychol, 47*:419, 1954.
43. OLES, J., AND OLDS, M.E.: Mechanisms of voluntary behavior. In Heath, R.G. (Ed.) : *The Role of Pleasure in Behavior*. New York, Harper & Row, 1964, p. 23.

44. PUJOL, J.F., MOURET, J., JOUVET, M., AND GLOWINSKI, J.: Increased turnover of cerebral norepinephrine during rebound of paradoxical sleep in the rat. *Science, 159*:112, 1968.
45. SCHILDKRAUT, J.J., AND KETY, S.S.: Biogenic amines and emotion. *Science, 156*:21, 1967.
46. SCHILDKRAUT, J.J., AND HARTMANN, E.: Seventy-two hours on an island: Effects on the turnover and metabolism of norepinephrine in rat brain. Paper presented at the annual meeting of the Association for the Psychophysiological Study of Sleep, 1969.
47. SIEGEL, D.: Unpublished thesis, Wesleyan University, 1969.
48. SIEGEL, D., AND LEAF, R.C.: Effects of septal and amygdaloid brain lesions in rats on mouse killing. Paper presented at the annual meeting of the Eastern Psychological Association, 1969.
49. SMITH, D.D., KING, M.B., AND HOEREL, B.G.: Killing: cholinergic control in the lateral hypothalamus. Proceedings of the 77th Annual Convention of the American Psychological Association, 1969.
50. STEIN, L.: Amphetamine and neural reward mechanisms. In Steinberg, H., de Reuck, A.V.S., and Knight, J. (Eds.: *Ciba Foundation Symposium on Animal Behaviour and Drug Action*. London, J. and A. Churchill, Ltd., 1964a, p. 91.
51. STEIN, L.: Reciprocal action of reward and punishment mechanisms. In Heath, R.G. (Ed.) : *The Role of Pleasure in Behavior*. New York, Harper, 1964b, p. 113.
52. STEIN, L.: Psychopharmacological substrates of mental depression. In Garattini, S., and Dukes, M.S.G. (Eds.) : *Antidepressant Drugs*. Amsterdam, Excerpta Medica Foundation, 1967.
53. STEIN, L., AND WISE, C.D.: Release of norepinephrine from hypothalamus and amygdala by rewarding medial forebrain stimulation and amphetamine. *J Comp Physiol Psychol, 67*:189, 1969.
54. STEINER, S.S., AND ELLMAN, S.: REM deprivation lowers intracranial self-stimulation thresholds. Paper presented at the annual meeting of the Eastern Psychological Association, 1969.
55. STEINER, S.S., BEER, B., AND SHAFFER, M.M.: Escape from self-produced rates of brain stimulation. *Science, 163*:90, 1968.
56. STERN, W.: Effects of REM sleep deprivation upon the acquisition and maintenance of behavior in the rat. Paper presented at the annual meeting of the Association for the Psychophysiological Study of Sleep, 1969a.
57. STERN, W.: Pharmacological modification of the effects of REM sleep deprivation upon active and passive avoidance in the rat. Paper presented at the annual meeting of the Association for the Psychophysiological Study of Sleep, 1969b.
58. TEITELBAUM, P.: *Physiological Psychology*. Englewood Cliffs, Prentice-Hall, 1967.
59. TEITELBAUM, P., and CYTAWA, J.: Spreading depression and *recovery from lateral* hypothalamic damage. *Science, 147*:61, 1965.
60. VALENSTEIN, E.S.: The anatomical locus of reinforcement. In Stellar, E., and Sprague, J.M. (Eds.) : *Progress in Physiological Psychology*. New York, Academic Press, 1966, p. 149.
61. WEDEKING, P.W., AND BABINGTON, R.G.: Effects of neurological agents on seizures elicited by low intensity brain stimulation in rats. *Pharmacologist*, in press, 1969.
62. WISE, C.D., AND STEIN, L.: Facilitation of brain self-stimulation by central administration of norepinephrine. *Science, 163*:299, 1969.
63. WOODS, J.W.: Taming of the wild Norway rat by rhinecephalic lesions. *Nature, 178*: 869, 1956.

Chapter 17

Hypoxia as a Model for Drug Effects on Behavior

STEPHEN A. WEINSTEIN

The evaluation of the effects of a pharmacologic agent on cerebral function involves analysis of effects at several levels ranging from metabolism to behavior. Each new drug must be considered within the context of the action of other substances whose effects are already established. It is of utmost importance for the understanding of drug action, to ascertain the functional relationships between observed effects at different levels.

Oxygen availability is one of the prime determinants of cerebral function and any significant deficiency is reflected by alterations in metabolism, blood flow, temperature, electrical activity, and behavior of the organism. Because of its broad ranging effects, its quantifiability, and its susceptibilty to control the manipulation of oxygen levels provides an excellent means for altering cerebral function and observing the relationships of changes over a broad range of function.

Our laboratory has focused on the behavioral, respiratory, and electrophysiological changes produced by decreases in oxygen and/ or increases in carbon dioxide. The results which we have obtained can be divided into the following categories:

1. the interaction between sensory stimuli and increases CO_2 on the respiratory system;
2. the conditionability of cardiovascular and respiratory effects produced by in-increased CO_2 and decreased O_2;
3. the motivational properties of increased CO_2 or decreased O_2;
4. the decrements in performance of learned motor responses produced by hypoxia;
5. the conditionability of decrements in performance produced by hypoxia;
6. factors which improve performance in hypoxia; and
7. the interaction between motivation and the deleterious effects of hypoxia on behavior.

The regulation of respiration is one of the prime means for maintaining tissue oxygen and since there is usually a reciprocal relationship between O_2 and CO_2, chemoreceptive tissues responsive to both have developed with peripheral receptors responding primarily to oxygen lack and central recptors to CO_2 excess. There is also a responsivity to sensory inputs. The first series of studies elucidate the interaction between sensory and chemical stimuli and the second, the differences in the conditionability of their respiratory effects.

Fowle and Weinstein (1) demonstrated that the increase in ventilation produced by increased CO_2 was independent of and additive to the respiratory effects of cutaneous electrical stimulation and that sodium pentobarbital decreased the sensitivity to CO_2 but not the effect of cutaneous electrical stimulation upon the reticular formation. This is illustrated in Figure 17-1.

One of the important aspects of this study derives from the observation that, as the CO_2 concentration increases above 5 per cent in the awake animal, the parallel displacement of the CO_2 response curve by the cutaneous electric shock is disrupted, and in fact, there is often a reversal in the tendency of

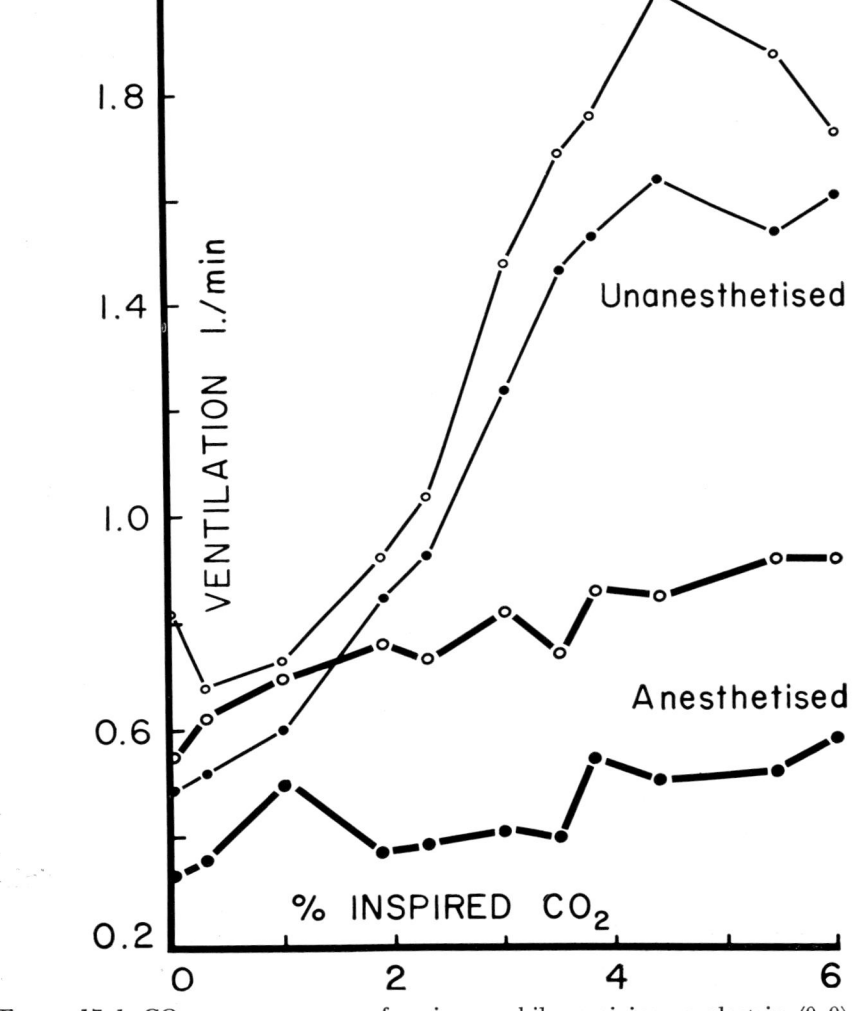

FIGURE 17–1. CO_2 response curves of a pigeon while receiving an electric (0–0), and not receiving a shock (0–0) with and without sodium pentobarbital.

ventilation to rise with increased CO_2. Under anesthesia, the displacement remains parallel with CO_2 concentrations as high as 9 percent and there is no reversal. We interpreted this as indicating a significant aversive sensory component produced by CO_2 concentrations above 5 percent. This aversive component, eliminated by anesthesia, is distinct form direct sensory effects upon the reticular formation of cutaneous electrical stimulation. This interpretation fits well with our later findings that the ventilatory response to CO_2 concentrations below 6 percent are not classically conditioned (2), while according to Birukov et al. (3) classical conditioning of the ventilatory response occurs with very high CO_2 concentrations. This conditioning being a function of the aversive sensory component.

It should be emphasized that although increased CO_2 and decreased O_2 do not elicit respiratory changes which are conditionable, they do provide motivation for the acquisition of an escape response (4). Figure 17-2 illustrates the results obtained in an escape conditioning experiment in pigeons. The latency of the escape response is inversely related to the concentrations and directly related to the interval between presentations.

Figure 17-3 illustrates the changes in heart and respiratory rate in rats that occurs during learned escape from 6% CO_2. There is a fall in heart rate and an increase in respiratory rate during the CO_2 presentation. However, even after ten days with up to fifteen trials per day, there is no change in either measure during the warning signal that precedes each CO_2 presentation. These results lend additional support to the report of Weinstein and Fowle which indicated a lack of respiratory and cardiovascular conditioning when 6% CO_2 was used as the unconditional stimulus in birds.

Having demonstrated the motivational properties of O_2 and CO_2, we looked at their interaction (5). Mice were trained to escape from 4% CO_2 and were then subjected to varying levels of hypoxia. Figure 17-4 illustrates the results of this study. Mild levels of hypoxia produce a decreased latency of escape, but as the hypoxia becomes more severe, the latency increases. This early facilitation of the escape response fits well with the finding of Nielson (6) indicating an increased ventilatory response to CO_2 produced by hypoxia. Within the physiological range the learned responses parallel the ventilatory response. This parallelism disappears when the deleterious effects of hypoxia upon neural function begin to predominate. This is clearly demonstrated in the effects of hypoxia upon self-stimulation.

Figures 17-5a,b illustrate the effects of hypoxia upon self-stimulation of the hypothalamus. When electrodes are implanted in the medial forebrain bundle of the rat and the current is adjusted to produce maximal self-stimulation rate, there is a graded decrement in performance, with 14% O_2 producing virtually no decrement and with 8% O_2 producing a significant slowing (7). If the same rats are tested after the current is decreased, a very different pattern emerges, with 14% O_2 producing a decrement equal of that produced by 8%.

It becomes apparent that just as the ranges of chemical and sensory stimulation determine their interaction, the level of motivation determines, within certain ranges, the magnitude of the performance decrement produced by hypoxia. The issue does not rest there, for another set of factors enter into the performance decrement produced by hypoxia. Past experience markedly alters the effects of hypoxia upon behavior. These effects are manifested in two ways. First there is a conditioning of the suppression of behavior produced by low oxygen (8). Rats with implanted hypothalamic electrodes were allowed

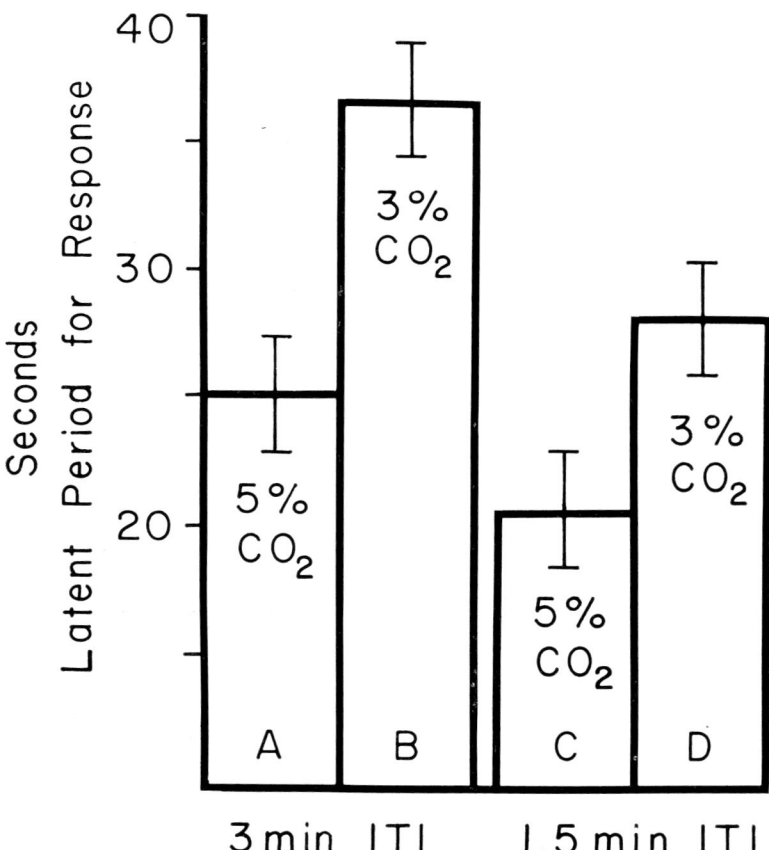

FIGURE 17–2. One standard error of the mean is indicated for each treatment combination.

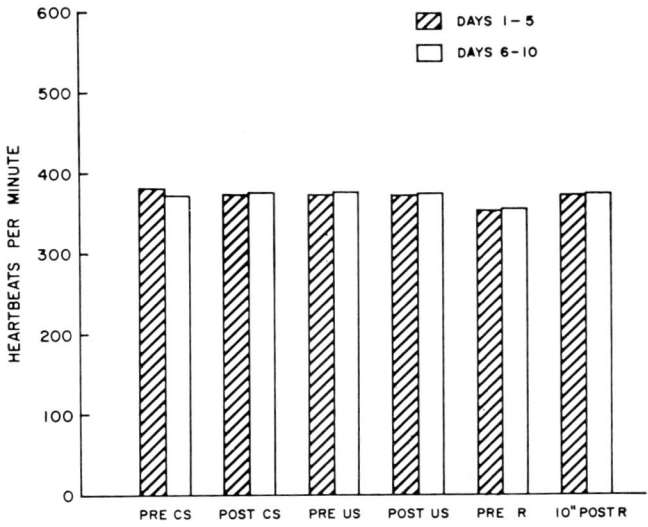

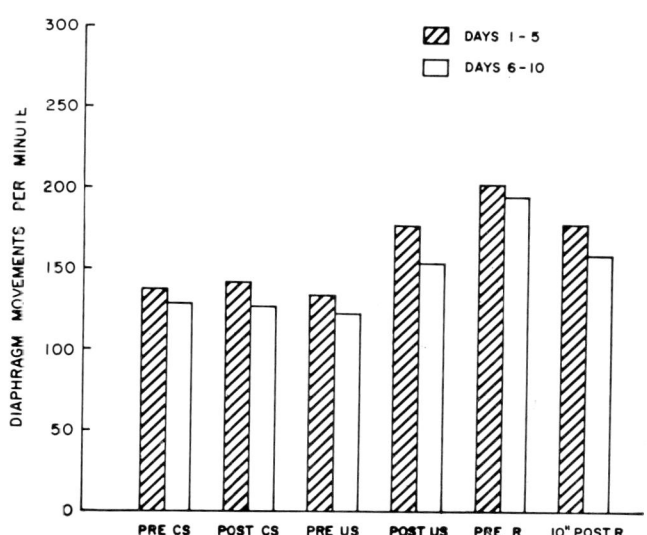

FIGURE 17-3. Mean heart rate and respiratory rate for 800 trials in rats escaping from 6% CO_2. The interval between 11 heart beats and 5 diaphragmatic movements was measured just prior to CS onset, just after CS onset, prior to US (CO_2) onset, after US onset, prior to the escape response, and ten seconds after the escape response.

to self-stimulate on a variable interval schedule (mean interval: 15 sec). Periodically, during a one hour session, they received a warning signal followed by a rapid reduction of inspired oxygen from 21% to 6%. After several days of conditioning, the suppression produced by the hypoxia was conditioned. Although 8% O_2 produces a marked decrement in self-stimulation, conditioned suppression cannot be obtained, unless the O_2 level is low enough to completely eliminate self-stimulation (i.e. below 8% for short exposures). CO_2 concentrations as high as 10% do not produce conditionable suppression, although when 4% CO_2 is presented in air to an animal previously conditioned with 6% O_2 there is a suppression identical to that produced by the hypoxia. We postulate that this is due to the elicitation of increased respiration which is the conditioned signal for suppression. In essence the conditioning sequence is as follows: (1) tone and light on, (2) O_2 decreases, (3) mild hypoxia, (4) increased ventilation, (5) increased hypoxia, and (6) suppression of behavior. Although experimentally we intend the light and tone to act as the conditional signals, the ventilatory increment becomes the

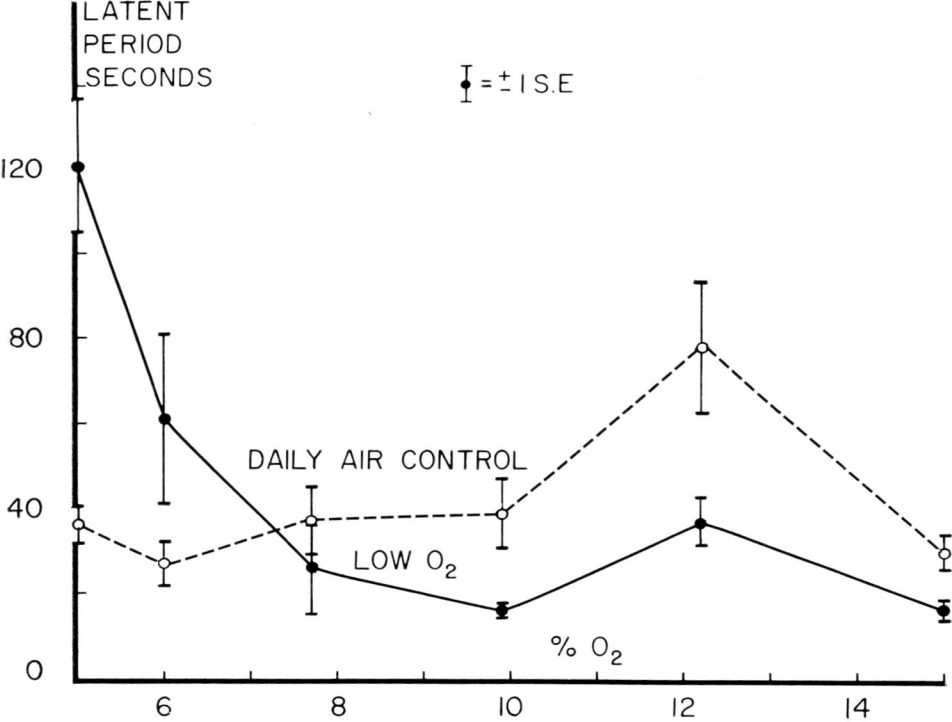

FIGURE 17-4. The results obtained in one animal illustrating the effect of hypoxia upon latent period for learned escape from CO_2. Open circles are means for escape from CO_2 in 21% O_2 on the same day as the hypoxia trials indicated by the solid circle directly above and below.

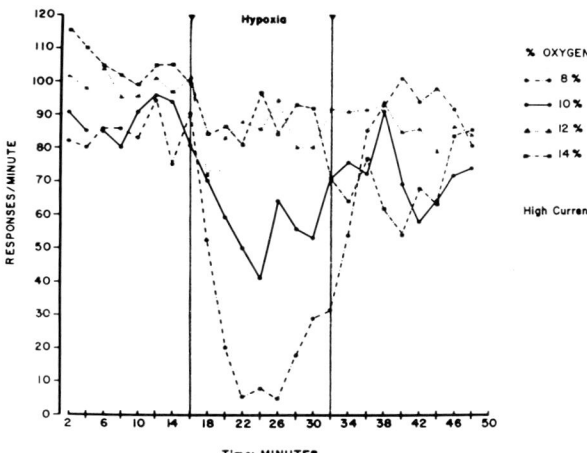

FIGURE 17–5a. Mean self-stimulation rates for four animals in sequential two-minute period; first in air, then in 16 minutes of low oxygen and during recovery in air. Animals were stimulated with high current levels sufficient to produce self-stimulation rates between 80 to 115 (high motivation) responses per minute in air.

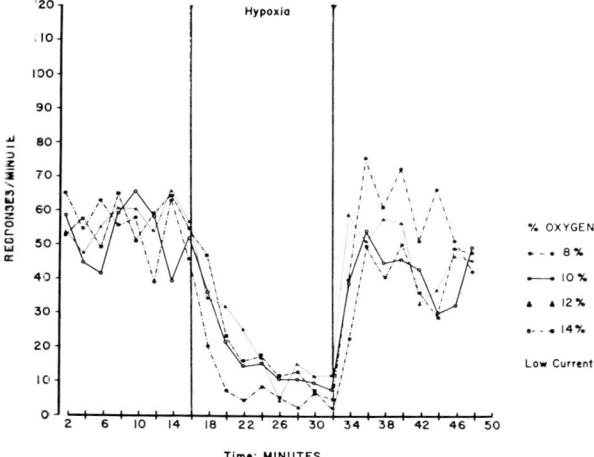

FIGURE 17–5b. Mean self-stimulation rate for four animals in sequential two-minute period; first in air, then in 16 minutes of low oxygen and during recovery in air. Animals were stimulated with current levels reduced to produce self-stimulation rates between 40 to 65 (low motivation) responses per minute in air.

effective C.S. . Proof of this assertion is derived from an additional set of observations. As conditioning continues, (at about day 7) some subjects do not suppress to the C. S. (light and tone). When these animals are given 4% CO_2, they immediately terminate self-stimulation. If the testing interval is broken down into 30-sec periods and the data analyzed over the course of conditioning, it becomes apparent that the animals use the first thirty seconds of the test period to determine if they are in fact in low oxygen. They do this by using their ventilation as a discriminative stimulus. If they are hyperventilating, they stop pressing and complete suppression ensues. If on the other hand they are not hyperventilating, they start self-stimulation and continue throughout the test trial. This testing of the environment, utilizing the ventilatory response as a discriminative stimulus does not occur during the initial stages of conditioning, This can be seen in Figures 17-6 and 17-7 (see legend

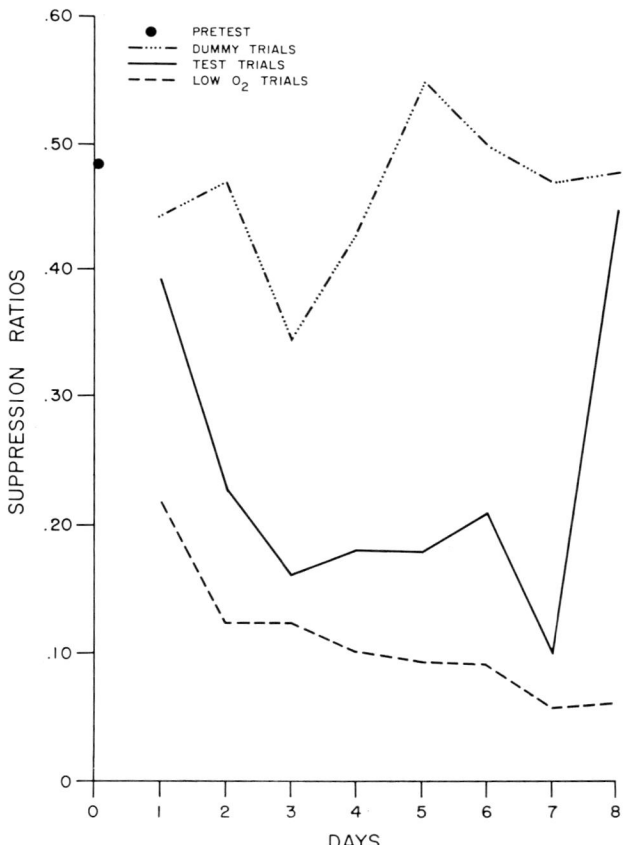

FIGURE 17–6. This illustrates the mean suppression ratios for 8 days of conditioning for the dummy, test and conditioning trials. The mean pretest ratio (.48) is shown on the ordinate.

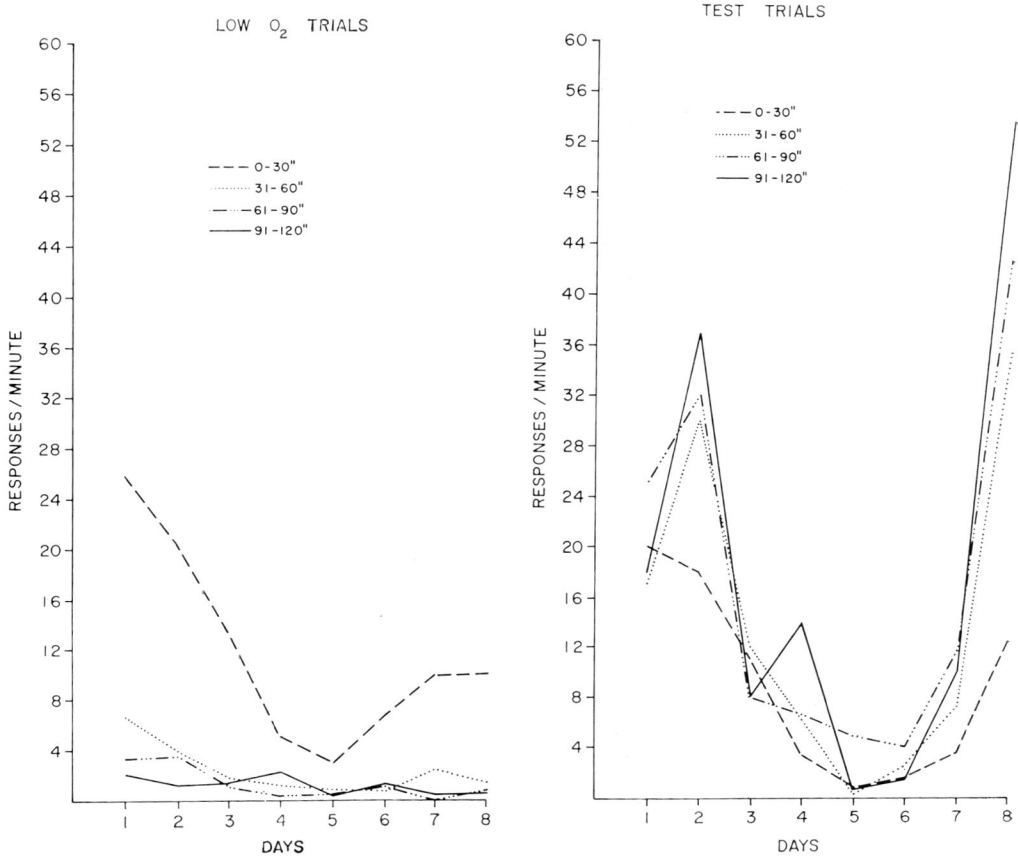

FIGURE 17-7. This illustrates the mean number of responses for 7 animals for consecutive 30-second periods during conditioning (low O_2) and test trials as a function of days of training.

for further explanation). This use of the ventilatory response as a discriminative stimulus is feasable because the initial conditional signal (light or tone) does not elicit a ventilatory response and there is a constant difference between the conditioning trials with low O_2 (in which there is always hyperventilation), and the test trials without low O_2 (never hyperventilation). Thus, nonconditionability of the ventilatory response to CO_2 increase, or O_2 decrease provides the basis for potentially vital discriminations about the nature of the gaseous environment.

The second effect of experience is more difficult to explain. When rats are placed in 8% O_2 for sixteen minutes per day, there is a gradual improvement on each daily exposure (9). This is illustrated in Figure 17-8. This adaptation is not that usually attributed to "acclimatization" as can be seen in Figures 17-9 a, b, c, d, e, which demonstrate that there is no alteration in pH, pO_2, PCO_2, hematocrit, or oxygen saturation in rats during an identical pattern of low O_2 exposure.

This adaptation to repeated hypoxic exposure may well indicate highly specific adaptive mechanisms within the central nervous system. Whether these are predominately due to psychological or physiological-biochemical factors has yet to be determined. This is discussed in detail in a recent publication (9).

It becomes evident that the history of exposure to altered gaseous environments is an important factor in determining performance. Whether an improvement or decrement results is determined by the nature of this experience. One must exercise great caution in any attempt to evaluate the action of a chemical alteration on performance and neural function and carefully weigh both psychological and physiological effects.

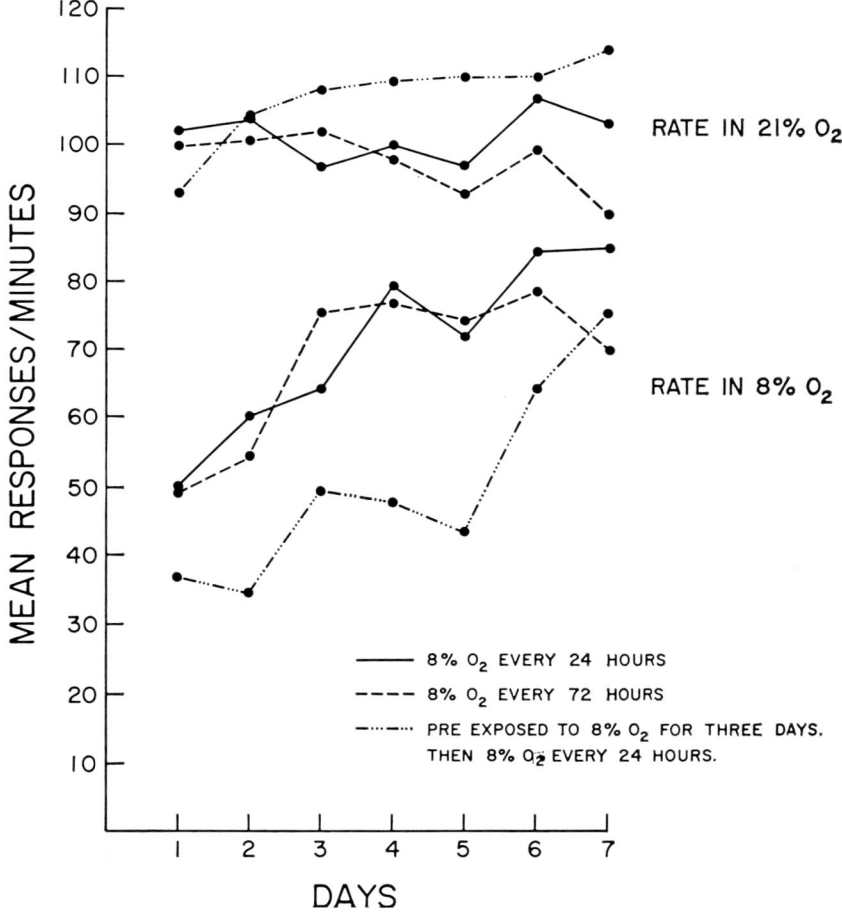

FIGURE 17–8. Hypothalamic self-stimulation rates for three groups of eight rats each on exposure to 8% O_2 under three conditions as indicated on the illustration.

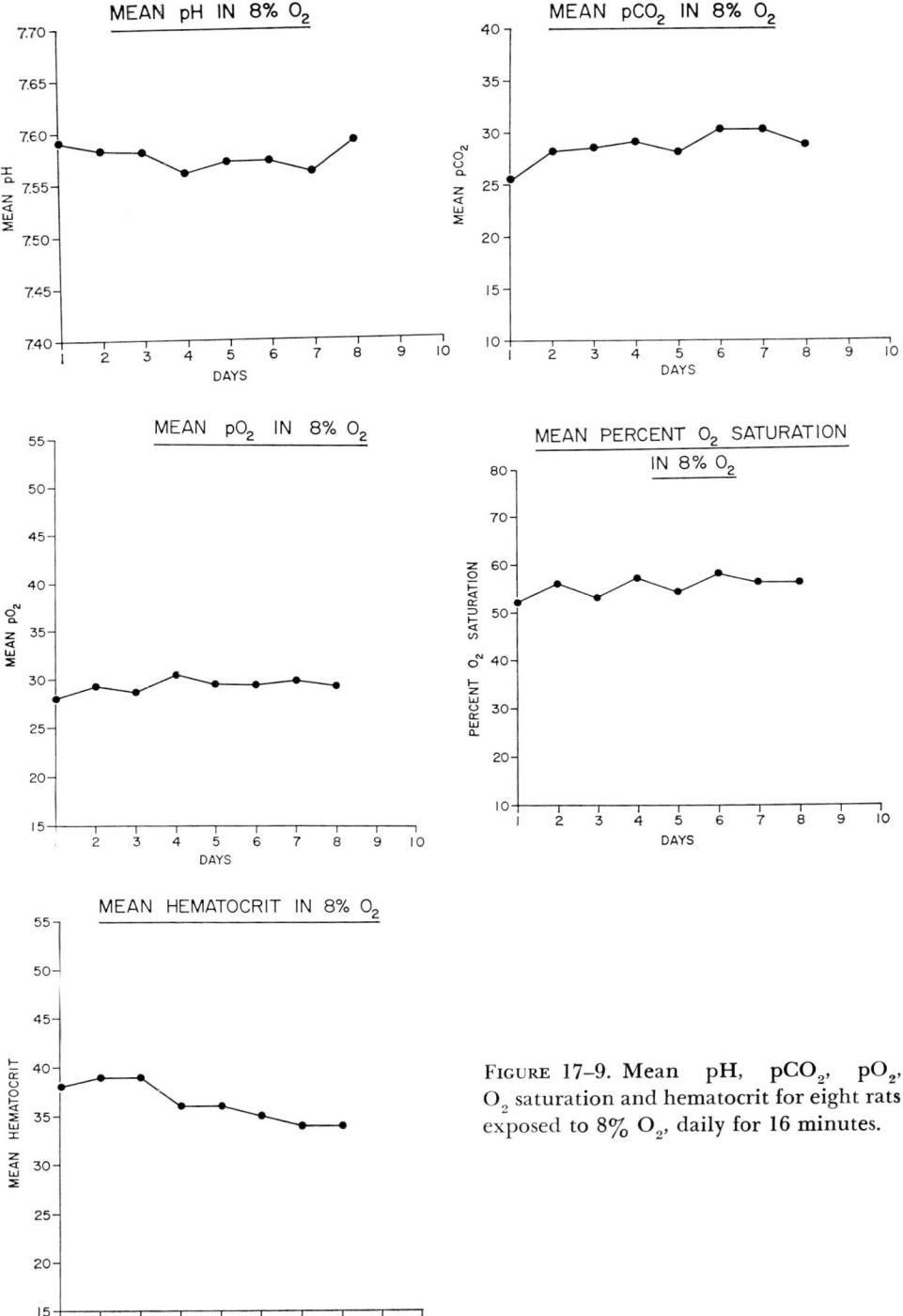

FIGURE 17-9. Mean pH, pCO_2, pO_2, O_2 saturation and hematocrit for eight rats exposed to 8% O_2, daily for 16 minutes.

The multiple actions of respiratory gases as sensory stimuli, reinforcers, and impairers of neural function are dependent upon the absolute and relative concentrations of each gas. Under some circumstances, a decrement in performance produced by hypoxia can be eliminated by the addition of CO_2 to the inspired air (10). This is illustrated in Figures 17-10 a, b, c, d, e. This improvement in performance is related to the direct actions of CO_2 upon the oxygen dissociation from hemoglobin, respiration, and cerebral blood flow. On the other hand, when psychological factors become active the expected effects of CO_2 upon performance in hypoxia are reversed. This was illustrated in the conditioned suppression experiment where CO_2 actually enhanced suppression in hypoxia.

The behavioral evaluation of any chemical agent is highly complex and as illustrated in this paper must take into account a large number of factors. The multiple effects of past experience, the interaction with motivational level and differential actions with other drugs or altered metabolic states are some

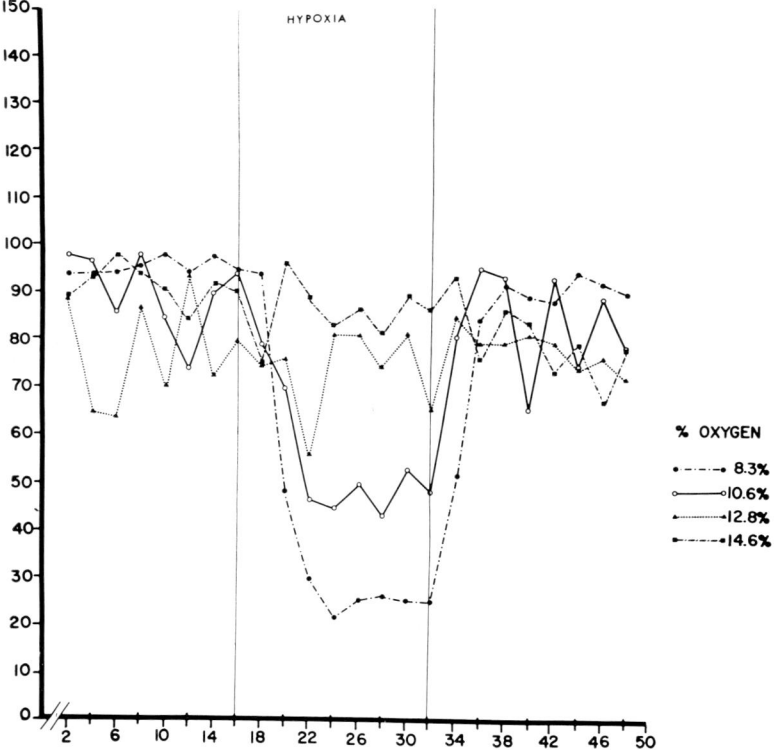

FIGURE 17–10a. Lever pressing rates for successive two-minute periods in air (0 to 16 minutes) in hypoxia (16 to 32 minutes) and in air (32 to 48 minutes) with no CO_2 present during the hypoxic period. Each curve represents the mean performance of the same six animals run each day in a control period in air followed by a sixteen-minute period in hypoxia and a sixteen-minute recovery period in air.

of the prime considerations. Behavioral scientists should tread cautiously when attempting to analyze drug effects on behavior, and simple screening procedures must be regarded as a naive and potentially dangerous approach.

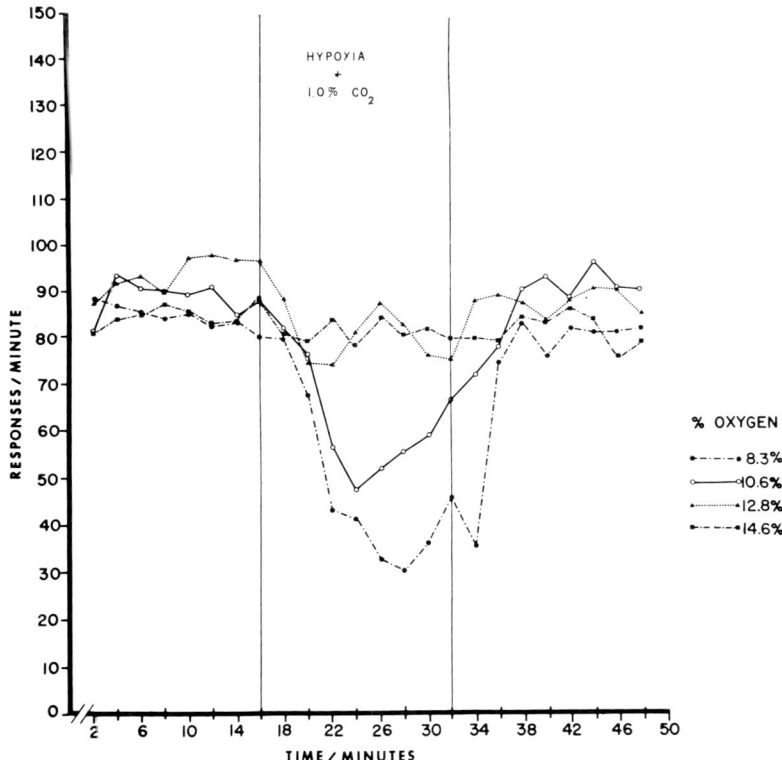

FIGURE 17–10b. The effect of 1% CO_2 in self-stimulation rates during hypoxia. Successive lever pressing rates are shown in air (0 to 16 minutes) in hypoxia and 1% CO_2 (16 to 32 minutes) and in air (32 to 48 minutes).

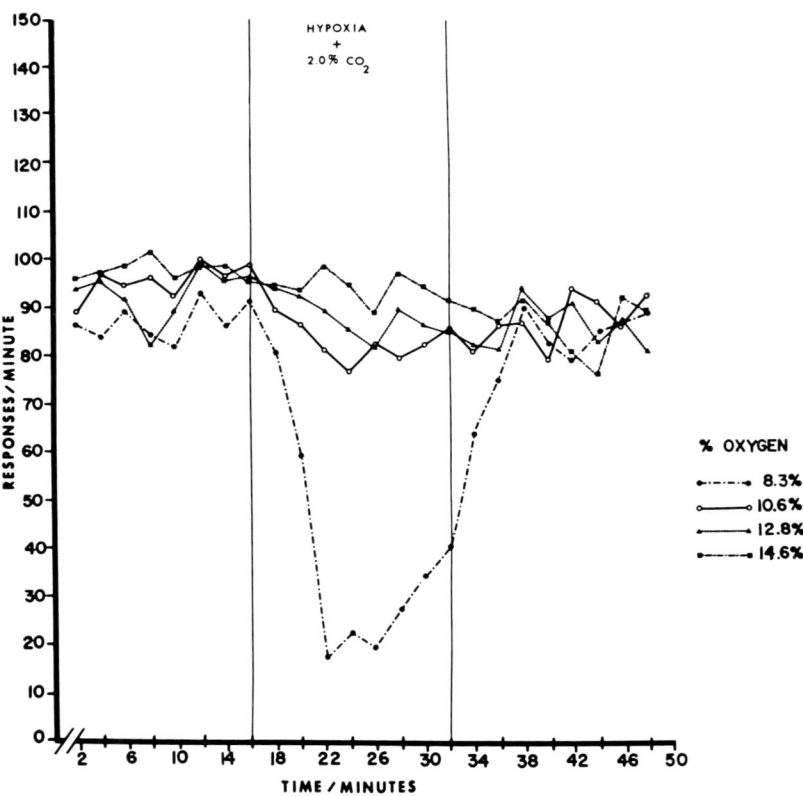

FIGURE 17–10c. The effect of 2% CO_2 on self-stimulation rates during hypoxia. Successive lever pressing rates are shown in air (0 to 16 minutes) in hypoxia and 2% CO_2 (16 to 32 minutes) and in air (32 to 48 minutes).

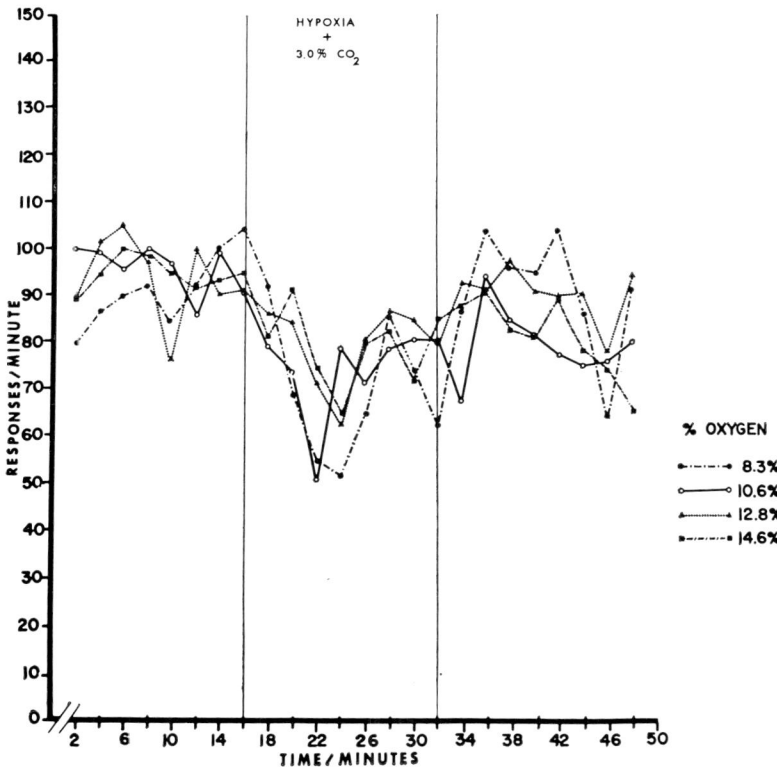

FIGURE 17–10d. The effect of 3% CO_2 on self-stimulation rates during hypoxia. Successive lever pressing rates are shown in air (0 to 16 minutes) and in 3% CO_2 (16 to 32 minutes) and in air (32 to 48 minutes).

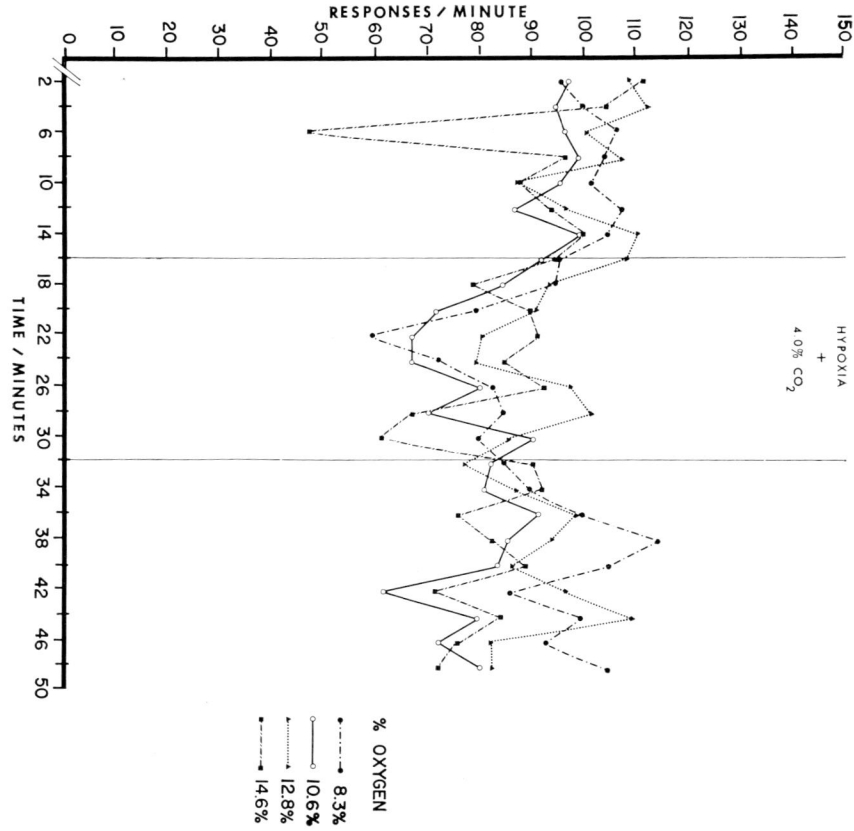

FIGURE 17-10e. The effect of 4% CO_2 on self-stimulation rates in hypoxic environment.

REFERENCES

1. FOWLE, A.S.E., AND WEINSTEIN, S.A.: Effect of cutaneous electric shock on ventilation response of birds to carbon dioxide. *Amer J Physiol, 210* (2) :293-298, 1966.
2. WEINSTEIN, S.A., AND FOWLE, A.S.E.: Respiratory conditional reflex formation with CO_2 and electric shock as unconditional stimuli. *Cond Reflex, 1* (2) :117-124, April-June 1966.
3. BIRYUKOV, D.A., KOTNEVA, E.A., SHLYAFER, T.P., AND YAKOVLEVA, M.I.: Phylogenetic and ontogenetic patterns in development of reflex regulation of cardiac activity and respiration in animals. *Trans Supp, 22*:80-85, 1963.
4. WEISTEIN, S.A.: Carbon dioxide as a reinforcer in escape conditioning. *Cond Reflex, 2*:118-126, 1967.
5. WEINSTEIN, S.A.: The effect of hypoxia upon learned escape from carbon dioxide. *Psychon Sci, 6* (3) :91-92, 1966.
6. NIELSEN, M., AND SMITH, H.: Studies on regulation of respiration in acute hypoxia. *Acta Physiol Scand, 24*:293-313, 1952.

7. ANNAU, Z., AND WEINSTEIN, S.A.: Hypothalamic self-stimulation: Interaction of hypoxia and stimulus intensity. *Life Sci, 6*:1355–1360, 1967.
8. ANNAU, Z., AND WEINSTEIN, S.A.: Conditioned suppression of hypothalamic self-stimulation based on low oxygen levels. *Comm Behav Biol, 2*:1–6, 1968.
9. WEINSTEIN, S.A., AND ANNAU, Z.: Behavioral and physiological measures of adaptations to brief repeated hypoxic exposures. *Comm Behav Biol,* In press, 1969.
10. WEINSTEIN, S.A., AND ANNAU, Z.: The effects of carbon dioxide in hypothalamic self-stimulation during hypoxia. *Comm Behav Biol, 1* (4):223–229, 1968.

III

Concluding Discussion on Biochemicals

WALTER B. ESSMAN

It is difficult to summarize in a few words all of the ideas which have been generated by the panelists and the excellent data presented, inasmuch as we have heard of results with chickens, pigeons, and rats, all of which point to several levels of interrelationship on both the species level as well as the theoretical level between animal behavior, drug effects, and cerebral function.

In the case of Dr. Adler's data and commentary, I believe that we have seen a most elegant illustration of the Cannon and Rosenbleuth hypothesis relating the development of ablation induced supersensitivity; it was most interesting to observe that the alteration in convulsive thresholds by selective lesions of the central nervous system in the rat did not result in any changes in the biogenic amines measured. I wonder, in this regard, if this could not, in some way, be reconciled with the observation that a majority of drugs, which act as anticonvulsants, have been shown to affect the level of one or more biogenic amines in the brain, or their turnover.

In Dr. Cherkin's presentation, we have been presented with an interesting demonstration of a dose-dependent relationship reflected in his consolidation model. Perhaps what we have seen here is not only an illustration of a modification of the consolidation process, but a modification of something more, which may go beyond consolidation, per se, and involve the storage phase of memory. There have been some interesting negations of classical neurologisms employed in Dr. Cherkin's data, the persisting notion of retrograde amnesia, requiring post-traumatic amnesia, has been elegantly cast away, as has the the concept of retrograde amnesia requiring a losss of consciousness. Dr. Cherkin has also illustrated that the concept of a quantifiable unit, at least on a theoretical level, allows us to conceive of the engram as part of an active consolidation process involving more than an initial phrase during which such an engram becomes vulnerable, through its relative instability, to disruption.

Dr. Leaf's comments illustrated the importance of multiple neurochemical systems actively regulating the behavior which his work has been concerned with, and it might be appropriate to point out that multiple sites, important for neurochemical activity, also play a role in these behaviors.

Dr. Weinstein's data present us with an interesting model, particularly appropriate for the pharmacologist. An ideal source of experimental interaction may well be provided by a system within which alterations in the ED or LD of drugs, specifically agents of a psychoactive character, may be studied. In this connection, combinations of hypercapnia or anoxia, or both, affecting the regulation and maintenance of body temperature, have been indicated to alter the central effects of anticonvulsants, monoamine oxidase inhibitors, and other psychoactive agents.

Perhaps one way in which an appropriate summary of the panel presentations may be presented is to view each of the contributions as representative of a model system, within which drug effects, their central action, and behavior may be interrelated. Such interrelationships hold exceedingly interesting ideas for future research and exploration of the role of cerebral mechanisms underlying drug action and relating such action to the modification of behavior.

PART V

VASODILATORS

Chapter 18

Cerebral Blood Flow

D. HYWEL DAVIES

The topic of cerebral blood flow is one which falls more naturally into the field of activity of the neurologist rather than the cardiologist. As practising clinical cardiologists we are obviously concerned with the heart as a pump, with the blood vessels as pipes, and with the economy of those vascular territories which sustain the major impact of cardiac disease. In practice this means the lungs liver and kidneys. The central nervous system is involved less commonly, at least by gross clinical assessment, and when it is involved it is as a result of two main processes—embolism and arterioclerosis—affecting the carotid vessels and the arteries distal to them. Sometimes we see, and have to deal with, psychoses appearing a few days after major heart surgery: whether these are embolic, metabolic, or environmental is not clear, though probably due to a combination of the last two factors. The conditions of the intensive-care unit—where the patient often has little sleep, where there is constant interference for purposes of taking temperatures, measuring blood pressures, dealing with drainage tubes giving injections etcetera, and all this with a light shining constantly in the patient's eyes—are probably such as to encourage this complication. It seems not to happen to the more stoical patients, but rather to the more nervous and imaginative ones.

In looking at the topic of cerebral blood flow, therefore, I thought I might approach it by examining what seemed to me to be acceptable in this field, in terms of knowledge and attitude, and what is less acceptable. Some things seem to be fairly well established. First the anatomy, though we should be aware of the variability of the collateral mechanisms between case and case as well as the variations which may occur normally on the general anatomical theme.

Second, there seems to be good understanding of at least some of the factors which control cerebral blood flow. These are the pressure gradient across the cerebrovascular territory, the resistance of that territory, and the viscosity of the perfusing blood. The pressure gradient merits some thought in the respect of the effect of changes in systemic blood pressure, particularly hypotension. It is of interest that hypotension, to the order of about one half the normal mean pressure, does not cause significant diminution of cerebral blood flow in normal man. However, under conditions of hypoxia and hypercapnia, vasodilation is present as a result of these which makes the relationship between pressure and flow a passive one, and hypotension will then cause a fall in cerebral blood flow. Conversely, when hypotension is present, hypoxia and hypercapnia fail to produce their usual increase in cerebral blood flow, presumably due to the fact that cerebral vessels are already maximally dilated in order to maintain flow in the face of low pressure. These considerations are of importance in the management of cardiogenic shock, when the further insult of hypoxia in someone whose blood pressure is low can be of considerable significance to the patient's cerebral function. Such hypoxia can of course easily arise owing to impairment of lung function, either chronic or the consequence of acute heart failure.

The relationship between arterial pCO_2 and cerebral blood flow has been well defined, though it seems to me that sufficient credit is sometimes not given for the power of the organism to adapt to changes in pCO_2; in other words, one sees corrections being made in the value given for the cerebral blood flow according to the arterial pCO_2 level without allowance being made for its chronicity. In chronic lung disease, for instance, the arterial pCO_2 is chronically elevated and the patient loses his ventilatory sensitivity to pCO_2. It would be surprising if CO_2 did not, in the same circumstances, lose some or all of its acute effects on the cerebral blood flow.

The third point that seems fairly well established is the methodology of measurement of cerebral blood flow. The original nitrous oxide methods of Kety and Schmidt have been amply vindicated by subsequent developments in isotope techniques, including those of intra-arterial injection by the Scandinavian workers especially (Larssen, Hoedt-Rasmussen etcetera). The latter is elegant but of course traumatic—or, to use the current in-phrase in cardiology, "invasive"—and not repeatable with any frequency for this reason. Other workers, such as Mallet and Veall in England and McHenry in this country, have therefore developed the inhalation method, using ^{85}Kr or ^{133}Xe, with external counting over the cranium. It is likely that it is in this area, using more refined techniques and perhaps different sorts of emitters, that the main impact of the technology will come on clinical practice. The measurement of cerebral blood flow has been an interesting experimental tool, but its effects hitherto on clinical practice have not been great.

To turn then to what seems to be generally less acceptable in this area. One thing which concerns me is the question of hypoxia. We have heard the results of experiments which have used hypoxia as one of the tools. I do not wish to discuss the meaning of these experiments nor their interpretation, but rather to dwell a little on the significance of chronic hypoxia. One comes to this from observation of patients with chronic disease of the lungs or of the heart leading to cyanosis, or a persistently reduced oxygen saturation in the arterial blood. Is there in fact such a thing as chronic hypoxia, in the sense of a chronic deficiency of oxygen supply, in the whole organism. Six or seven years ago we were interested in lactate production as a determinant of ventilatory drive in cyanotic heart disease, reasoning *a priori* (and, as it turned out, wrongly) that they should be great lactate producers. In fact, they do not produce a great deal of lactate on exercise, being forced to stop by breathlessness and fatigue before lactate levels reach high values. This, together with the fact that oxygen consumption remains appropriately normal under virtually all circumstances, suggests that there is no deficiency of oxygen supply to tissues and that adaptation is adequate. Any thesis which invokes the deleterious effect of chronic hypoxia is therefore ill-founded, and this applies to the brain as to other tissues. A tissue is presumably concerned primarily with the number of oxygen molecules of oxygen that it receives rather than the partial pressure at which it receives them. Again, extrapolation from acute experiments with hypoxia to the chronic state is not permissible. It is unlikely that cerebral damage arises from chronic generalized hypoxia per se—many very blue children are very bright indeed—rather one must postulate local factors such as arterial disease, embolism, or repeated episodes of acute hypoxia.

One other subject of interest is the pharmacodynamics of vasodilators in regard to the cerebral circulation. Here again I must seek a parallel in cardiology. One of the therapeutic paradoxes of cardiology is as follows: the drug dipyridamole increases coronary flow markedly, both in the isolated heart and in the intact body, yet if we give it to patients with angina their symptoms become worse. On the other hand, as has been known for one hundred years, nitroglycerine leads to a dramatic improvement in symptoms, yet we can show no increase in coronary blood flow as a result of its use. The answer is probably that generalized vasodilation of the territory leads to a run-off from the ischemic area distal to a narrowed vessel. There is thus no necessary relationship between the total blood supply to an organ and the perfusion of ischemic zones. The use of vasodilators to improve the cerebral function is therefore fraught conceptually with at least two hazards; one, that they will lead to generalized vasodilation in the body as a whole and thus to diminished blood flow; two, that even if an increase of cerebral blood flow were to be shown as a result of their use, this might, as in the heart, be at the expense of ischemic areas in the brain. This is a fundamental issue in the use of vasodilators, and I believe the tests of therapeutic adequacy must, at least for the present, remain empirical.

Since you ask me to give my views about drugs in general, I can hardly refrain from doing so. I believe that drugs in this society—and I am not referring to drugs of addiction which overall are a minor problem much magnified—probably do as much harm as they do good. L.J. Henderson said that it was not until 1912 that a random patient consulting a random physician with a random disease stood a better than 50:50 chance of being improved as a result of the encounter. Clearly there are some drugs which stand out by reason of the fact that they are efficacious—antibiotics for infections, B 12 for pernicious anemia—but of the tens of thousands of different drugs available these are few. Many of the remainder are toxic to some degree or other, and I wonder if, taking the whole range of prescribing, Henderson would find that today the net result was debit or credit, to the patient I mean, not the business.

The problem lies not only in the demand by the patients, which according to Osler singles us out from our Simian ancestors, but in the character and motivations of the doctor. This is a topic which I would like to develop if there were only time.

There was a newly commissioned officer drilling his troops on the Cliffs of Dover during World War II. As they marched toward the cliff-edge he forgot the word of command to turn them about and stood speechless. A seasoned sergeant-major was heard to remark, "For Heaven's sake say something, Sir, if its only goodbye!" So often the physician's reaching for his prescription pad is his way of saying goodbye to his patient.

What I call "Everest therapy" is the treatment of something because it is there rather than because it is doing harm, and this applies to the therapy of hypercholesterolemia, hyperglycemia, hyperuricemia, overweight. There is in us an inordinate desire to try to make everyone regress towards some concept of the norm. Since most things that are worthwhile stem from the unusual, this is indeed a regression. It is unfortunately frequent to find that it is the therapy that does the harm.

Chapter 19

Clues to Cerebral Circulatory Disturbance From Ocular Fluorescein Angiography

LEMUEL T. MOORMAN

The fundus of the eye has always been implicated as an important source of information related to systemic diseases especially in vascular disorders. The circulation of the eye is intimately associated with that of the brain since they both arise from the same arterial tree and respond almost identically to neurocirculatory and humoral influences. The important and common circulatory disturbances related to the brain are atherosclerosis, or hardening of the large arteries, and hypertension with its attendant small vessel constriction and associated arteriolar sclerosis. Atherosclerosis is an intimal deposition of lipoidal substances followed by calcification and scarring occurring in true arteries. Since true arteries are not present in the eye except in the vicinity of the optic nerve, atherosclerosis is not often seen in the eye. There has been a common misconception in the past that atherosclerosis is an important eye-ground finding.

The important vascular eye-ground finding which can be correlated with vascular disturbances of the brain is hypertension with its two major signs, narrowing and arteriolar sclerosis.

The evaluation of the funduscopic findings in the eye is of great significance in evaluating small vessel conditions of the eye and brain. In grading the eye grounds, we try to dissociate the findings of hypertension or peripheral vasoconstrictive phenomena from the long-term stress-induced finding of arteriolar sclerosis (Fig. 19-1). One is functional change and the other is an actual organic change. We make an effort to determine the amount of constriction of the arterioles graded from 1 to 4 to indicate the amount of peripheral resistance or vasoconstriction. Grades 1 and 2 are milder degrees of constriction and grade 3 indicates increased constriction, resulting in extravasation of some of the blood elements from the vessel, and grade 4 indicates this condition plus the finding of edema of the optic nerve. In grading the separate condition of arteriolar sclerosis, we grade the eye-ground in terms of the amount of decrease in transparency or translucency of the vessel and the amount of A-V compression at the crossing (Fig. 19-2). Grade 1 indicates a mild increase in the opacification of the arteriole or decrease in its translucency, combined with a widening of the light streak. Grade 2 is an increase in the degree of this with moderate compression of veins. Grade 3 indicates a copper-wire effect due to further widening of light streak and opacification of the arteriole, combined with considerable compression of the veins. Grade 4 indicates marked compression of the vein in conjunction with further opacification of the arteriole which is called a silver-wire arteriole.

CLASSIFICATION OF HYPERTENSION AND
ARTERIOLAR SCLEROSIS
(SCHEIE)

HYPERTENSION	ARTERIOLAR SCLEROSIS
1. MILD NARROWING	1. INCREASE IN LIGHT REFLEX
2. FOCAL NARROWING	2. A-V COMPRESSION
3. FOCAL NARROWING WITH HEMORRHAGES AND EXUDATES	3. COPPER WIRE ARTERIOLES
4. EXAGGERATION OF ABOVE WITH ADDED PAPILLEDEMA	4. SILVER WIRE ARTERIOLES

FIGURE 19–1. Factors in the differentiation of hypertension from arteriolar sclerosis.

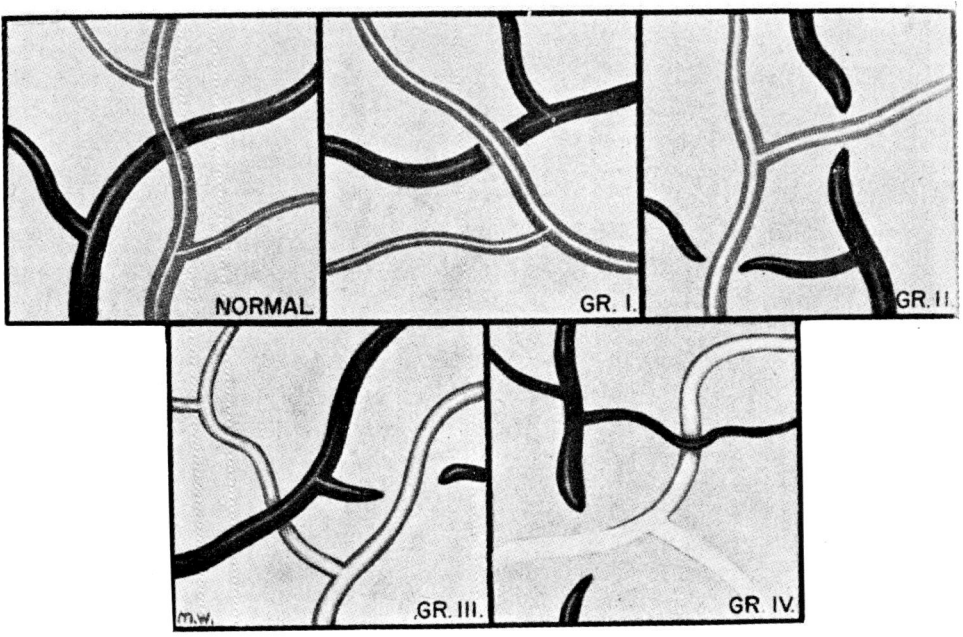

FIGURE 19–2. Classification of the degree of arteriolar sclerosis.

As stated above, hypertension and arteriolar sclerosis do exist together, but the amount of one can be markedly dissociated from the amount of the other seen in the same patient. For example, one may have a great deal of narrowing in an acute hypertension, being associated with very little arteriolar sclerosis (Fig. 19-3). On the other hand, one may have a great deal of hypertension associated with a large amount of arteriolar sclerosis if the hypertension has been going on for a long time. There may also be associated findings in the other direction, namely a long-standing low-grade high blood pressure causing minimal narrowing of the arterioles but rather marked sclerosis (Fig. 19-4).

If one is interested in studying circulatory disturbances and vasodilator responses of the brain, it is important to recognize that a patient with acute marked narrowing of the arterioles without much long-term changes of ar-

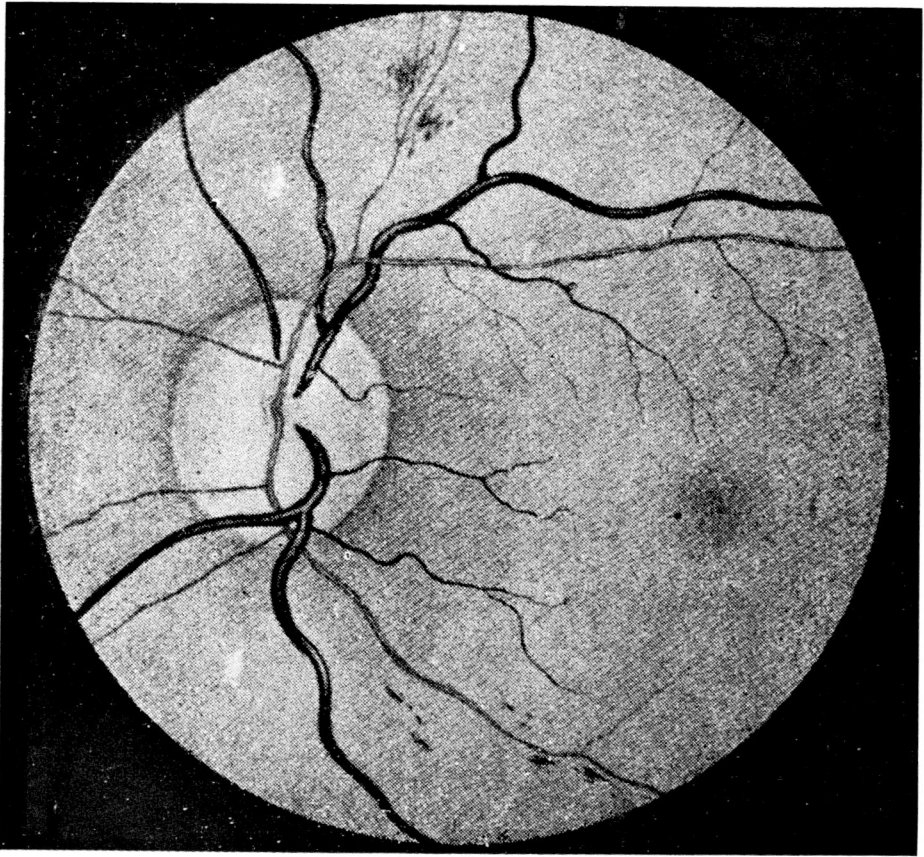

FIGURE 19-3. A case showing the marked narrowing of arterioles in hypertension, with no concurrent arteriolar sclerosis.

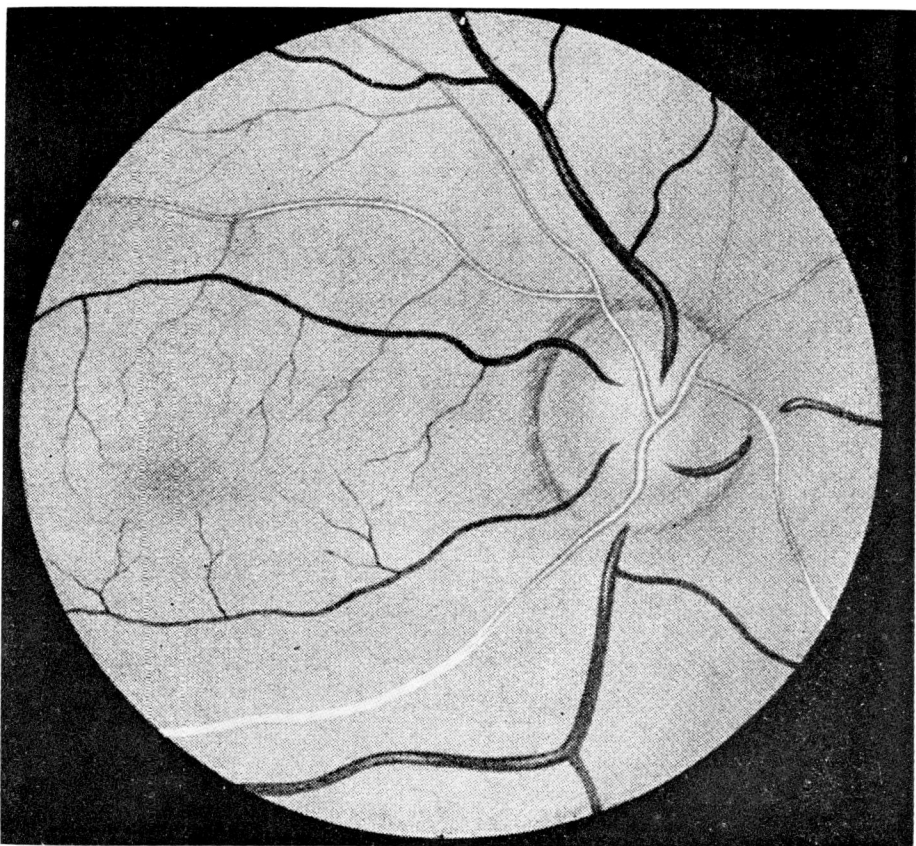

FIGURE 19-4. A case showing very little narrowing of arterioles with a marked sclerosis.

teriolar sclerosis will respond much better to vasodilator therapy than one who has a lot of arteriolar sclerosis. Conversely, one with a great deal of sclerosis and one with not very much narrowing would be expected to respond less well to vasodilator treatment. It is quite possible, by studying the eye-grounds ophthalmoscopically and photographically, to determine the therapeutic responses to antihypertensive and vasodilator drugs. We not only see the ophthalmic counterparts in terms of symptoms related to the circulatory disturbances, but we also see the funduscopic manifestations of these vessel changes while the patient is under therapy. When the patient with blurred vision due to hypertensive retinopathy is seen with the cerebral symptoms of dizziness and headache related to hypertensive necephalopathy, we know that the same thing is happening in both the brain and the eye, and we can see the improvement in the eye-grounds as the patient improves clinically and symptomatically. Figures 19-5 and 19-6 show the eye-grounds before and after treatment. In the more advanced cases, such as this one, it is very obvious that these changes are occurring. In the less severe and more chronic cases, and in nonhypertensive cases where the changes may be more subtle, one could see the need for more accurate masurements in the case where clinical observation may not provide enough accuracy. For purposes of clinical research, this can be done photographically. A grid, such as the one shown in Figure 19-7, can be placed in the Zeiss fundus camera so that the vessels can be magnified and measured at certain distances from the optic nerve. Whereas this is pretty accurate in many cases, there is still a need for more accuracy in studying subtle but definite changes in caliber.

Certain difficulties in observation are encountered when one realizes that the optical density of the vessels with varying amounts of arteriolar sclerosis give a false interpretation of the actual caliber of the vessel. It is thought that the vessels of the fundus act as refractive lenses in giving certain appearances, such as widening of the light streak, an early finding in arteriolar sclerosis.

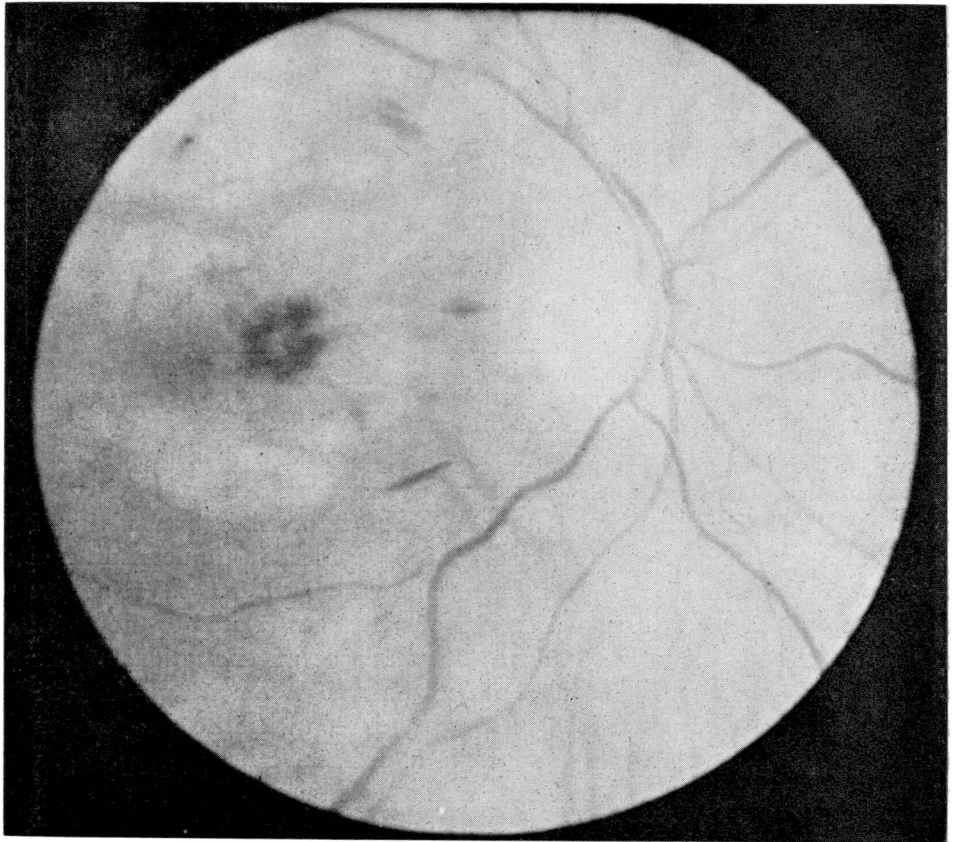

FIGURE 19-5. A case of severe hypertension with eyeground findings before treatment. Narrow vessels, hemorrhages, and exudates.

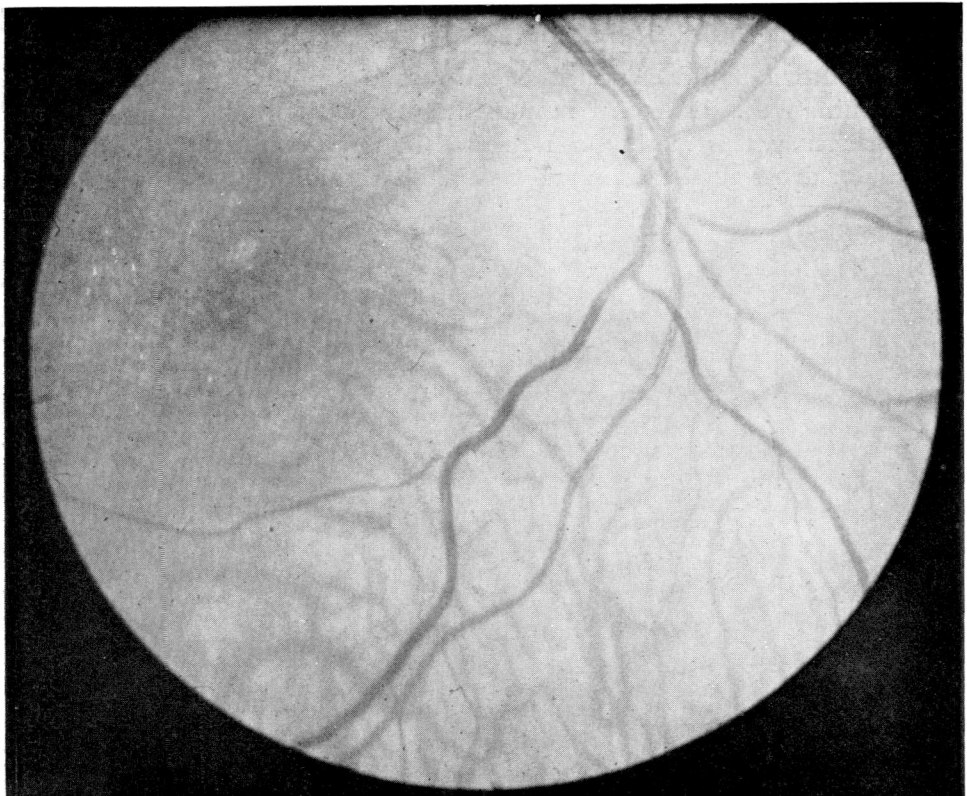

FIGURE 19-6. Same case as in Figure 19-5, showing widening of arterioles and absence of hemorrhages after treatment.

The increased amount of hyalinization of the arteriolar wall results in increased refractive power which apparently magnifies the normal light streak of the vessel, causing the widening. This same type of change may result in apparent narrowing or changing caliber of an arteriole when it is not actually true. The method for eliminating or obviating this abnormal refractive state of the arterioles in study of vascular caliber is the use of fluorescein angiography, in which the fluorescein is injected into the vessel by way of the antecubital vein of the arm and is allowed to circulate throughout the eye. Within ten or twelve seconds, the intravenous sodium fluorescein is seen in the eye with a special ultraviolet filter coursing through the arterioles. Within another second or two, the dye is coursing through the veins. Following this, the dye permeates the small vessels of the eye and gradually is absorbed into the hepatic and renal excretory systems. It is largely gone from the circulation within thirty to sixty minutes. Figure 19-8 shows the vascular outline before fluorescein, and Figure 19-9 shows it with fluorescein in the vessels. This can be used to study a wide variety of vascular abnormalities of the eye other than just the caliber of the vessels. Since the fluorescein dye is almost completely nontoxic and does not affect the vasculature of the eye, and since it does eliminate the disturbing refractive abnormalities related to variations in translucency, this method can be used by anyone studying the effect of vasodilator drugs on the brain and eye. We have found that the image of an arteriole containing fluorescein dye is 10 to 20 per cent larger than the same one in an ordinary photograph.

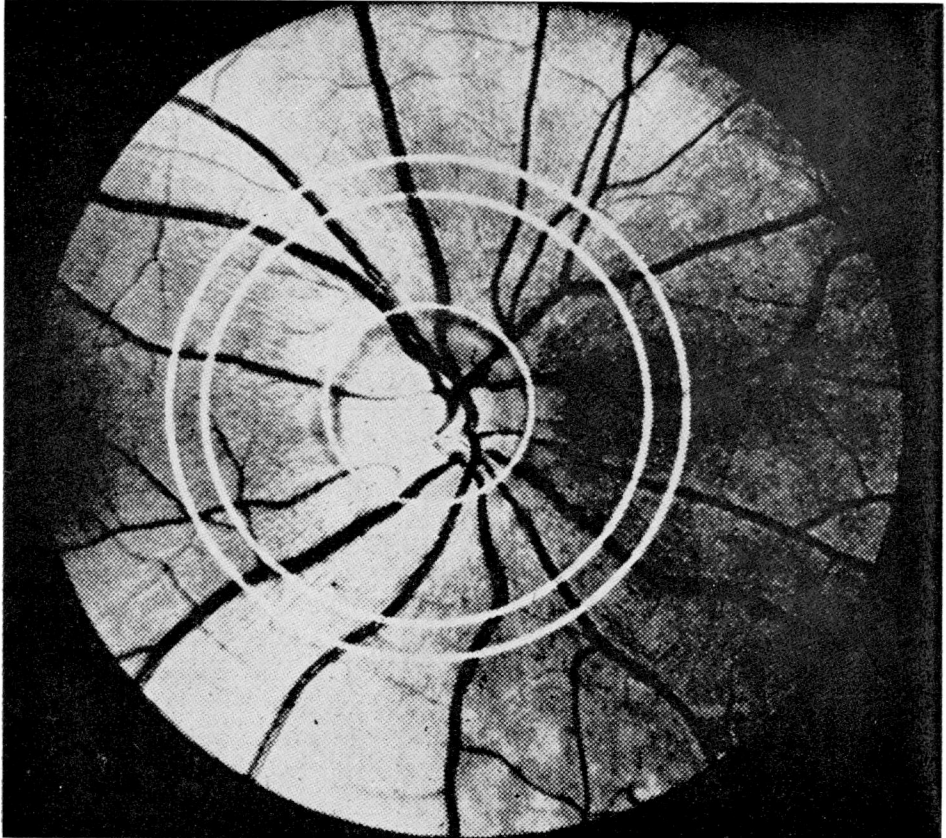

FIGURE 19-7. Grid mounted in Zeiss Retinal Camera, as an aid in accurate measurement of vessels.

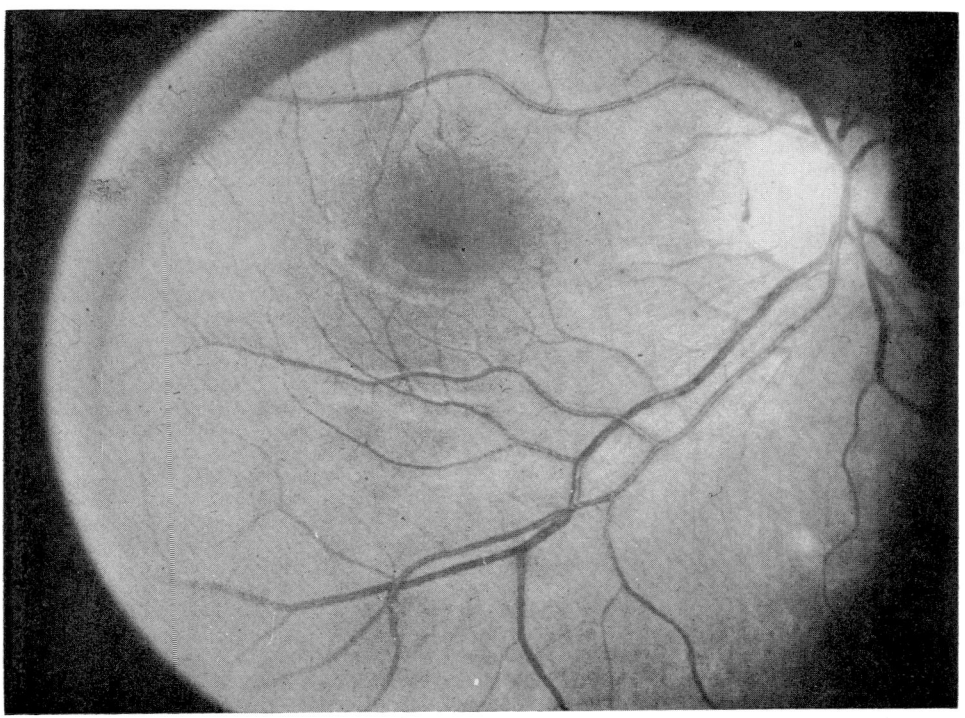

Figure 19-8. Retinal picture showing the size and outline of vessels before fluorescein injection.

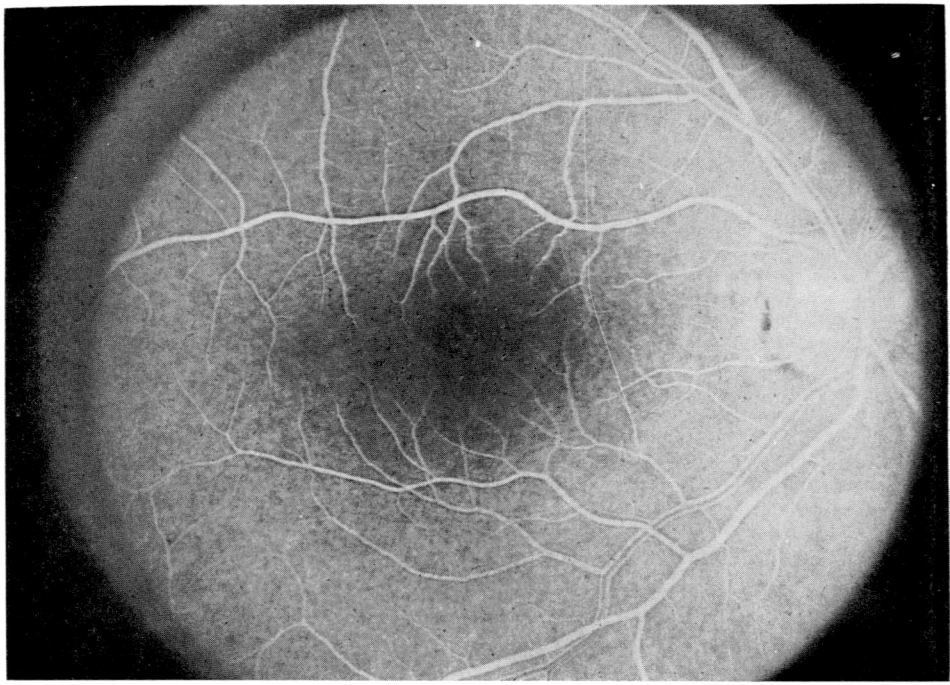

FIGURE 19-9. Retinal picture showing slightly larger size and clearer outline after fluorescein injection.

CONCLUSION

1. Atherosclerosis of brain and other major organs is not reflected in the eye, but small vessel disorders of the brain are frequently mirrored in the eye.

2. Known correlations between small vessel behavior in the brain and eye make further research o nthis subject highly desirable.

3. Since variation in caliber of vessels in the eye is so easy to photograph and measure, this may be a very valuable parameter for study of the effect of vasodilators on small vessels of the cerebral cortex in conjunction with psychological tests and these studies.

4. Fluorescein angiography provides a more accurate measure of actual vessel size than ordinary photography.

REFERENCES

1. SCHEIE, HAROLD G.: Evaluation of ophthalmoscopic changes of hypertension and arteriolar sclerosis. *Arch Opthal,* 49:117, 1953.
2. BEHRENDT, THOMAS, AND DOYLE, KATHRYN E.: Reliability of image size measurements in the new Zeiss fundus camera. *Amer J Ophthal,* 59:896, 1965.

Chapter 20

Sensorineural Hearing Loss

WILL P. PIRKEY

During the past fifteen years, students of otology and audiology have attempted to identify and provide information on the sites of lesions within the human central auditory system. This effort has stimulated a proliferation of "cortical" or central auditory tests. This field is wide open for all kinds of new experiments, but the groundwork has been provided. These initial investigations, in our opinion, have provided many, particularly those of you in the Cortical Function Laboratory, an opportunity to entertain a variety of suggestions and with the motivation for continuing investigations.

First of all historically, audiologists have developed relatively reliable and clinically usable audiometric measures for detecting lesions in the peripheral auditory system including the acoustic nerve. Distrubances of the peripheral mechanism readily induce errors of intensity, frequency, pitch, or loudness which may be identified and attributed to various etiologic factors. Thus, numerous so-called site of lesion tests may demonstrate various patterns of response which may be associated with certain otologic disturbances. By contrast, however, lesions in the auditory cortex (the middle and posterior portion of the superior temporal gyrus) may not be accompanied by any discernible symptomatology. As Jerger so aptly put it, "a tiny piece of wire inadvertently dropped into the labyrinth during stapes surgery can cause severe or even total deafness in that ear; yet an entire temporal lobe can be removed and the effect on hearing is so slight that we must go to very great lengths to show that the patient's auditory system is not entirely normal." Frequency and intensity are not generally affected by such lesions. A loss of threshold sensitivity does not usually occur. Consequently, the allusive nature of the auditory symptoms deferred the "clinical demand" for central auditory tests. It became obvious that conventional audiometric procedures were of little, if any, value diagnostically. It became apparent that the mere analysis of the parameters of frequency and intensity became less significant at levels above the cochlear nuclei. Thus, tonal-stimuli and the capacity to discriminate between single sound elements were abandoned in favor of "sensitized" or distorted speech material: verbal stimuli made difficult by reducing the redundancy of the sound message.

Bocca and his colleagues in Italy demonstrated that patients with temporal lobe tumors had considerable difficulty understanding distorted speech in the ear, contralateral to the lesion. This contralateral phenomenon has been demonstrated in many studies and is probably related to the fact that a greater number of nerve fibers from one cochlea go to the opposite temporal cortex and appears to be independent from hemisphere dominance. Bocca's group systematically varied the redundancy of the speech message by means of acceleration of rate, periodic interruption, low-pass filtering, and variation in message length. The reduction in redundancy seemed to place a heavier burden upon the higher auditory mechanism.

Since Bocca's breakthrough, many techniques using speech material have been suggested. Also, tests involving localization judgments, employing Tonal, noise or click stimuli have been studied; however, a clinically useful technique which would not be affected by peripheral hearing loss remains to be developed. Verbal stimuli, which can be used in an infinite variety of ways, has been favored. Some researchers have employed: selective distortion, usually accomplished by acoustic filtering; time distortion, usually accelerated speech; "fusion testing," alternating speech rhythmically between ears so that each side received only half of the message; and finally, competing messages, two messages are usually presented simultaneouely, one to each ear. Jerger, among many others, believes the competing message to be the most promising.

Obviously, each procedure may be modified in a number of ways. No matter which technique, modification or combination of procedures, however, the common goal has been to identify and localize the phantom-like lesions in the higher auditory centers by reducing the redundancy of the verbal message. By reducing the redundancy, the auditory task is increased and the integrative processes of these higher centers are challenged. As mentioned previously, the patient with a lesion of the auditory cortex has no difficulty with standard speech audiometric procedures. His perception of a verbal message is a synthetic rather than an analytic process; and since speech is known to be a highly redundant phenomenon, he is supplied with more information than is actually needed and utilizes the normally superfluous information to compensate for any pathological deficit. When the redundancy of the message is reduced to the point where he can no longer compensate adequately, his test performance suffers in a unique fashion.

In other words, at the present our methods of testing give us only gross answers concerning lesion of the cerebral cortex. These answers are greatly influenced by pathology in the cochlea.

To determine the influence of vasodilators, or any disease, on the auditory cortex requires a detailed and careful auditory evaluation to rule out peripheral damage; then another battery of tests to examine the auditory cortex.

Even then our results are nonspecific as to type of lesion or the exact location in the auditory cortex.

Findings are more specific in the peripheral and auditory nerve areas.

The cochlea is influenced by vascular dyfunction. Vasodilators have played a major role in the treatment of both auditory and vestibular disease restricted to the cochlea and to the vestibular area for many years. It is widely suggested today that the cochlear vessels may play an important role in such pathological conditions as congenital and hereditary deafness, presbycusis, sudden deafness, viral labyrinthitis, and Meniere's disease. A lack of detailed information on the vascular anatomy has led to these suggestions which are often without adequate morphological and physiological foundation.

The inner ear is supplied by only one main vessel—the labyrinthine artery. Its origin is the following: vertebral, basilar, anterior inferior cerebellar, labyrinthine. It divides at the inner acoustic meatus to form the vestibular artery and the common cochlear artery, which again divides into the vestibular-cochlear and the cochlear or spiral modiolar artery.

The vestibular branch of the vestibular-cochlear artery supplies the basal end of the cochlea and the vestibulum. The cochlear branch supplies one-fourth of one-half of the basal turn of the cochlea and anastomoses with one or two branches of the spiral modiolar artery, which supplies the remaining portion of the cochlea.

Within the cochlea itself there are extensive anastomoses of capillaries, arteriols, and venules. There is separation of the vessels supplying the scala vestibuli and the strai vascularis from those supplying the basilar membrane and the organ of Corti.

Due to the extensive anastomoses, all parts of the cochlea probably have a more or less constant circulation even in the event of small peripheral flow disturbances. This suggests that higher degrees of perceptive hearing impairments of vascular origin must either be due to extensive vascular injuries peripheral to the capillary regions or due to injuries in the larger vessels in the modiolus or in the inner acoustic meatus. A definite interruption of the circulation in the end arteries, the labyrinthine or the common cochlear arteries would result in a serious loss of hearing. One the other hand, interruption of the circulation in the vestibular-cochlear or spiral modiolar arteries need not lead to serious impairments since these vessels in man anastomose with one another in the basal turn.

Small injuries peripherally, i.e. in single radiating arterioles or collecting venules, will probably not result in a clinically detectable change of hearing due to good anastomosing possibilities in a spiral direction. In the human cochlea there are also relatively good alternative pathways for the blood in case of circulation interruption in either of the spiral veins.

The high frequency of high tone loss of different etiologies suggests that the most vulnerable parts of the cochlea are situated within the areas supplied by the vestibular-cochlear artery and in particular the vestibular branch.

It has been suggested that exposure to noises may cause vascular spasm which in turn is detrimental to the proper function of the cochlea. Demonstrations show that noise decreases the oxygen tension in the scala media and also that the cochlea is more vulnerable to noise during a simultaneous lack of oxygen.

The response of the cochlear vessels to excessive cochlear stimulation corresponds to that observed for the cerebral vessels. There appears to be an increase in oxygen utilization of cells in the cochlea upon increased functional demand. There is an increase in blood flow, but not a dilation of blood vessels, arterioles, or arteries. The increase in blood flow is probably due to a local increase in CO_2. This increase in blood flow will allow for an increase in oxygen extraction from the blood to help support the increased demand on the organ of Corti. Experiments with guinea pigs show no increase in vasoconstriction or in vasodilation to stimulation of 120 dB of noise; there is a marked decrease in cochlear microphonic response. Anoxia causes a decrease in cochlear microphonics, increased in blood flow, and a decrease in oxygen tension.

Different forms of noise and several other causes of injury often result in an audiometric high tone loss. The basal turn of the cochlea appears to be most vulnerable. The oxygen consumption of the stria vascularis is greater at the base; and the ability to carry out anaerobic metabolism is poorest developed in the base and in the organ of Corti.

It could thus appear the reason for the common injuries due to noise at the basal turn can be the high oxygen consumption and the poor anaerobic metabolism and not due to vascular spasm or to any anatomical vascular reason.

Available oxygen in perilymph is rapidly used up (within approximately 30 seconds) after obstruction of blood supply. This is similar to the findings in endolymph, cerebral cortex, and in cardiac muscle.

Experiments using various medications in attempting to show the effect of vasodilation have been in most cases unsatisfactory. Epinephrine causes an increase it cochlear blood flow but only minimal changes in oxygen tension of perilymph; an elevation of CO_2 causes both increase in cochlear blood flow and increase in oxygen tension. When there is venus obstruction 8% CO_2 causes an increase in cochlear blood flow, an increase in oxygen tension, and an increase in cochlear microphonics. When there is venus obstruction, intravenous epinephrine also cause an increase in cochlear blood flow and an increase in oxygen tension and an increase in cochlear microphonics. This is not found in a normal cochlea.

The lack of adequate research limits our knowledge concerning the relationships of generalized arteriosclerosis to decrease in blood supply to the cochlea with resulting decrease in oxygen tension. Likewise, the possibility of thickening of the arterioles and arteries secondary to a high cholesteral blood level must be considered. Certainly we know that in many cases of sudden sensorineural hearing loss treated as an emergency with vasodilators, such as intravenous histamine, Cyclospasmol®, and with heparin, there will be a return to normal hearing. Lack of autopsy material, however, limits our knowledge as to the etiology of the sudden hearing loss—Was it a vascular spasm? Was it an embolis of the major end artery, which on medication was dissolved with eventual dissemmination throughout the smaller arterioles where the extensive anastomosis prevented any major loss of hearing? Was it a viral infection? or Was it an allergic response, which would have improved on no treatment at all?

Those of us who see a number of these patients feel that treatment within seventy-two hours after the onset of sudden hearing loss gives a much higher percentage of return of function.

I hope this paper will stimulate an increase in research concerning the relationships of all types of medication, but particularly vasodilators to the cochlea and to sensorineural hearing loss. Any new knowledge concerning the reaction of the cerebral cortex vessels would be of benefit in the general knowledge of the entire sensorineural hearing mechanism.

Chapter 21

The Effects of Vasodilators on Psychological Test Performance in Patients With Cerebral Vascular Insufficiency

W. LYNN SMITH

A considerable amount of research has been done on the physiological effects of vasodilators on cerebral circulation, but there are very few systematic behavior studies demonstrating measurable effects of vasodilating agents on higher cortical brain functions (1 to 4). A double-blind study recently conducted in Northern Ireland incorporated both monitoring of cerebral blood flow and mental tests and showed evidence of improvement in mental functions following cyclandelate (2). The six psychological test measurements employed in that study were quite general, however, and not directly related to psychological dimensions more consistent with studies of mental deterioration (3). The three exploratory studies presented there were designed to examine changes in specific psychological and psychophysical functions involving parameters consistent with studies of mental deterioration and with clinico/anatomical correlates in elderly patients with moderate cerebral arteriosclerosis who were being treated with various vasodilators.

The test selection of repeated measures for these studies was further determined by previous drug studies conducted in the Cortical Function Laboratory, as well as clinical studies involving the relationship of abilities and deterioration in the elderly. This paper is a report on three vasodilators: papaverine HCl, cyclandelate, and isoxsuprine HCl.

METHODOLOGY

Subjects included sixty patients seen over the past year in three separate studies of twenty each, ranging in age from sixty to seventy-five years of age. All were patients or staff physicians at Porter Memorial Hospital, Denver, with the exception of ten patients, half of the isoxsuprine HCl population,

Note: These studies were supported and vasodilator medication supplied by: Ives Laboratories New York, New York (cyclandelate as Cyclospasmol); Marion Laboratories, Kansas City, Missouri (papaverine HCl as Pavabid); Mead Johnson, Evansville, Indiana (isoxsuprine HCl as Vasodilan).

The author gratefully acknowledges the contributions of Stephen K. Campbell, Ph.D.: Jack B. Lowrey, M.D.; M. J. Philippus, Ph.D.; John A. Davis, M.D., Robert Wrathall, M. A.; Jerry Oslinker, M.D., and N. H. Tracy for their assistance in collecting and evaluating these data and of Robert T. Lewis, Ph.D., President of Applied Behavior Sciences, Inc., for his efficient arrangement of half of one of the studies reported in this chapter.

who were tested in Los Angeles by a cooperating research team of Applied Behavior Sciences, Inc. All patients were diagnosed by their physicians as having moderate arteriosclerosis and represented the middle and upper-middle class socioeconomic level. None of the patients were taking medication regarded by their physicians as having cerebral effects during the study except the experimental compounds of cyclandelate, papaverine, and isoxsuprine HCl. All tests were performed in the Cortical Function Laboratory under the supervision of its director, a clinical psychologist.

MATERIALS

Of the nine subtests selected for these studies, six appropriate tests directly relating to symptomatology were from the Wechsler Adult Intelligence Scale and its alternate form, the Wechsler-Bellevue Intelligence Scales for Adolescents and Adults, Form II, i.e. Comprehension, Information, Digit Span, Digit Symbol, Similarities, and Picture Arrangement. Respectively, these tests assess judgment, remote memory, recent memory, learning of new material involving relationship of symbols, verbal abstraction, and visual-spatial sequential functions. These two intelligence scales are equivalent forms and were selected to avoid practice effects.

A few comments are necessary about the rationale for those tests excluded from and included in this study series. The Wechsler tests and their sensitivity to mental deterioration in the elderly may be spuriously influenced in some instances by the nature of the items and may be reflecting threat or boredom, or both, and not deterioration per se. For example, the four "Don't Hold" tests as pure measure are rather suspect in the elderly, especially Digit Symbol and Block Design. Although many, including Wechesler, regard the Digit Symbol subtest as being most sensitive to organic changes of the eleven subtests in the scale, its scores can be affected by varying forms of writing difficulty and a tendency in older people to concentrate on neatness at the expense of speed. (11). However, after much consideration, it was decided to include it but with the instructions altered to correspond with these criticisms.

A similar problem holds true for Blocks and led to the omission of the Block Design subtest, which, although correlating highly with the Raven Matrices, has an added visual-motor factor which could contribute to lessening its effectiveness as a drug discriminating test. It might also be added that visual-motor tasks fall off with aging much sooner than verbal-symbolic ones and temptingly could lead to loading the test battery in that direction. In the elderly, however, in contrast to youth where Block Design is a sensitive measurement of organic cortical dysfunction, activities and life situations of the elderly involve heavy reliance on verbal-symbolic functions where, on the other hand, children are much closer to and interested in visual-spatial activities. Within the rationale of test selection for these studies was the awareness of the constant problem of anxiety in the elderly person, especially enhanced with the problems of vascular insufficiency, anxiety which can easily reach catastrophic proportions, seriously undermine testing rapport and lead to underachievement. Other tests used were the Raven Coloured Progressive Matrices, Babcock Sentences 22 and 23, Critical Flicker Fusion, and the Wechsler Memory Scale.

PROCEDURES

The design of papaverine and cyclandelate studies were open, premedication and postmedication testing without placebo. The twenty subjects in each study were selected both as hospital inpatients and outpatients for their first testing. All postmedication testings were conducted in the same laboratory, but all on an outpatient basis. The order of the subtests was randomized for each patient and the alternate form of the subtests was randomly assigned across the subjects.

After the baseline testing was completed, cyclandelate was prescribed at a daily level. The first ten subjects were given 800 mg daily (200 mg q.i.d.) while the remaining ten were given 800 mg (200 mg q.i.d.) for four days, 1200 mg (400 mg q.i.d.) for the next four days, and 1600 mg (400 mg q.i.d.) for the remaining six days. In the papaverine study the physicians prescribed papaverine at the recommended daily level of two 150-mg capsules twice a day or 600 mg daily. After the patients had been taking the medications for fourteen days, they returned for the second testing sequence. As an added measure, the subjects were required to return the medication at the time of the second testing so that it could be determined that the proper amount of medication had been taken. To ensure that the patients were taking the proper dosage at regular intervals, the cooperation of a family member was solicited to provide the necessary supervision.

Alternate forms of the subtests, except for the Raven and Critical Flicker Fusion, were administered at the second testing and again the test order was randomized for each patient.

The isoxsuprine HCl study varied in that it was drug/placebo and double-blind crossover in design. The above procedure conditions were adhered to except testing was performed after the drug and placebo condition and the dosage was two 10-mg tablets four times a day, or 80 mg daily.

RESULTS AND DISCUSSION

Test Patterns Before and After Receiving Papaverine HCl

In the papaverine and cyclandelate studies difference scores were used to indicate changes from premedication to postmedication tests. Mean changes were then analyzed by means of a t test. There were no significant differences between means at the acceptable confidence level of $p= .05$ in the papaverine

TABLE 21-1
A TEST PATTERN COMPARISON BEFORE AND AFTER RECEIVING PAPAVERINE HCL

Test	Statistic		df
Similarities	$X^2 = 10.52$	$.005 < p < .01$	df = 2
Picture Arrangement	$X^2 = 10.84$	$.001 < p < .005$	df = 2
Memory Quotient	$X^2 = 8.32$	$.01 < p < .025$	df = 2
Wechsler Memory Scale		$.01 < p < .025$	
CFF	$X^2 = 9.58$	$.005 < p < .01$	df = 2

study. Failure to find significant differences was due in part to a large variance associated with the sample on all of the tests and subtests employed. While individual changes on the tests were occasionally quite large, others were negative or very small. Responses to the drug were largely unique to each subject due in part, at least, to the standard dosage of 600 mg.

A *post hoc* comparison, using chi-square, of the frequency of positive or negative changes in each test was then performed. A hypothesis of equal change on each test was tested. It is interesting to note that significantly more changes occurred for four of the tests than hypothesized (see Table 21-1). There were significantly more changes in a positive direction for the Similarities and Picture Arrangement subtests from the Wechesler-Bellevue Intelligence Tests and also for the Memory Quotient of the Wechsler Memory Scales as well as the Critical Flicker Fusion Test. Significantly fewer changes than expected were found in the Babcock Sentence Test. In accordance with studies which have established association between certain areas of the brain and certain intellectual functions, these results suggest changes to specific areas as well as generalized changes in cortical function. However, as mentioned in the foregoing, anatomical correlates of given intellectual tasks may not apply as readily to the elderly.

The Effects of Cyclandelate on Psychological Test Performance

The changes in tests between premedication and postmedication conditions again were handled by difference scores and mean changes were analyzed statistically by means of a t test. There were three significant differences between means at the acceptable confidence level of $p = .05$ with one exceeding that level at $p = .01$ (see Table 21-2). Thus, four of the nine subtests evinced good postmedication increases: Comprehension, Similarities, and Picture Arrangement subtests of the Wechsler Intelligence Scales and

TABLE 21·2
TEST PATTERN COMPARISON BEFORE AND AFTER RECEIVING CYCLANDELATE

	$\bar{d}$	Sd	t Actual	df	TWO-TAIL CRITICAL t VALUES		UPPER TAIL CRITICAL t VALUES	
					t.95	t.99	t.95	t.99
Comprehension	1.500	0.701	2.140*	19	2.093	2.861	1.729	2.539
Information	0.800	0.468	1.709	19	2.093	2.861	1.729	2.539
Digit Span	1.400	0.690	2.029†	19	2.093	2.861	1.729	2.539
Similarities	1.800	0.672	2.680*§	19	2.093	2.861	1.729	2.539
Babcock Sentences	0.100	0.069	1.449	19	2.093	2.861	1.729	2.539
Picture Arrangement	1.650	0.755	2.185*	19	2.093	2.861	1.729	2.539
Digit Symbol	0.350	0.386	0.907	19	2.093	2.861	1.729	2.539
Raven	5.350	3.640	3.006†	19	2.093	2.861	1.729	2.539
CFF	1.550	1.123	1.256	19	2.093	2.861	1.729	2.539

* Significant at <.05
† Significant at <.01
‡ Two-tail   p <.05
§ Upper tail   p <.01

the Raven Coloured Progressive Matrices Test. It should be clarified that these significant differences are arrived at through a two-tail critical t value where no assumption is made regarding difference score changes. By employing an upper tail critical t value, an assumption of change being likely, more discrimination is seen which makes for significance for Digit Symbol and elevates Similarities. These results, however, are being discussed through the more conservative procedure.

These cyclandelate results are very similar in quality to those achieved in the papaverine study. Where papaverine pre/post medication score changes failed to achieve significance because of large variance associated with the sample, further analysis using chi-square showed significantly more changes occurring in four tests, i.e. Similarities, Picture Arrangement, Memory Quotient and Critical Flicker Fusion. Cyclandelate on a similar sample elicited unilateral increases in identical tests of Similarities and Picture Arrangement, plus Comprehension and the Raven Matrices. Surprisingly, Critical Flicker Fusion, regarded as a general power factor (5), did not show significant difference scores in either the papaverine or cyclandelate studies as expected, although a *post hoc* analysis of papaverine data showed postmeasurement considerably greater than expectancy. As to Wechsler Memory Scale comparisons, inadvertently, an insufficient number of pre/post medication Memory Scales were administered in the cyclandelate study for adequate statistical comparison. The Raven, however, in the cyclandelate study, showed the highest increases of all the subtests. By employing a different critical t value, however, Similarities manifested equal significance and Digit Span, recognized as sensitive to organic changes, reached acceptable significance.

It is noted that the cyclandelate dosage levels, 800 mg daily for the first ten patients and 1600 mg daily for the second ten, did not result in any statistically significant differences in any of the subtests. The two medication groups would have been a good problem for analysis of variance, however, the results with the t suggest it would not yield further significance. A spot check of computing t scores using nine degrees of freedom also showed no significance in those checked.

As indicated, it is interesting to note that several of these parameters selected as sensitive measures for both the cyclandelate and papaverine HCL vasodilator studies appear to be sensitive measures to changes in increased vascular flow or distribution. Although these present cyclandelate study findings reveal more statistical significance than those achieved in the papaverine study using the same parameters, variables as differences in population, differences is psychological examiners, and lack of placebo controls preclude definitive comparisons. Also, the cyclandelate study may have been unusually fortunate in not having subjects who respond to the drug with a shunting effect which makes for very poor performance.

As to isoxsuprine HCl, after an inspection of the data of nineteen of twenty patients studied statistical significance is expected in Similarities and Visual Reproduction subtests. One common denominator of measured improvement for all three vasodilators is the Similarities subtest, a test of abstraction.

Interpreting these results in terms of neuropsychological studies of McFie and others, especially A. Smith, vasodilators could be regarded as influencing the highest cortical functions, verbal symbolic, with some increase to secondary visual-spatial functions. In terms of differential anatomical/intellectual correlates, Comprehension, Similarities and Picture Arrangement and Visual Reproduction subtests can be regarded as posterior frontal lobe functions, the first two associated with left and the latter to right hemisphere functions. The Raven Coloured Matrices are highly correlated with Block Design which in turn is a reliable measurement of right parietal lobe function; there is some demonstration, also, that the Raven Matrices are related to dysphasic functions produced by vascular or neoplastic lesions of the left hemisphere (9). Also Picture Arrangement and Visual Reproduction (memory for designs) are highly correlated with one another and lesions of the posterior frontal anterior temporal area on the right (8). The tests employed in these studies, especially in considering its elderly population, are felt insufficient to entertain this type of conclusion as these results involve and reflect measurements sensitive to anxiety level and could very well be explained in terms of decreased anxiety. Those with moderate cerebral vascular insufficiency are very aware of their lowered abilities and this awareness brings a great deal of agitation which may well contribute to functioning below their present capacities. After vasodilator, this anxiety element may largely disappear, and we may be attributing changes too much to the drug action. We might well be facing a similar problem in researching vasodilators as we face in studying antianxiety drugs in drug/placebo design and, until we use drugs, placebo, and nothing sequence the results could be disputed.

CONCLUSION

Three separate vasodilator studies on the elderly, each involving a single drug, either cyclandelate, isoxsuprine HCl, or papaverine HCl have yielded both similar and yet quite different results. Precomparisons and postcomparisons on nine differen tests sensitive to changes in cortical brain functions in one group of twenty patients all diagnosed as having moderate cerebral vascular insufficiency revealed overall significance in difference scores for four tests for cyclandelate, i.e. Comprehension, Similarities, and Picture Arrangement subtests of the Wechsler and the Raven Matrices. These significant tests are largely verbal symbolic, reflecting changes in the highest cortical functions. The largest post-testing increase was in the Raven Matrices, a test regarded as assessing visual-spatial functions, as well as a generalized factor, a factor of generalized intelligence which the Progressive Matrices are thought to measure (9).

The papaverine HCL results are very similar in quality but did not yield the same kind or degree of statistical significance as those achieved in the cyclandelate study. It is thought that papaverine pre/post medication score changes failed to achieve significance because of uniform dosage and large variance associated with the sample as well as shunting effect in several cases which led to a serious lowering of the post medication scores. However, a chi-square analysis revealed significantly more changes occurring in four tests than hypothesized, i.e. Similarities, Picture Arrangement, Memory Quotient, and Critical Flicker Fusion. The isoxsuprine HCl study, although the study is not yet completed, is expected to result in statistical significance of change attributable to the drug in Similarities and Visual Reproduction subtests.

Increased measurements following isoxsuprine HCL, papaverine HCl, and cyclandelate share two common parameters which are regarded as resulting from the effects of vasodilators; i.e. verbal abstract and visual-spatial functions. The statistical significance in these parameters is certainly suggestive, however, because two of the three studies were open, those results should be viewed cautiously and not as conclusive evidence for therapeutic efficacy without further study involving placebo control. Follow-up studies on papaverine HCl and cyclandelate, both with palcebo control in a double-blind crossover design, are now underway.

REFERENCES

1. EICHORN, O.: The effects of cyclandelate on cerebral circulation. *Vasc Dis 2* (No. 6): Nov. 1965.
2. BALL, J.A.C., AND TAYLOR, A.R.: Effect of cyclandelate on mental function and cerebral blood in elderly patients. *Brit Med J, 3*:525–528, Aug. 1967.
3. SMITH, W. LYNN, PHILIPPUS, M.J., AND LOWREY, J.B.: A comparison of psychological and psychophysical test patterns before and after receiving papverine HCl. *Curr Ther Res, 10*:428–431, Sept. 1968.
4. SMITH, W. LYNN, LOWREY, JACK B., AND DAVIS, JOHN A.: The effects of cyclandelate on psychological test performance in patients with cerebral vascular insufficiency. *Curr Ther Res, 10*:613–618, Dec. 1968.
5. SMITH, W. LYNN, AND PHILIPPUS, M.J.: *Neuropsychological Testing in Organic Brain Dysfunction.* Springfield, Charles C Thomas, 1969.
6. HALSTEAD, W. C.: *Brain and Intelligence: A Quantitative Study of the Frontal Lobes.* Chicago, Chicago University Press, 1947.
7. LURIA, A.R.: *Human Brain and Psychological Processes.* New York, Harper & Row, 1966.
8. McFIE, JOHN: Psychological testing in clinical neurology. *J Nerv Ment Dis, 131*:383–393, 1960.
9. REED, H.B.C., AND REITAN, R.M.: A comparison of the effects of the normal ageing process with the effects of organic brain damage on adaptive abilities. *J Geront. 18*:177–179, April 1963.

10. DeRenzi, E. et al.: The influence of aphasia and the hemispheric side of the cerebral lesion on abstract thinking. *Cortex, II* (No. 4):399–421, Oct. 1966.
11. Wechsler, D.: *The Measurement of Adult Intelligence.* Baltimore, Williams & Wilkins, 1944.
12. Kaufman, A.: The substitution test: a survey of studies on organic mental impairment and the role of learning and motor factors in test performance. *Cortex IV* (No. 1): 47–64, March 1968.
13. Smith, A.: Intellectual functions in patients with lateralized frontal tumors. *J Neurol Neurosurg Psychiat, 29*:52–54, Feb. 1966.
14. Smith, W. Lynn, and Davies, D.H.: Pre-post surgical cortical function studies on open-heart surgery cases. Unpublished observations, 1969.
15. Smith, W. Lynn, Wrathall, R., Lowrey, J.B., and Oslinker, J.: Psychological Study of Elderly Patients with Cerebral Vascular Insufficiency Treated with Isoxsuprine HCl (Vasodilan) and Placebo. In preparation.

PART VI

FINAL PANEL

Final Panel

Moderator: JOSEPH E. BOGEN

Dr. Bogen: In the hope that they may be of interest to you, I might mention several small items. Dr. Davies pointed out that we understand, or there is a general acceptance of the idea, that blood flow is related to pressure and resistance according to Ohm's law. You may be interested to know that Dr. Van Harreveld (who is not here to say this himself) once developed some equations including the elastic recoil of the vessels, thus including a factor of "capacitance." So, instead of talking about the resistance, he has a term called "impedance" which is a complex of the resistance and the capacitance (1).

I would like to second Dr. Davies' point about iatrogenic disease. I do not often see people with hypokalemia from diuretics; but it is almost a daily occurence to see somebody whose high blood pressure has been treated aggressively and who has been very dizzy for the past month or so and then gets well as soon as the blood pressure is regarded as a compensatory phenomenon to be tolerated rather than suppressed.

Dr. Moorman showed a picture which deserves wide publicity—the change in caliber of an arteriole. Spasm in cerebral vessels is a very real thing. Perhaps I am saying something unnecessary but I constantly encounter people who think that it is a myth. There is no question about the spasm of the blood vessels—you can often see it with your bare eyeball at surgery; and we see it on angiograms all the time.

One other item . . . Dr. Pirkey mentioned dichotic stimulation, in which material is put into both ears at the same time. Now, if you put words into the right ear and into the left ear simultaneously and then ask the patient afterwards to tell you how many of these words he remembers (the usual right-handed patient), the percentage of words which he will recall going into the left ear is somewhat lower than in the right. Since the right-handed person is talking with the left hemisphere, this hemisphere which is giving you feedback—telling you what it hears—is evidently more attentive to the right ear than it is to the left ear. Now, Milner and Taylor came out from Montreal to test in this way some of our patients who had the corpus callosum split (2). You see now what would be predicted, that is, an even greater disparity, because the left hemisphere has difficulty drawing on the right hemisphere—and indeed that is the way it turns out. The person repeats back a very high percentage of the words piped into the right ear and practically none from the left ear. This is not attributable to a peripheral hearing loss on the left, because the patient will reliably repeat the words from the left ear, if that is the only ear which is stimulated. So this finding which is barely detectable in normal people has very clear support from the splits; the discrepancies are so great that statistical measures are no longer necessary to see the difference.

Which brings me to a question which has to do with the problem of before and after statistics. If we have patients being considered for an operation, what it boils down to is the pre post condition—if they are going to be better afterward than before. We only have one chance—only one prestate and one poststate. But the experimental pharmacologist has tremendous advantage because a drug can be started and stopped repeatedly. While listening here for the last couple of days, it seems to me that this advantage has not been exploited in doing double-blind crossover studies when there is only one crossover. Would not the information double or possibly quadruple if there were some recrossing? Well, I see people shaking their heads and I would appreciate it very much if someone could elucidate this problem for me. I see Doctor Essman shaking his head and furiously puffing his cigar. Would you like to speak first?

Dr. Essman: I think probably Doctor Hakerem has had much more experience with some of the problems associated with the double-blind crossover and your suggestion of double or triple crossover....

Dr. Hakerem: It is a statistical nightmare. We did an intensive study on several drugs at once—each patient received six weeks on drugs, three weeks of inbetween drugs and then again drugs or placebos. When we analyzed the data it was open to too many problems as to the effect, the overall effect of each of the drugs as well as the placebo and which came first or last. How much of the drugs remained in the system was not explained—and is not easily explained.

Dr. Bogen: Well then you need a longer period before you cross back over.

Dr. Hakerem: Yes. But then this would be about three times the nine weeks and would become totally unwieldy.

Dr. Adler: There are so many problems associated with the type of suggestion that you make, on a pharmacological basis. First of all, enzyme induction (which has come into its own in the past few years and is not readily appreciated by people who give drugs) can very profoundly alter the type of response that you are going to get. I would guess that there are at least fifty common drugs which have been shown to cause enzyme induction which alters the metabolism of that and other drugs . . . some for as long as several months after a single administration. Now this is something that is not usually taken into account. Secondly, genetic differences in people are often ignored. The way the drug is handled by the particular person is something which can effect this type of study. Lastly, drug interactions—you very rarely find a patient who has been on only one drug. He has been on a variety of drugs and the type of interaction is almost impossible to predict. I am not trying to negate the value of crossover study but I think that to just chain these and continually go back and forth will give as much spurious information as valuable information. Furthermore, you usually cannot find what the patient has been taking—either prescribed or nonprescribed. If you have an institutionalized patient it is, of course, somewhat easier but at the same time we know so little about the long-term effect of any of these drug therapies that to say that if we take a patient off for two weeks or four weeks and then to make the necessary assumption that the patient is drug-free is not true. You can measure levels of phenothiazine for a long time in the brain after it has been given chronically. You cannot see any overt effects on many occasions, but if you give another drug which could add to, or be antagonized by it, you are going to pick up an effect of which you understood practically nothing.

Dr. Haward: In addition to what Doctors Hakerem and Adler said there is an ethical problem: one is not sure whether the drug is the right drug for the particular patient. If one finds that there are some genuine beneficial results, it could be argued, I think, that you should stop the trial; and in fact you would have a burden to justify extending trials for the purpose of obtaining more information.

Dr. Bogen: Let's suppose that in a single crossover you have attained what you consider to be a sufficient probability that there is a significant difference. But you do not know what caused it—that is the problem. If you are sitting on a horse and you say in a firm voice, 'Mush' and the horse starts running, you have no problem recognizing there is a significant difference in the horse's velocity. But what makes him go? Maybe he was bitten by the bluetail fly. The way you actually decide is that you stop the horse and you say 'Mush' again, and he goes again. To show a significant difference is a far cry from showing the causal relationship, it is the *repeated* manipulation of the independent variable which gives you confidence that there is some dependence.

Dr. Hakerem: The problem is, What is the independent variable?—one that has the same value with repetition. In other words, what Doctor Adler was saying, one of the big problems with the crossover, is the washout of the drug. As he mentioned, phenothiazine may have a persistent level for four to six months after administration. Now, assuming you crossover and go back to the placebo and wait that period of time, then you go back to your drug again; now is the result attributable to an inadequate washout period?

Dr. Bogen: You would then have a way to defend a negative result, but if you have a positive result, it would be very convincing.

Dr. Smith: The comment on human studies and the problem of repeated measures: I got caught in this bind when using a so-called Florida design in a diphenylhydantoin study where everyone was on a placebo for a while, then baseline tested, and then switched over to the next condition, placebo or drug condition, then finally crossed over again to the remaining condition. In this type of design one can have a better check on placebo reaction as there are two placebo groups. But in order to do this, i.e. employing several conditions and using intelligence measures, we get into serious measurement problems. We do not at this time have three alternate forms of an intelligence scale so with just three conditions we get involved in all sorts of problems, e.g. contamination of subtests, subtest items, practice effect on some performance items and so on. Actually we are very limited in choosing from available design procedures in studies involving humans.

But back to the question of repeated crossovers. In the ethosuximide series I presented yesterday the double-blind crossover study was preceded by an open study so the series actually involved two crossovers for six subjects. Those who were on the drug before the second drug/placebo study fell off in verbal functions when placed on the first placebo condition but increased in the same functions when crossedover to the remaining drug condition. These two crossovers provide valuable reinforcing data to clarify actual drug effect. Fortunately, where the dependent variable is verbal function, practice effect is not a factor in intelligence testing with repeated measures.

Dr. Bogen: Perhaps we can move on to another problem. Yesterday we were shown a sigmoid curve such that if we manipulate in the proper range, then it appears that there is some dependence of y on x. Now, if we move the entire curve along the z axis and you happen to be in the wrong place, you are not going to be able to find any range of x where y varies markedly with x. This is not just a three-dimensional surface; you are actually dealing with many dimensions. Now, if a man is an effective experimental tactician, that is what he is good at. He manipulates the other variables until he finds some range where he can demonstrate an effect. Indeed, if a man is a good enough experimenter, he will always get a significant difference of some kind. How do we decide whether this is of consequence to us?

Dr. Haward: This is very clear in the study which I showed yesterday morning; the justification for showing significance at the two-hour level was just because in actual practice this is the sort of time basis one is working with. There would be no justification for showing a six-hour level or even the first minute level. We have got to justify the parameters in terms of the real life problem.

Dr. Cherkin: That raised a question I wanted to ask you. I assume there are some strong practical reasons why it is not feasible to restrict the watch time to an hour because it seems to me that would solve your problem in a nonpharmacological way.

Dr. Haward: Yes, two problems enter here. One consists of administrative problems in changing over shifts because it means complete replacement of staff. The second thing is that there is a psychological need to have a degree of consistency—an historical knowledge of what is happening. If you come in when the aircraft is already on the screen, you do not know its entire history and therefore, you cannot pick up the nuances which are being followed. You do not know when you take the aircraft over, say ten miles within the air field, that in fact the pilot finds it very difficult in the storm center and therefore should be given priority. This sort of information which is not necessarily made explicit by the preceding controller may be very important in justifying decisions which the controller makes. So that one would really want as long a period as possible from the purely task point of view...

Dr. Cherkin: And that would argue for extending the watch period...

Dr. Haward: Yes, indeed.

Dr. Cherkin: But you do not do that.

Dr. Haward: No. The watch period is a compromise between the physical needs of the controller and the psychological needs of the task.

Dr. Turner: May I comment on a still more general level of discourse, with reference to what Dr. Smith has called "horizons in psychopharmacology"? If people are going to use drugs and drugs are going to be used on them, may we predict just a little bit about where we are going? The M.D. prescribes a large number of official drugs, and very largely these are toward relief of pain, fear, or to keep people from bothering others. But there is another group that are also official, such as the impending fluorides, DDT, carbon monoxide, and others which may cause general pollution and affect everybody. In addition to having still unknown psychopharmacologic effects, these can cause many people to have anxiety. Then there are a lot of drugs which are being used, and will always be used, for purely personal satisfaction, let's call these "people's drugs," and these, many times, are forbidden by official authorities. We know about hallucinogens and cocaine and so on. The use of these depends, in part, upon what population density does. I suppose almost everyone here is familiar with the work of Calhoun on rats (9, 10), showing that when the population density reaches the square of the optimal (generally, the optimal is somewhere between 8 and 12; in other words, if you get between 64 and 144 animals within a certain space), the whole population becomes so unstable that mothers will abandon their young; there is a great deal of cannabalism, and there are other extreme forms of behavioral disturbance in normal animals. Such findings suggest some questions about increasing density of human populations.

What kind of drugs may we expect to be developed or to be used, both as "people's drugs", and as those used but not considered "official"? Some of these, like alcohol, improve our acceptance of decreased interpersonal space. There are others, such as LSD and so on which lead to a narcissistic absorption so that those intoxicated do not care about interpersonal relations. Then, there are some aphrodisiacs which are not currently available but they will be. I understand (having had no experience with them) that they prolong sexual excitement and satisfaction and increase the sense of sexual gratification (11). This suggests that there will be other drugs which will do more than merely promise a reward and will actually bring about the consummate joys of gratification.

Again, because of the increase in population and the certainty that we are on the edge of worldwide famine, I think there will be developed other drugs such as cocaine which will permit persons to avoid the pain of hunger, or drugs such as the amphetamines which will suppress hunger. Then, the use of drugs which have already been introduced for suppression of fear must be varied greatly, enlarged in scope and activity.

A third group of approaches to psychopharmacology is preventative. We have not only the thalidomide experience but Nature itself producing a large number of genetic variations with deformity. There is on the horizon a way of altering the genetics of the individual after birth, beyond that which has been done in terms of just giving a special diet, or giving insulin (4).

Dr. Bogen: May I ask a question? There are many people here who are representatives of pharmaceutical firms. Would it be betraying a trade secret if I ask you—Are you people about to introduce little gadgets which will supply defective enzymes for people, say for diabetes or some other genetic defect? If so, it must be a trade secret!

Dr. Turner: No, as far as I know, it has not actually been done, but it is in the literature. For instance, both Hurler's and Hunter's syndromes are mucopolysaccharidoses, in which an enzyme defect leads to the appearance of a mucopolysaccharide which is deposited in various tissues. There are different polysaccharides for these two types. If fibroblasts in tissue culture are grown together, they each supplement the other so that the tissue culture now becomes competent and the mucopolysaccharides do not appear. If you grow them with normal cells, the culture is competent (12). An experiment done by Benoit on two accasions back in 1961 and 1966 is another example of the kind of thing I mean (8). They had some red ducks; I have forgotten the strain. They injected a liver homogenate of the red duck into the peritoneal cavity of a newly hatched white duckling. As the young duck grew to maturity, it had a lot of red feathers and red bill. When these ducks were inbred the F-1, F-2, F-3 generations down to F-6 continued to have a mixture of red and white. When they were outbred to their original ancestors, they gradually segregated again, the white into the red.

Now I do not want to go into a lot of other experiments which suggest to me that there are already the beginnings of mechanisms, procedures, which will permit major genetic defects to be overcome as the cells of the individuals affected become competent for the production of the normal enzyme. I do not know whether this would lead to propagation of aberrant genes in the next generation and increase the genetic load. These, I think, are a few of the areas in which psychopharmacological studies in the future will be extended.

Dr. Bogen: Is anybody else concerned about increasing the genetic load? That seems to be a major contribution of the medical profession. Dr. Turner discussed what is on the horizon and did a very thorough job, it seems to me, but there may be contributions from the audience.

Dr. Venn: I feel that there is one area of possible research that is being sorely neglected and needs further looking into—and that is cortical dysfunction in the aging person. For example, we cannot find any validated grading systems for judging such dysfunctions. We have no drugs, and I include the vasodilators, that have a predictable effect on cortical dysfunction of the aged. At this stage, it is a negative horizon, I am afraid.

Dr. Bogen: We are all familiar with the fact that a lot of persons who are aged and have difficulty thinking also have large ventricles in the brain. Now one of the reasons, of course, is that there is a steady fallout of nerve cells. We are all losing brain cells at a steady rate every day; and eventually we run out, if we do not die of something else first. But there is another cause for large ventricles in addition to hydrocephalus *ex-vacuo*. It is now recognized that there is an occult or nonresorptive hydrocephalus in which the ventricles are large, not because the brain has shrunk, but because the fluid cannot get out of the ventricles properly. If a ventriculojugular, or some other shunt, is put in, sometimes there is a remarkable improvement. There is here, then, an opportunity for some help in the question of senility, and of course as we improve our survival with respect to other disease, this is going to be a bigger and bigger source of concern. At the present time there is no way to decide which is the proper cause; and in fact the only good test now is to put in a shunt and see if the patient gets better. Now a question has been raised as to whether this is merely a pressure problem. Since many of the people who have resorptive hydrocephalus do not have increased pressure, it may be that the failure to circulate fluid properly is not a mechanical problem at all but that metabolic products are not being carried away with sufficient rapidity. So far as I know, no chemical studies have been done in this particular field.

Dr. Hakerem: There would be no end of metabolic products to look for. Perhaps instead of thinking about these problems, we would do better to concentrate for a while on sharpening our tools. Becoming expert in a particular method, for example pupillography, can be in itself a lifetime study.

Dr. Pirkey: With respect to possible increase in pressure in the fluids within the ear, as we learn more about Meniere's disease we find that there is a precursor of this disease which we call endolymphatic hydrops for want of a better name. There is increased pressure inside the cochlear duct. We find that many people with severe, uncontrolled Meniere's disease have an obstruction of their endolymphatic duct and the cerebrospinal fluid cannot get back into the cerebrospinal system. This causes a marked dilatation system.

Dr. Bogen: You are fairly confident there that it is a mechanical problem?

Dr. Pirkey: Yes. That is right, in many cases. Now of others with the same symptoms, probably 50 per cent have a dilatation but we cannot prove an obstruction of the outlet. Certain types of audiometric testing are abnormal in the very early beginning of an increase in pressure. So, even though the hearing is normal in routine tests, we can determine whether there is a beginning increase in pressure in one ear. By giving certain medications, particularly histamine, you can show that the fluid pressure is decreased. Then, the patient stops the histamine and the pressure returns, as in a crossover study. Then, if you start histamine again the pressure drops and that is an example where you can cross back over.

Dr. Bogen: Thank you very much.

Dr. Turner: We might take note of a possible role of androgens and anti-androgens in modifying human beings (4). For instance, anti-androgen given to rats during some phases of development will (if I am not mistaken) make the males come out as females (5, 6). There is the case of a man who introduced his six-year-old son to mutual sexual activity. (7). He wanted to stop and could not, so he applied for help and they gave him an anti-androgen which is now on the market—it reduced his androgen level in the blood and urine to extremely low amounts and stopped his sexual drive entirely.

Dr. Cherkin: Evolution took pretty good care of man's behavioral aberrations; and then we escaped evolutionary control by introducing civilization and so the human horizon seems simultaneously limitless and controllable. This may include the development of psychopharmacologic agents that will assist us to modify our behavior appropriately until we learn how to do it ourselves. In other words, we have to invent our own future. . . .

Dr. Turner: Yes—aggression is one area. I think the overall point is that we have had a wonderful feedback mechanism where defects were eliminated by evolution, and we have lost that now. We have denied ourselves of it and we have to find a substitute. One more comment, if I may be permitted. There are methods now in development which can permit a single installation of a silicone-coated drug, for instance in a specific locus in the brain, to control behavior for a significant part of a lifetime (3).

Dr. Bogen: How about synthesizing big molecules, for example, in putting together a virus? Doctor Turner pointed out that no matter what problem we discuss, we always come back to the population increase. A suggestion was made by one of our panelists the other day—he left early and might not want to take the credit for this idea—that we might be able to tailor-make a virus to solve the population problem . . . a temporary sterility, say of a year, and the virus spreads around the world in perhaps every three years, to give everybody a fair chance. . . .

Dr. Cherkin: That's not a question of synthesis of drugs, is it? It is a question of political feasibility.

Dr. Bogen: Isn't it true though that the political problem is not as sticky as one would think, because the attitudes of whole populations of people change when the practicality of some action is apparent, as with The Pill the people can see it, the ordinary fellow who is not specially educated, then the entire political view, the overall aura seems to change.

Dr. Essman: Maybe what we need is some way to resolve our communication on one hand and perception on the other. It is not only in the experimental subjects that their communications somehow do not reconcile with—perception. What we really have to identify is who the communicators are and who the receivers are, and I think all of these problems bring us back to Dr. Hakerem's point about sharpening our tools before trying to use them.

Dr. Smith: It is most impressive that we seem to have divided into two camps in this discussion, not so much on the basis of our supposed specialties as on the basis of some personal preference for emphasizing either means or ends —whether we should concentrate on *what* to do or on *how* to do it. In spite of which, it has been a most stimulating and informative exchange, and I should like to thank again all of the participants.

REFERENCES

1. VAN HARREVELD, A., ELLIS, C.H., AND WOLFGRAM, F.J.: An analysis of the cardiovascular action of levo-epinephrine and levo-nor-epinephrine. *Arch Int Physiol*, 60: 420–421, 1952.
2. MILNER, B., TAYLOR, L., SPERRY, R.W.: Lateralized suppression of dichotically presented digits after commissural section in man. *Science*, 161:184–186, 1968.
3. FOLKMAN, JUDAH, AND MARK, VERNON, H.: Diffusion of anesthetics and other drugs

through silicone rubber. Therapeutic implications. *Trans NY Acad Sci,* ?:1187–1195, 1968.

4. MICHAEL, RICHARD, P. (Ed.) : *Endocrinology and Human Behavior.* Proceedings of a conference held at the Institute of Psychiatry, London, May 1967. London, Oxford University Press, 1968.

5. MONEY, JOHN, AND EHRHARDT, ANKE: Prenatal hormonal exposure: Possible effects on behavior in man. In Michael, R.P. (Ed.) : *Endocrinology and Human Behavior.* London, Oxford University Press, 1968.

6. HAMADA, H., NEUMANN, F., AND JUNKMANN, K.: Intrauterine Antimaskuline Beeinflussung von Rattenfeten Durch ein Stark Gestagen Wirksames Steroid. *Acta Endorcr, 44*:380–388, 1963.

7. TURNER, M.D.: Comments and discussion to Zubin, Evans, and Katz. American College of Neuropsychopharnacology presentation at the December 1968 meeting at Puerto Rico Sheraton Hotel, San Juan, Puerto Rico.

8. LEROY, PIERRE, AND BENOIT, J.: Resultats obtenus sur des sujets de troisieme et de quatrieme generations, issues de Pouled de Rhode Island traitees au sang de Pintade, *C R Acad Sci,* May 1963.

9. CALHOUN, J.B.: Ecology and Sociology of the Norway Rat. *Public Health Service Publication, #1008.* US Department of Health, Education, and Welfare, Bethesda, Maryland, 1962.

10. CALHOUN, J.B.: Space and the Strategy of Life. Presented at A.A.A.S., 135th Annual Meeting, Dec. 1968.

11. EVANS, W.: Aphrodisiac Chemicals. Presented at the meeting of the American College of Neuropsychopharmacology, San Juan, Puerto Rico, Dec. 1968.

12. FRATANTONI, J.C., HALL, C.W., AND NEUFIELD, E.F.: Hurler and Hunter syndromes: Mutual correction of the defect in cultured fibroblasts. *Science, 162*:570–572, July 1968.

Subject Index

Acetylcholine, 85
Achievement interest, Dexedrine effect, 91
Acoustic nerve, 247
Action instigational factors, 71
Activating systems, 72
Activation, 71
Active behavioral inhibition, 208–211
Adaptation, hypoxic exposure, 224
Addiction, 106
Adrenergic substances, pupil effect, 60
Aerobic conditions, 29
Aerospace medicine, 105
Aged, see Aging, Elderly, and Senile Patients
Aggression, 206
Aggressive actions, brain damage result, 178
Aggressive children, 142
Aging, 44, 188
Agitation, cerebral function, 258
Air traffic control, 103, 105, 110, 267
    anxiety reaction, 109–110
    concentration measurement, 115
    pemoline testing, 106–108
    studies, 112–113 table
Alcohol, 268
Alcoholic delirium, CPZ treatment, 50
Amino acids, 32
    convulsibility relation, 183
Amino acids' release, asphyxiation, 33
Amitryptyline, 205
    avoidance tasks, 170 table
Ammon's horn, 14
Amnesia,
    animals studies, 156
    ECS effect, 168
    experiments, 188–195 figs.
    studies, 194–196 figs.
Amnesic effects, 152
    ECS, 153, 160, 163, 164, 165 table
    flurothyl, 188
    Indoklan, 188
Amphetamines, 73, 79, 85, 204, 268
    avoidance tasks, 170 table
    brain damaged animal, 177
    brain damaged subjects, 180 table
    cognitive functioning effect, 89
    hyperkinetic children therapy, 93
    locomotor activity, 177, 178
    memory effect, 91
    mental fatigue relief, 105
    overeating, 179 table
    side effects, 110
    vigilance enhancement, 92
Amusia, right hemisphere lesions, 37
Amygdaloid functions,
    behavioral index, 202–205
    inhibition, 206
    lesions' effect, 206
    norepinephrine, behavioral effects, 207
    regulatory role, 211
        cortical excitability, 201
Amytal injection, 37
Analeptic drugs, memory effect, 91
Anancastia,
    students, 111
    treatment resistance, 112
Anatomical correlates, 3–37
Androgens, 270
Anesthesia, 188, 192
    brain acetylcholine levels, 169
    CO_2 response, 217
    nembutal, 15
Anger activation, 72
Angina, dipyridamole contraindicated, 236
Animal studies,
    amphetamine effect, 91
    amygdaloid function, 202–205
    asphyxiation, 29
    avoidance tasks, 170
    brain damage, 177–185 figs.
    CO_2 response, 216–230 figs.
    convulsion depressant, 201
    corpus callosum, 7
    cortical activation, 85
    cortical structure, 15, 17 figs.
    drugs compared, 170 table
    ECS effects, 152–154, 155 table, 156, 162–167 tables
    EEG alteration, 161
    flurothyl, 188
    imipramine, 162–163, 164–167 tables, 168–169 table
    lithium effects, 151, 156–157 table, 160–161 tables, 169
    magnesium in brain, 157–159 fig.
    memory, 187–197 figs.
    noise effects, 250

pentylenetetrazol, 162
post-tetanic potentiation, 21 fig.
REM sleep deprivation, 209
retina, 32–33
sodium pentobarbital effect, 216 fig.
sympathectomy, 60
tetanic stimulations, 18
thiazesim, 201
Anti-androgens, 270
Anti-anxiety agents, animal studies, 202
Antibiotics, 237
Anticholinergic hallucinogens, 50
Anticipation, learned, 70
Anticipation threshold, lowering, 79
Anticonvulsant action, drugs, 205
    phenytoin, 112
Anticonvulsants, 122
Antidepressants, 73, 74, 79, 205
    animal experiments, 202
    avoidance effect, 171
    effects, 75 table
    imipramine action, 162
    thiazesim, 201
Antihistamines, 202, 204
Antipsychotics, 74
Anxiety, 73
    air traffic control, 109
    elderly patients, 254
    skill effect, 104
    students, 111
    tranquilizer therapy, 105, 112
    vasodilator effect, 258
Apathetic patient, drug selection, 56
Apathy, 73
Aphrodisiacs, 268
Appetite loss, 73
Applied Behavior Sciences, Inc., 253
Arithmetic, 44
Arithmetic performance, stimulants' effect, 89
Arousal,
    action instigation, 71
    reduction, 162
    suppression, 161
Arousal level,
    hyperkinetic children, 93
    stimulants' effect, 140
Arousal systems, 72
    CPZ effect, 49
Arteriolar sclerosis, 238, 238 fig., 240 fig., 241 fig.
    cochlea blood supply, 250–251
Aspen Institute, xiii
Asphyxiation studies, 30, 31
    central nervous tissue, 29
    cerebral cortex, 30
Atherosclerosis, 238, 246
Attention span, 122
    improvement, 136
Audiology, 247
Auditory cortex, 247
    lesion, 248
    lesion detection, 247
Auditory verbal dysgnosia, 122
Autonomic recovery, hyperkinetic children, 93
Autonomic symptoms, slow learners, 122
Avoidance acquisition, 209 table, 210
Avoidance tasks, drugs compared, 170 table
Axons, 33

B12, 237
Babcock Sentences, 254, 256 table
Barbiturates, 73, 78, 79, 202
    brain-damaged subjects, 180
    effects, 75 table
Behavior,
    brain-damage effect, 176
    drug effects, 215–231 figs., 227
    drug effects on children, 142
    improvement, 136
    methylphenidate effect, 140
    neurological translation, 27
    vasodilators' effects, 252
Behavior disorders, stimulants' effects, 86–88 fig.
Behavioral activation,
    drugs' effects, 75 table
    regulation by psychotropic drugs, 69–81
Behavioral depression, 180
Behavioral inhibition, 208–211
Behavioral plasticity, brain systems, 205–208
Behavioral sedation, 152
Behaviorally disturbed children, 86–99 fig.
Belligerance, 73
Belligerant patient, chlorpromazine, 56
Bender-Gestalt tests, 94
Benzedrine, children's treatment, 86, 87–88
Biochemicals, 149–232
Biogenic amines, brain-damaged subjects, 183
Bipolar activation, 72–73
Block design tests, 9–11 figs., 44, 129, 253, 258
    Dilantin improvement, 99, 100–101 table
Blood flow, 215
    cerebral, 243–237
    cochlea, 250
Blood pressure, 76, 263
    raising, 85
Blood vessels, constricting, 85
Blue children, 236

Subject Index

Boredom, 110
Boutons, 27
Brain,
    acetycholine anesthesia, 169
    dysfunction, 49
    dysfunction in children, 136
    functions, ethosuximide effect, 131
    imipramine's effects, 162
    magnesium levels, 157–159 table
        elevation, 169
    metabolism, higher functions, 151
    monoamines, 158
    pupillary dilation tie, 60
    serotonin, lithium effect, 158, 159
    synaptosomes, 158
Brain damage,
    animal studies, 177
    drug response afterward, 176–186 figs.
    verbal function loss, 131
Brain-damaged adults, testing, 46
Brain stem,
    conduction enhancement, 105
    reticular formation, 5, 6 fig.
    sites, 12
Brain systems, behavioral plasticity, 205–208
British psychiatrists, 41

Caffeine, side effects, 105, 106, 110
Callosal section, 7
Cambridge Cockpit, 104
Canada, 263
Cannon and Rosenbleuth hypothesis, 231
CO_2, cochlear blood flow increase, 250
pCO_2 level, cerebral blood flow, 235
Cardiac muscle, 250
Cardiogenic shock, 235
Carotid sinus, 12
CAT, pupil studies, 62
Categories, xiii
Central nervous system, drug action and
    functions, 151–175
Central nervous tissue, electrolyte changes,
    29–35
Cerebral arteriosclerosis, 252
Cerebral blood flow, 234–237
Cerebral circulatory disturbance, ocular
    fluorescein
    angiography, 238–246
Cerebral cortex, 5, 250
    asphyxiation, 29–30
    excitability, 14
    freezing study, 30
    lesion, 248
Cerebral dysfunction, learning difficulties, 122
Cerebral function, oxygen availability, 215

Cerebral Function Symposium, xi, xiii, xiv
Cerebral vascular insufficiency, vasodilators'
    effects, 252–260
CFF, 43, 44, 254
    tests, 255 table, 256 table, 257, 259
Channel capacity tests, 114–115 fig.
Character disorders, 42
Chemoconvulsant, 188
Children,
    blue, 236
    Dilantin therapy, 99–102
    drug effects, 142
    emotionally disturbed, 86–88
    learning problems aid, 121–133
    psychotropic drugs studies, 134–147
    stimulants' effect, 86–88
    visual-spatial tests, 253
Chlordiazepoxide, 205
    avoidance tasks, 170 table, 171
Chlorpromazine, see CPZ
Cholinergic substances, pupil effect, 60
Cholinesterase inhibitor, 203
Cholinomimetric drugs, animal studies, 203
Chronic hypoxia, 235
"Clear thinking," 46
CNS,
    assessment of functions, pupillography, 59–
        68
    changes in man, 41–52
    excitation, 73
    induced change, 49–50
    stimulant, 85
Cocaine, 267
Cochlea, pathology, 248
Cochlear blood flow, epinephrine effect, 250
Cochlear microphonics, anoxia's effect, 250
Cognitive behavior, lithium salts, 153
Cognitive decrements,
    chlorpromazine, 112
    promethazine, 112
Cognitive function,
    children's therapy, 142
    improvements, 49–50
    levels, 114
    phenothiazines effect, 141
    stimulants' effect, 88–94 figs.
Cognitive maps, 71
Cognitive measures, 43
Cognitivist, learning theory, 70
Commisurotomy, 9, 10 fig., 11
Compensatory drugs, 74
Comprehension,
    convulsive therapy, 48 fig.
    cyclandelates effects, 256 table

Computer of Average Transients, see CAT
Concentration ability, 145
  DPH's effect, 111–113
  drug aid study, 112–113 table
  noisy environment, 114
  objective factors, 113
  pemoline's effect, 103–111
  phenytoin therapy, 112
  subjective factors, 113
  tests, 114–115 fig.
Conceptual nervous system, 41
Confusional delirious state, CPZ effect, 50
Connectionists, 6
Convulsant drugs, 192, 198
Convulsant thresholds, brain damage effect, 181–185 figs.
Convulsant potency, fluorothyl, 188
Convulsions, 122
  avoiding, 151
  thiazesim action, 201
  urea-induced, 151
Convulsive therapy, 46–48 figs.
Coordination,
  convulsive therapy, 47, 48 fig.
  impairment, meprobamate, 105
  two-hand, 44
Core-withdrawn symptoms, phenothiazine therapy, 55
Corpus callosum, 5–14
Corpus callosum split, 263
Cortex,
  electrical studies, 36
  role
Corti, organ of, 250
Cortical activation, 85
Cortical desynchronization, 208
Cortical Function Laboratory, 247, 252, 253
Cortical functions,
  limbic regulation, 201–214
  pharmacology, 201–214
  pupil motility, 59
Cortical structure, 15–18 figs.
CPZ, 42, 78, 205, 208
  avoidance tasks, 170 table
  behavior, 180
  changes in man, 41–52
  children's therapy, 141–142
  cognitive decrements, 112
  excited patient, 56
  physiological action, 49–50
  studies, 53–54
  test changes, 44 fig.
  tests, 45–46
  thinking improvement, 112
  see also Largactil

Cranial injury, 188
Critical Flicker Fusion, see CFF
Crystalline eserine, 203
Cyanotic heart disease, 236
Cybernetic hypothesis, 76
Cyclandelate, 252
  cerebral function, 258–259
  mental function improvement, 252
  psychological test effects, 255–258 table
  studies, 254
Cycloid psychoses, 73
Cyclospasmol, hearing loss therapy, 251

Davis apparatus, anxiety tests, 104
Deactivating systems, 72, 73
Deafness, congenital and hereditary, 249
Deanol acetamidobenzoate, 85, 94–95, 121
  children's therapy, 136–141 tables
Dendrites, 15–16
Denver, Colo., 252
Depressant action, thiazesim, 201
Depressed persons, imipramine effect, 152, 161
Depression, 73
  cortical cells' depolarization, 32
  imipramine therapy, 152, 161
  O_2 deprivation, 31
  psychic energizers therapy, 112
  symptoms, students, 111
Detectors, 76–77
Dexedrine, children's therapy, 86, 87, 88, 89, 91, 93
Dextroamphetamine, 79
Dextroamphetamine, 78
  children's therapy, 86–87, 136–141 tables
Dextroisomers of catecholamines, 203
Diagnosis, hearing loss, 247
Dichotic stimulation, 263
Diencephalic function disturbance, 93
Differential drug activity, 56
Digit span, 44
  concentration measurement, 114
  cyclandelate effects, 256 table
Digit symbol substitution, 44
Digit Symbol tests, 253
Dilantin, emotionally disturbed children, 99–102
Diphenylhydantoin, see DPH
Dipyridamole, angina contraindication, 236
Discharge rate increase, 57
Discriminant function analysis, Maholonobis D2, 45–46
Ditran, confusion inducement, 50
Diuretics, 263
Dizziness, 241, 263

Subject Index

Donnan forces, 32
Dose level, 146
Double-blind studies, 115–116
  ethosuximide, 123
DPH, 121, 145
  children's therapy, 99
  concentration effect, 111–113
  error reduction, 121
  fatigue relief, 116–117
Dreyfus Medical Foundation, 99
Drives, 69, 70, 71
  students, 111
Drug-impaired performance, 112
Drugs,
  central nervous system action, 151–175
  damaged brain's response, 176–186 figs.
  predicting response, 43–58
  sensitivity, 143
  students, 112–113 table
Durham University, 111
Dyscopia, 9, 11
Dysgraphia, 9, 10 fig., 11
Dysphoric reactions, 106

Eating, amphetamine effect, 179 table
Eating behavior, brain damage effects, 176, 177
ECP data, 64
ECS, 41, 152–153, 188, 192, 194, 196, 198, 209
  amnesic effect, 160, 163–165 table
  animal studies, 162–165 tables
  avoidance acquisition, 210
  RNA response, 163, 165–166 table
  serotonin response, 159–160, 166–168 fig.
ECT, 78
Ed50, animal studies, 202
Edinger-Westphal nucleus, 60
EEG, 42
  changes, 41
  children's patterns, 121–133
  convulsive therapy, 46, 47 fig., 49
  CPZ effects, 45–46, 50
  nomenclatures tests, 131 table
  patterns' significance, 132, 147
  slow learners, 122
Efficiency decrement, 110
Ego mechanisms, 69
Ego psychology, 71
Elderly,
  mental difficulties, 269
  mental tests, 253
  vasodilator therapy, 252
  visual-motor ability, 253
  see also Aging, and Senile patients
Electrical activity, 215
Electrical gradients, 22

Electrical stimulation, pupil effect, 60
Electrical studies, cortex, 36
Electrical transmission, 5
Electroarchitectonic map, 22, 23 fig.
Electroconvulsive shock, see ECS
Electroconvulsive therapy, see ECT
Electrocorticogram arrest, 29
Electrograms, abnormal, 122
Electrolytes, 76
  changes in central nervous tissue, 29–35
  extracellular and intracellular, 30
Electron microscopy, 27, 31
Electronic frequency analyzer, 42
Emotionally disturbed children, 86–88 fig., 99–102
Encephalitis, 188
Energizers, 73
England, 235
Engram, 197, 198
Engram forming functions, 26
Environmental influences, 55–56
Epilepsy, 7
  DPH therapy, 99
Epileptogenic foci, pentylenetrazol effect, 181
Epinephrine, 85
  cochlear blood flow increase, 250
Erotomania, 73
Errors,
  anxiety relation, 105
  reduction by diphenlhydantoin, 121
  reduction by pemoline, 121
Erythrocytes, 157
Ethological theory, 70
Ethosuximide, 122–123, 147
  brain damaged subjects, 185 fig.
  IQ score, 126 tables, 127, 128
  learning problem aid, 121–133
  tests, 131 table
  verbal cognition, 128, 131
  verbal IQ effect, 125 table
Euphoria, 73
  lithium salts therapy, 151
Excitability, measurement, 14–28
"Excitation-retardation," 73
Excited patient,
  chlorpromazine, 56
  lithium salts therapy, 151
Excitement, pupillary dilation, 62
Extrapyramidal symptoms, thioridazine, 55
Eye, diagnostic value, 238

Fatigue, 71, 94, 110
  DPH relief, 116–117

effect on vigilance, 104–105
pemoline aid, 116–117
stimulants' relief, 105
Fear,
activation, 72
pupillary dilation, 62
suppressants, 268
Feverishness, 110
Fibers of Bergmann, 30, 31
5-HIAA, 167
levels, 158–159
lithium studies, 160 tables
5-HT,
ECS alteration, 153
levels, 158–159
lithium studies, 160 tables
5-hydroxyindoleacetic acid, ECS effects, 153
5-hydroxytryptamine, transcallosal response effect, 12
5-phenyl-2 imino-4-oxo-oxazolidin, 106
Flight surgeons, 105
Fluorescein angiography, 243-246 figs.
Fluphenazine, apathetic patient, 56
Flurothyl,
brain-damaged subjects, 181, 182 fig.
memory experiments, 190–193 figs.
memory processing effects, 187–200
Flurothyl-induced seizures, brain-damaged subjects, 184–185 figs.
Forebrain removal, 206
14–6 positive spike EEG patterns, children aided, 121–133
France, xi
Frequency spectra changes, 42
Frustration tolerance, low, 73

Genetic defects, animal studies, 268–269
Genetic variations, 268
Germany, 67
Gestational behavior, 72
Gilles de La Tourette disease, pupillary changes, 66
Glucose, 76
Glutamate, 33
Glutamic acid, 32
Grand mal convulsions, 41, 122
Grand mal convulsive treatments, effects, 46–48 figs.
Granule cells, 15
Greeks, 69, 187
GSR recovery times, hyperkinetic children, 92
Guessing situation, pupillary response, 62–63, 65 fig.

Habits, 69, 70

Hallucinations, drug treatment, 55
Haloperidol, 66, 205
thinking improvement, 112
Hand steadiness and unsteadiness, 44
Hardening of arteries, 238
Harmaline hydrochloride, brain-damaged rats, 180
Harvard Infusion Pump, 181
Headache, 241
children, 122
Hearing, 263–264
Hearing loss,
drug alleviation, 251
sensorineural, 247–251
sudden, 251
Heart disease, cyanotic, 236
Heart failure, hypoxia, 235
Heart muscle, stimulating, 85
Hemiplegics, testing, 46
Hemispere relationship, 102
Hemisherectomy patients, 132
Heparin, hearing loss therapy, 251
High tone loss, injury, 250
Higher functions, central nervous system, 151–175
Hippocampal pyramids,
excitability, 19
polarization, 20–22 figs
Hippocampus,
excitability, 14–28
post-tetanic potentiation, 18–20 figs., 25
transmittive apparatus, 27
Hippus, 62
Histamine, 270
Holism, 5
Holland, 5
Hormones, 71
Horner's syndrome, 60
Hospital findings, 54
"Hospital-prone" patient, 57
Hullian theories, 69, 70, 71
Humor loss, 73
Humoral transmission, 5
Hunger suppressants, 268
Hunter's syndrome, 268
Hurler's syndrome, 268
Hydrocephalus, 269
Hyperactive children, see Hyperkinetic children
Hyperactivity, 73
methylphenidate, 140
Hyperarousal, 49
Hypercholesterolemia, 237
Hyperglycemia, 237
Hyperkinetic children, 86, 88, 136, 141, 142

amphetamine therapy, 93
dexedrine effect, 89
methylphenidate, 140
Hyperpolarization, 14
Hypertension, 238, 240 fig., 242–243 figs., 263
classification, 239 fig.
Hypertensive encephalopathy, 241
Hyperuricemia, 237
Hyperventilation, 223
Hypervigilance, 110
Hypokalemia, 263
Hypopolarization, 14
Hypotension, cerebral blood flow fall, 234–235
Hypothalamic areas, brain damage, 176–177
Hypothalamic excitability, imipramine effect, 162
Hypoxia,
cerebral blood flow, 234, 235
chronic, 235
drug effects in behavior, 215–231 figs.
low blood pressure, 235

Iatrogenic disease, 263
Idiot savant, 102
Illinois studies, children, 142
Imipramine, 42, 73, 74, 77, 78, 152, 205, 209, 210
animal studies, 162–163, 164–167 tables, 168–169 table
avoidance tasks, 170 table, 171
brain effects, 162
depressed patients therapy, 161
effects, 75 table
sleep effects, 162
rage response effect, 162
RNA response, 163
serotonin response, 167, 168 fig.
Impedance measurement, 30
Imprinting, 70, 71
Impulse conduction, arrest in asphyxiation, 33
Incentive motivation, 71
Incentive-reward, 72
Indoklon, 188
Information, cyclandelate effects, 256 table
Injury, high tone loss, 250
Inner ear, 249
Instinctual ties, 71
Insulin, 268
Intellectual impairment, amphetamine, 110
Intelligence, concentration link, 115
Intelligence tests,
digit span, 114
stimulants' effect, 89

Interactions of drugs, 265
Interhemispheric transfer, 7
Involutional disorder, convulsive treatment, 46
Ion pumps, arrest, 29
IQ score, ethosuximide, 126–128 tables
IQ tests, 42
Ireland, 252
Iris of eye, 59
Irritability, 110
lithium salts therapy, 151
Ischemic areas, brain, 236
Isoxsuprine HCl, 252
cerebral function, 258–259
cerebral function tests, 258
study, 254
Isotope techniques, cerebral blood flow measurement, 235
Italy, 247

Killing, animal studies, 205–206
Killing activation, animal studies, 203, 204
Killing inhibition, animal studies, 203, 204, 207
Knee-jerk, 27
Korsakoff psychosis, 188
^{85}Kr inhalation, 235

Labyrinthine artery, 249
Lactate production, 236
Language capacity, lateralization, 9
Largactil, xi
Latency reaction, neocortex, 23
Latency variation, 25
Law of Denervation Sensitivity, 181
L-dopamine, 203
Parkinson's disease, 66
Learned anticipation, 70
Learning, 70, 147
enhancement, stimulant drugs, 85–98
facilitators, 83–147
studies with children, 121–133
impairment, meprobamate, 105
theories, 27
early, 69
Lethargy, 151
Li_2CO_3, see Lithium carbonate
Limbic regulation, cortical function, 201–214
Limbic system, 26
Lithium carbonate, 73, 74, 78, 151
animal studies, 160–161 tables, 169
avoidance tasks, 170 table, 171
brain serotonin, 159

effects, 75 table
  norepinephrine effect, 160–161
  treatment, 156–157 tables
Lithium salts, see Lithium carbonate
Locomotor activity,
  amphetamine effect, 180 table
  brain damaged animal, 177
London Gatwick Airport, 106
Los Angeles, Calif., 253
Lowenstein pupillograph, 61–62
LSD, 268
  psychedelic effects, 11–12
Lung disease, cerebral blood flow, 235
Lung function, hypoxia, 235

Mackworth curve, 110–111
Magnesium,
  brain action, 169
  brain levels, 157–159 table
  psychotropic drug evaluation, 170
Maholonobis D², discriminant function analysis, 45–46
Maladaptive behavior, 41
Man,
  chlorpromazine changes, 41–52
  CNS changes, 41–52
Mania, cause, 73
Manic behavior, lithium carbonate therapy, 151
Manic-depressive psychosis, 73
  imipramine therapy, 152
  lithium salts therapy, 151, 159
MAO inhibitors, 73, 74, 77, 78
  effects, 75 table
Mating behavior, 72
Medication responses, 79
Memory, 153
  amphetamine effect, 91
  animal studies, 187–197 figs.
  retrieval, 197–198
  short-term, 197
  tests, 253, 259
Memory consolidation, 152, 194–196
Memory processing, fluorothyl effects, 187–200
Memory Quotient tests, 255 table, 257, 259
Meniere's disease, 249, 270
Mental activity, pupillary responses, 62
Mental deterioration, elderly, 253
Mental disturbances, Indoklon therapy, 188
Mental fatigue, 105, 110
Mental functions, cyclandelate therapy, 252
Mental hospital population drop, xi
Meprobamate, 205
  anxiety reduction, 112

avoidance tasks, 170 table
  coordination impairment, 105
  learning impairment, 105
Metabolism, 215
  central nervous system, 151–175
Methodology, pemoline assessment, 106
Methyl anthranilate, 190
Methyl atropine, 203
Methyl scopolamine, 203
Methylphenidate, 85, 121
  behavior effect, 140
  children's therapy, 88, 136–141 tables
  hyperactivity, 140
Microelectrode, 23
Monoamine oxidase, imipramine, ECS effects, 167
Monoamine oxidase inhibitors, 112
Monosynaptic reflex activity, 29
Montreal Children's Hospital, 134, 135 table, 136, 137 table, 142
Mother ties, 70–71
Moths, 72
Motivation,
  children, 143
  improvement, 141
Motor activity, phenothiazines' effect, 141
Motor skills, drugs' impairment, 105
Mucopolysaccharidoses, 268
Multiple factor handling, 110
Muscle afferent system, 27
Music, right hemisphere, 37

Narcotic action, tranquilizers, 169
National Institute of Mental Health, see NIMH
Nembutal, 15
Neocortex, 26, 27
  excitability, 14–28
  polarization, 22–26 figs.
Nervous patients, 234
Nervous system, signal transmission, 26
Nervousness, caffeine, 110
Neural function, respiratory gases' effect, 226 fig.
Neuroendocrine functions, brain lesions effect, 176
Neuroleptic drugs,
  animal studies, 202
  thinking improvement, 112
"Neuronal hook-up," 64
Neurophysiology, 27
Neuropsychological action,

chlorpromazine, 41
  stimulants, 140
Neurotic children, 88
Nicotine sulfate, avoidance tasks, 170
NIMH, 53, 54
  environmental influences study, 55–56
  phenothiazine study, 55
Nitroglycerine, 236
Noise,
  animal studies, 250
  concentration effort, 114
  hearing injury, 250
Noradrenaline, excessive and insufficient, 73
Norepinephrine, 203, 204, 206, 209, 210
  behavioral effects, 207, 208
  lithium effect, 160–161
Normalizing drugs, 74, 79, 116
  action, 77, 78
  phenothiazines, 74
Normetanephrine increase, imipramine treatment, 161
"Normothynoleptics," 161

Object assembly, 129
Objective factors, concentration, 113
Obsessional personality, students, 111
Ocular fluorescein angiography, cerebral circulatory disturbance, 238–246
Ohm's law, 263
Olfactory pheromones, 72
1-a-methyl-tyrosine, 204
Oral drives, 69
Orphenidrine, 121
Oscillograph recordings, 15
Osmolarity, 76
Osmotic equilibrium, 32
Outpatient, schizophrenia, 56–57
Overweight, 237
O_2,
  cerebral function, 215
  concentration energy need, 114
  cochlea, 250
  deprivation studies, 30, 31
  lack, central nervous tissue, 29
  tension, CO_2 effect, 250
Oxygen, see O_2

Pain activation, 72
Papavarine HCl, 252, 257
  cerebral function, 258–259
  studies, 254–255 table
Parachlorophenylalanine, 204

Paranoid symptoms, environment enfluence, 56
Parkinson's disease, pupillary response, 66
Pathophysiology, reparative drugs, 74
Patients,
  cerebral vascular insufficiency studies, 252–259 figs.
  nervous types, 234
Peer perceptions of behavior, 87
Pemoline,
  assessment experiments, 106–108 figs.
  concentration effects, 103–111
  error reduction, 121
  fatigue relief, 116–117
Pentylenetetrazol,
  animal studies, 162
  brain damaged subjects, 181
  epileptics' sensitivity, 181
Perceptual-analytical testing, 46
Perceptual disorganization, 109–110
Performance,
  deterioration, 110
  drug impairment, 112
  enhancement, stimulant drugs, 85–98
Personality tests, Dexedrine effect, 91
Petit-mal, 122
  therapy, 147
Pharmacology, cortical function, 201–214
Phenobarbital, sleep effects, 50
Phenothiazines, 41, 73, 74, 78, 79, 121, 134
  children's therapy, 141–142
  effects, 75 table
  efficacy, 53–54
  intelligence effect, 91
Phenytoin,
  beneficial effects, 112
  concentration aid, 116
  studies, 112–113 table
Pheromones, 72
Photographing pupil, 61
Photo-Metrazol threshold, hyperkinetic children, 93
Physiological repair, CPZ effect, 49–50
Picture arrangement tests, 255 table, 266 table, 257–259
Pilots, 105
Placebo,
  predicting response, 53–58
  value, 115–116
Pleasure incentive, 72
Pleasure-pain, 79
Polarization,
  hippocampal pyramids, 20–22 figs.
  neocortex, 22–26 figs.

Pollution, 267
Porter Memorial Hospital, 121, 252
Porteus Maze Performance, stimulants' effect, 91
Post-encephalitic disorders, children, 86
Post-tetanic potentiation, 14–28
Predicting response to drugs, 53–58
Prefrontal lobotomies, 91
Presbycusis, 249
Procyclidine, 42
Promethazine, cognitive decrements, 112
Proprioceptive system, 27
Psychedelic effects, LSD, 11–12
Psychiatric illness,
    behavioral activation regulation, 69–81
    drugs' effects, 75 table
    electroconvulsive therapy, 41
    psychotropic drugs' use, 69–81
    students, 111
Psychiatrist, 46
Psychiatry, xi, 72
Psychic energizers, depression relief, 112
Psychoactive agents, 205
    children's therapy, 121
    comparison, 170–171 table
    higher functions, 151
Psychoanalysis, ethological theory impact, 70
Psychodynamic theories, xi
Psycho-effective drugs, pupillary effects, 67
Psychological factors, CO_2 effect, 226
Psychological measures, 42–44 table
    convulsive therapy, 47
    vasodilators' effect on performance, 252–260
Psychological performance,
    convulsive therapy, 47
    cyclandelate effects, 255–258 table
Psychological treatments, 41
Psychology, 72
Psychoneurosis, 42
    convulsive therapy, 41
Psychoneurotic children, 86
Psychopathology, 72
Psychopaths, children, 86
Psychopharmacology, 267
Psychotic children, 86, 142
Psychotic depressions, 42
    convulsive treatment, 46
Psychotic disorders, students, 111
Psychotic patients,
    CPZ effect, 49
    pupillary response, 66, 67
    sleep patterns, 50
Psychotic states, 72
Psychotropic drugs, 49
    animal studies, 202
    behavioral regulation, 69–81
    chtildren's therapy, 134–147
    debilitating effects, 202
    effects, xi, 75 table
    magnesium in evaluation, 170
    task performance, 143
    therapy, 42
Punishment, inhibition, 207
Pupil motility, 59
Pupillary dilation, 60
"Pupillary unrest," 62
Pupillography, CNS functions assessment, 59–68
Pupils, dilating, 85
Purkinje cells, 30

Rage, children, 122
Rage response, imipramine, 162
Raven Coloured Progressive Matrices, 253, 254, 256 table, 257, 258
    ethosuximide effect, 123, 124
Reading time, convulsive therapy, 48 fig.
Recall, CPZ effect, 46
Reflexology, 36
Rehabilitation, 57
Rejection sensitivity, 79
REM sleep, 208
    deprivation, 209, 210
Reparative drugs, 74
Reproductive behavior, 72
Reserpine,
    avoidance tasks, 170 table
    behavior effect, 180
Respiratory gases, sensory stimuli, 226 fig.
Response latency, 141
Response retention studies, 163–165 tables
Response selection, 71
Response to drugs, prediction, 53–58
Restlessness, lithium salts therapy, 151
Retarded children, 142
Retarded patients, stimulants' effect, 95
Retina, depression studies, 32–33
Retrograde amnesia, 231
    experiments, 188–192 figs.
Rheostat model, inconsistencies, 74
Rheostat theory, 78
Ribonucleic acid, *see* RNA
Right hemisphere, 37
Ringer's solution, 32
Ritalin,
    hyperkinetic children's therapy, 93
    intelligence test effect, 89

see also Methylphenidate
RNA,
    ECS effects, 152–153, 163, 165–166 table
    imipramine effects, 163
Rorschach tests, 43
    brain-damaged adults, 46
    CPZ effects, 43 table
    ethosuximide effect, 123, 124

Saline, avoidance tasks, 170 table
Scandinavia, 235
Schizo-affective psychosis, 73, 74
Schizophrenia, 41, 42
Schizophrenics,
    children, 102, 136
    convulsive therapy, 46
    CPZ treatment, 46, 49
    outpatients, 56–57
    phenothiazine treatment, 53, 54–56, 74
    pupillary response, 64
    sleep patterns, 50
    somatic therapies, 56
    students, 111
Sciatic stimulation, pupil effect, 60
Sedatives, 73, 94
Seizures, drugs blocking, 205
Self-image, 70
Senile patients,
    convulsive therapy, 49
    therapy, 269
    see also Aging and Elderly
Sensitivity to drugs, brain damage effect, 180
Sensorineural hearing loss, 247–251
Sensory distortion tests, 43
Separation anxiety, 70, 79
Separation from mother, 71
Septal "hyperirritability," 206
Serial retention tests, 43
Serotonin, 153
    ECS effect, 159–160, 166, 167, 168 fig.
    imipramine effect, 167, 168 fig.
    increase, 180
Sexual drive,
    drug control, 270
    drugs' effect, 268
Sexual preoccupation, children, 86
Short-term memory, 197
Side effects, phenothiazine, 55
Signal transmission, 26
Silver chloride, 30
Skin conductance level, hyperkinetic children, 93
Sleep, 208
    animal studies, 162

    drugs' effects, 50
    imipramine effects, 162
Social rehabilitation, 57
Social role, 70
Sociometric ratings, 87
Sodium chloride, asphyxiation action, 30, 32
Sodium diphenylhydantoinate,
    beneficial effects, 112
    concentration effects, 103–120
Sodium pentobarbital, 216 fig.
Sodium permeability, asphyxiation, 32
Sodium salts, 203
Soft transmission, 27
Somatic therapies, xi, 78
"Soup" school, 5
"Spark" school, 5
Speech, split-brain, 7
Speed in tests, 253
Spinal gray matter, asphyxiation, 30
Sphincter muscle, 59
Spiral modiolar arteries, 249
Split-brain studies, 7, 8 fig., 9
Stimulants, 73, 134
    animal experiments, 202
    arousal level, 140
    children's therapy, 121, 136–141 tables
    effects, 75 table
    fatigue relief, 105, 117
    learning enhancement, 85–98
    neuropsychological action, 140
Stimulation-inhibition, 78
Stomachache, children, 122
Stress thresholds, students, 111
Strychnine sulfate, 196
Students,
    concentration impairment, 111
    drug study, 112–113 table
    psychiatric conditions, 111
Subjective factors, concentration, 113
Sudden hearing loss, treatment, 251
Suicidal preoccupation, 73
"Supranuclear inhibition," 60
Survival drives, 72
Sussex University, 111
Sympatholytic drugs, 208
Symptoms, reduction by drugs, 57
Synaptic junctions, 27
Synaptic transmission, enhancing, 85
Synaptologists, 5

Tapping rate, 44
Task performance, psychotropic drugs, 143
Tavistock obsessional scale, 112
Temperature, 215

Temporal lobe tumors, 247–248
Tests, CPZ effects, 44 fig.
    see also names of specific tests
Tetanic stimulations, 18
Tetracyanopropene, 163
Therapeutic efficiency, 151
"Thermostat" theory, 74
Thalamocortical responses, 25
Thalidomide, 268
Thiazesim, 201, 204, 205
Thinking improvement, neuroleptic drugs, 112
Thioridazine, children's therapy, 141–142
Thought clarity, phenytoin, 112
Thought disorder, 41
Tissue deficiency drive, 71
Tissue needs, 71
Tofranil, 152
Tonal-stimuli, 247
Tonic midbrain, 85
Topism, 5
Tranquilizers, 73, 134
    anxiety relief, 105, 112
    effects, 75
    narcotic action, 169
Tranquilizer-barbiturates, 79
Transcallosal response, LSD effect, 12
Transmission patterns, 27
Tranylcypromine, avoidance tasks, 170 table
Tremors, 110
    harmoline effect, 180
Tricyanoaminopropene, 163
Trifluoperazine,
    apathetic patient, 56
    pupillary response, 66
Trimeglamide, 94
Tumors, temporal lobe, 247–248
"Turned-on-mind," 112
Twins, pupillary response, 64
l-tyrosine, 203

United Kingdom, 112
United States, 235
Univariate analysis, CPZ use, 42–45
University of Illinois, Children's Research Center, 134, 135 table, 136, 137 table, 140

Vasoconstriction, noise effect, 250
Vasodilation,
    hypoxia and hypercapnia, 234
    noise effect, 250
Vasodilators, 233–260
    behavior studies, 252
    cerebral circulation, 236
    cerebral vascular therapy, 252–260

drugs, 244
    performance effect, 252–260
    therapy, 241
Ventriculojugular, 269
Verbal cognition, ethosuximide, 128
Verbal deficiency, 132
Verbal functions,
    brain location, 131
    ethosuximide, 131
Verbal incontinence, 110
Verbal IQ, ethosuximide, 125 table
Verbal-symbolic tasks, elderly patients, 253
Vestibular-cochlear arteries, 249, 250
Veterans Administration, 54, 55
Vigilance, fatigue's effect, 104–105
Vineland Social Maturity Scales, 95
Viral encephalitis, 188
Viral labyrinthitis, 249
Vision, blurred, 241
Visual cortex,
    ablation results, 183
    thalamocortical responses, 25
Visual Reproduction tests, 258
Visuomotor tests, 43
    CPZ effect, 43–44
    elderly patients, 253
Visuospatial function, 37
Vocabulary tests, 129
Vocational rehabilitation, 57

WAIS, 99
Ward atmosphere, effects, 56
Water distribution changes, central nervous tissue, 29–35
Wechsler Adult Intelligence Scale, 253
Wechsler IQ Scales, ethosuximide effect, 123, 124
Wechsler Memory Scale, 254, 255 table, 257, 258
Wechsler tests, 10, 131
    ethosuximide effect, 128, 129
Wechsler-Bellevue Intelligence Scales, 253
Wechsler-Bellevue IQ tests, 42
Wechsler-Bellevue tests, 46
    convulsive therapy, 47–48 figs.
    CPZ effects, 44
WISC, 99
Withdrawal, 73
    phenothiazine therapy, 57
Withdrawn symptoms, environment influence, 56

^{133}Xe inhalation, 235

Zarontin, learning problem aid, 121–133
Zeiss fundus camera, 242, 244 fig.

Name Index

Adler, Martin W., ii, vii, 176–186, 231, 264
Akelaitis, A .J., 6, 7, 12
Alexander, T., 94–95, 97
Allikmets, L. H., 178, 185
Alpern, H. P., 189, 198
Andrews, John S., Jr., 201, 207, 211
Asher, E. J., 113
Ax, A. F., 72, 79

Bagington, R. G., 205, 214
Bailey, Mayme Y., 187
Baker, C. H., 110
Ballarminof, 60
Banuazizi, A., 189, 200
Barnes, K. R., 139, 143
Barondes, S. H., 91, 95
Barre, 7
Bartlett, Sir Frederick C., 104, 110, 117
Bartley, S. H., 104, 117
Beecher, H. K., 115, 117
Beer, Bernard, 201, 208, 214
Belmont, I., 46, 50
Benoit, J., 268, 272
Berger, F. M., 104, 117
Bernard, 99
Bindra, D., 71, 78, 80
Birch, H. G., 46, 50
Birren, J. E., 44, 50
Birukov, D. A., 217, 230
Bivens, L. W., 189, 200
Bocca, 247–248
Boelhouwer, C., 99, 102
Bogen, Joseph E., ii, vii, xiii, xv, 5–13, 36–37
Bohdanecky, Z., 189, 198, 199
Bostock, J., 95
Bowlby, J., 70, 71, 80
Bradley, C., 86, 89, 91, 95, 96
Brannick, L. J., 201, 212
Breitmeyer, J. M., 138, 143
Broadbent, D. E., 110
Bronk, D. W., 22, 27
Buckley, P., 95, 97
Burch, N. R., 94, 96
Burgemeister, B., 89, 98
Burke, J. C., 201, 212
Burkland, C. W., 132, 133

Cajal, R. y S., 27

Calhoun, J. B., 267, 272
Campbell, Berry, ii, vii, 14–28, 36
Campbell, Stephen K., 121, 252
Cannon, W. B., 181, 186
Carlton, Peter L., 201
Carrell, R. B., 104, 117
Castenada, A., 104, 117
Caties, V. G., 110, 115, 120
Cerletti, V., xi
Chen, Graham, 185
Cherkin, Arthur, ii, vii, 187–200, 231, 266, 267, 270, 271
Cherkin, Daniel C., 187
Chute, E., 104, 117
Cohen, H. D., 91, 95
Conners, C. Keith, ii, vii, xiii, 85–98, 121, 145–147
Craver, B. N., 201, 212
Crossman, E. R. F. W., 107, 117
Cure, C., 181, 186
Cytawa, J., 206, 214

Dandy, W. E., 7
Davies, D. Hywel, ii, viii, xiii, 234–237, 263
Davis, D. Russell, 104, 118
Davis, John A., 252
Davis, K. V., 138, 143
Davis, Russell, 109–110
Dax, 9
de Barenne, Dusser, 20
Dement, W. C., 209, 212, 213
Demetrescu, Mihai, 14–28
Didiergeorges, F., 204, 213
DiMascio, D., 112
Donnan, 32
Douglas, V., 134, 144
Drake, C. G., 181, 186
Drew, G. C., 104, 109, 110, 118
Dreyfus, J. J., 112
Duffy, E., 71, 72, 80

Eccles, A., 89, 97
Eisenberg, L., 86, 88, 96
Elleman, S. J., 210, 212, 214
Endroczi, E., 208, 212
Engelhardt, D. M., 54, 57
Epstein, A. N., 176, 177, 186
Epstein, L., 89, 93, 96

Essman, S. G., 151, 172
Essman, Walter B., ii, viii, xiii, xv, 151–175, 231, 264, 271

Feinberg, I, 49, 50
Fifková, E., 32, 33
Fink, M., 42, 49, 51
Fish, F. J., 73, 80
Fleming, J. W., 94, 96
Foerster, O., 7
Fowle, A. S. E., 216, 230
Freud, Sigmund, 70, 80
Fuguielle, A. R., 177, 186, 201, 212
Fulton, J. F., 27, 36

Garman, Mary A., 187
Gartside, I. B., 161, 172
Gasser, H. S., 36
Geller, 94
Glowinski, J., 210, 214
Goddard, G. V., 205, 212
Goldberg, M. E., 204, 212
Goldberg, Solomon C., ii, viii, 53–58
Golod, M. I., 151
Gonsky, M., 138, 143
Greenberg, J., 99
Guard, H. L., 121, 133
Guthrie, E. R., 113, 118

Hager, Joanne L., 201
Hakerem, Gad, ii, viii, 59–68, 264, 265, 270
Halstead, W. C., 131, 133
Hart, E. R., 12, 13
Hartman, E., 71, 210, 214
Harvey, J. A., 180, 186
Haward, Lionel, ii, viii, 103–120, 121, 144, 146, 265, 266, 267
Hauty, G. T., 111
Hebb, D. O., 41, 51, 113
Heilizer, 53–54
Helbing, J. C., 110
Heller, A., 180, 186
Henderson, J. K., 178, 186
Henderson, L. J., 236
Hess, E. H., 62, 67
Himwich, H. E., 78, 80
Hinton, G., 89, 97
Hippocrates, 9, 13
Hoedt-Rasmussen, 235
Holtzman, 178
Horowitz, Zola P., 178, 186, 201, 202–205, 212
Hubel, D. H., 14, 27
Huddleston, W., 95, 97
Hull, C. L., 69, 70, 71
Hyden, H., 163, 173

Jackson, J. H., 206, 212
Jarvik, M. E., 187, 189, 198, 199
Jerger, J., 247, 248
Johnson, Warren T., 201
Jouvet, M., 210, 214

Kahn, R. L., 49, 52
Kahneman, D., 62, 67
Kaplan, Rita, 99
Karli, P., 202, 203, 204, 206, 213
Kety, S. S., 235
King, M. B., 203, 214
Klein, Donald F., ii, viii, 49, 69–81
Kline, Nathan, 53
Knights, R. M., 89, 97
Knopp, W., 66, 67
Knowles, J. R., 111
Kopp, R., 189, 199
Koranyi, L., 208, 212
Kornetsky, C., 49, 51, 105, 119
Kraepelin, E., xi, 78
Krantz, J. C., Jr., 188, 199
Kris, E., 54
Kugle, R. B., 94–95, 97
Kurland, J., 99, 102

Laird, D. A., 114, 119
Lapin, I. P., 178, 185
Larrabee, M. G., 22, 27
Larssen, 235
Laties, V. G., 59, 89, 92, 97, 98
Lauber, H. L., 67
Laufer, M. W., 93, 97
LaVeck, G. D., 95, 97
Leão, A. A. P., 31, 34
Leaf, Russell C., ii, viii, 201–214, 232
Leaf, Susan R. P., 201
Lehmann, H. E., 46, 51
Leonard, C. A., 176, 186
Lerner, L., 203, 204, 213
Levine, Stephen, 59
Lewis, Robert T., 252
Loewenfeld, I. E., 60, 61, 67, 68
Loomis, T. A., 105, 119
Lorente de No, R., 27, 28
Lowenstein, O., 60, 61, 67, 68
Lowrey, Jack B., 252
Lucas, C. J., 111

Mackworth, N. H., 110
Magnus, Rudolph, 5, 12
Magoun, H. W., 71, 80
Mallet, 235
Marazzi, A. S., 12, 13

Name Index

Margules, David L., 201, 207, 213
Maynert, E. W., 183, 185
McCarthy, Duncan, 185, 203, 213
McFie, J., 131, 133, 258
McGaugh, J. L., 189, 197, 199, 200
McHenry, L. C., 255
Meagher, 7
Miller, A. J., 189, 200
Miller, A. T., Jr., 176, 186
Miller, Anits S., 201
Miller, E., 183, 186
Milner, B., 263, 271
Milner, P., 71, 80, 207, 213
Minde, Klans, 134, 144
Mirsky, A. F., 49, 51
Mitchell, G., 209, 213
Molitch, M., 89, 97
Moniz, S., xi
Moorman Lemuel T., ii, ix, 238–246, 263
Morden, M., 209, 213
Morgan, J. J. B., 114, 119
Moruzzi, G., 71, 80
Muller, S. A., 208, 213
Myers, H. F., 139, 143
Myers, R., 7, 12

Naquet, R., 60, 68

Oettinger, L., 94, 97, 122, 132
Olds, J., 71, 80, 207, 213
Olds, M. E., 207, 213
Orlando, R., 94, 96
Osler, Sir. Wm., 237
Oslinker, Jerry, 252

Paolino, R. M., 189, 200
Parry, J. B., 110
Pauling, Linus, 187
Pavlov, I. P., 50
Payne, R. B., 105, 111, 119, 120
Pearson, R. G., 106, 120
Philippus, M. J., 121, 133, 252, 259
Pirkey, Will P. ii, ix, 247–251, 263, 270
Poirier, L. J., 130, 186
Pollack, Max, ii, ix, 41–52
Pujol, J. F., 210, 214

Quartermain, D., 189, 200

Reed, H. L., 60, 68
Renshaw, B., 22, 27
Reynolds, R. W., 176, 177, 186
Rickels, K., 115, 120

Rosenblueth, A., 181, 186, 231
Routtenberg, A., 71, 78, 81
Rubin, L. S., 67, 68
Rubio-Chevannier, H., 162, 174

Sakel, M., xi
Salama, A. I., 204, 212
Salganicoff, Leon, 183
Satterfield, J., 93, 97
Schachter, D., 158, 174
Schildkraut, J. J., 160, 174, 210, 214
Schmidt, C. F., 235
Schou, M., 159, 161, 174
Seashore, C. R., 110
Seifert, R., 114, 120
Sequin, J. J., 180, 186
Shackleton, M., 94, 95
Shaffer, M. M., 208, 214
Siegel, David, 201, 203, 206, 214
Silverman, A. J., 94, 97
Smith, K. U., 6, 7, 12
Smith, D. D., 203, 214
Smith, W. Lynn, ii, ix, xiii-xiv, xv, 121–133, 147, 252–260, 266, 271
Sperry, R. W., 6, 7, 8, 12
Sprague, Robert L., 134, 136, 137, 138, 139, 143, 178
Sprott, R. L., 189, 200
Stark, P., 178, 186
Stavraky, G. W., 180, 186
Stein, Larry, 78, 81, 201, 207, 208, 214
Steiner, Solomon S., 201, 208, 210, 212, 214
Stephens, G., 189, 200
Stern, W., 209, 214
Stowe, F. R., Jr., 176, 186
Sutin, J., 22, 23, 27
Sutton, S., 62, 68

Taber, R. I., 189, 200
Tavistock, 112
Taylor, L., 263, 271
Teitelbaum, P., 206, 214
Tenen, Stanley S., 201
Thomas, Payne E. L., xv
Thompson, H. S., 62, 68
Tobias, M., 94, 98
Tolman, E. C., 70
Tomasch, J., 7, 12
Tracy, N. H., 121, 252
Turner, William J., ix, 99–102, 121, 267–268, 270–271, 272

Ulett, George A., xi-xii

Van Harreveld, Antonie, ii, ix, 22, 27, 29–35, 36, 37, 263

Veall, 235
Venables, R. H., 104, 120
Venn, R. D., 269
Vergnes, M., 203, 204, 213
Vogel, P. J., 7, 12

Ward, A. A., 60, 68
Wedeking, P. W., 205, 214
Weinstein, Stephen A., ii, x, 215–231, 232
Weiskrantz, L., 197–198, 200
Weiss, B., 89, 92, 97, 98, 110, 115, 120
Weiss, Gabrielle, 134, 137, 144
Weissman, Albert, 201

Wenger, M. A., 72, 81
Werry, John S., ii, x, 134–147
West, T. C., 105, 119
Weyl, T. C., 121, 133
White, C. E., 157, 175
Wiesel, T. N., 14, 27
Wise, C. D., 207, 208, 214
Woods, J. W., 202, 214
Wrathall, Robert, 252

Yates, A. J., 104, 120

Zimmerman, F. T., 89, 98

WITHDRAWN
UST
Libraries